An Illustrated Analysis of

Glass Prices
at Auction

2000-2008

2009 Edition

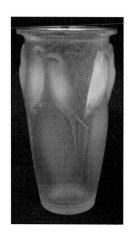

Editor: John Ainsley B.A., B.Ed., M.I.E.E.

An Illustrated Analysis of

Glass Prices at Auction

2000-2008

2009 Edition

Editor: John Ainsley

First published in Great Britain in 2008 by
Antiques Information Services Ltd. Wallsend House,
P O Box 93, Broadstairs, Kent CT10 3YR
Telephone: 01843 862069
Fax: 01843 862014
E-mail: enquiries@antiques-info.co.uk

Further details about the Publishers may be found on our website at
www.antiques-info.co.uk

ISBN: 978 0 9546479 5 7
Whilst every care has been exercised in the compilation of this book,
neither the Editor nor Publishers accept any liability for any financial
or other loss incurred by reliance placed on the information contained
in *Glass Prices at Auction*.

Printed in the United Kingdom
by Cromwell Press, Trowbridge, Wiltshire

Contents

Introduction

The Series

We now present *Glass Prices at Auction, our first 2009* Edition. Currently in print are *Ceramics Prices at Auction 2008*, *Furniture Prices at Auction* published in 2004, *Silver & Jewellery Prices at Auction* and *Picture Prices at Auction*, both published in 2005. The *Series* will continue. In 2009 we will also be publishing *A Beginner's Guide to Collecting*.

Price Guides in General

Price guides have usually followed the A-Z format, values quoted being controlled by publishers and/or editors. Many, not all, fulfil more of an information role than function as price guides! The reasons are clear. The estimates they contain are bound to be influenced to some extent by the commercial considerations of their publishers, although some now are basing their contents on actual sales following the success of this Series. In some cases it can be argued that it is the price guides which are leading the market rather than the market leading the price guides! 'Values' are often lacking an essential market context which is always present in a real sale and are therefore prone to misrepresentation and reader confusion, perceptions which we at *Antiques Information Services* are involved in frequently having to correct. Nor do they recognise secondhand objects are unique and values subject to a measurable set of criteria. It is therefore evident that estimates can never represent actual values. Using results from real sales, accompanied by the qualifications contained within the actual catalogue descriptions is a unique and ground-breaking development in the history of price guides. Readers of this Series, even experts, dealers and auctioneers are now frequently referring to our books.

The Rationale

Here are actual prices at auction from a mass of defined market situations representing the sales of 2,365 lots. In **Part I, Victorian & Twentieth Century Functional & Decorative Glass,** images have been placed in six price bands and in price order in the range £64,000 to £20 hammer. The price bands are arbitrary but provide a means of dividing the work into Sections, which aid the analyses and provide a format to help readers keep their bearings. However, certain categories of glass are so different and specialised that they deserve their own Sections. Hence I have included special sections on **Cranberry Glass, Perfumes & Scents, Paperweights and Dumps, Figures and Car Mascots, Stained and Painted Glass, Georgian Wine Bottles, Georgian Glass and Georgian Drinking Glasses.** The lots have not only been chosen to represent the various price ranges but also to represent glass types, categories and manufacturers from the last 300 years and from sales occurring between 2000 and 2008. In this period fashions and prices have changed and the book represents these changes. The rationale is the market. If you have used other price guides you will be aware of the difficulties. The A-Z format is a weakness in itself, bearing no relationship to sales which are a straightforward matter of when an item was sold, where it sold and what it sold for! Here, the actual numeric price order, overseeing the price bands, representing the top to the bottom *is* the essential ingredient which aids a grasp of the fundamental elements which *are* the market. Here one can analyse the market in many ways. The reader can browse any price range, or any Section. Using the *Index*, it is possible to make a study of a manufacturer, category or type of glass. Each Section is preceded by an Editor's analysis. It is recommended this be studied with the images and the captions. The analysis is not definitive and is quite unobtrusive: the subject isn't a science. Analyses may follow numerous paths at various levels. Hence, the Editor's analysis is personalised around the Editor's interests and knowledge. Reader will seek their own analyses based on their knowledge and interests.

Auction Arithmetic

Buying at auction

Most auctions publish only their hammer prices. The final price paid by the buyer is a matter of a private invoice not usually disclosed to the press. Auctions add on a buyer's premium dependent on the hammer price. You may pay 15% on a hammer price of say £1,000 but only 10% on a hammer price of £30,000. In addition there is VAT on the premium and in some cases VAT may be due on the hammer price as well, depending on the age and origin of the lot. We have added to each lot description both the hammer price and the approximate buyer's price (APB) which includes an average 15% buyer's premium plus VAT, i.e. 17.625%. Auction catalogues include the buyer's and vendor's terms and conditions and there are variations.

Selling at auction

The final cost to the vendor is again outside the public domain. There is a premium which on average will be about 15% of the hammer price. Then there is the VAT and there may be charges related to photographs, storage and even insurance. If you use this book to gauge how much you would receive if you were to sell an item, you subtract from the hammer price the amount added to give the APB. This is an important market statement. The real buying price and the real selling price will usually vary by about 35%. Again the catalogue will explain the terms and conditions relating to selling at auction. If the reader is in any doubt, auctions are always willing to explain their operations. And on viewing days, staff are usually on hand to offer information or advice on the lots themselves.

Glass Prices and the Market

This extensive study of the UK glass market sweeps across the leading manufacturing nations over three centuries. Here is glass from Gt. Britain, Eire, Germany, Czechoslovakia, France, Belgium, Scandinavia, the United States, Italy and Malta. Most of the British areas of manufacture such as Bristol, London, Stourbridge and the north-east are represented, but so are other nations and we may even add China. During the seventeenth century we can only rarely add names such as Ravenscroft to flint glass outputs, but resort to the generic *facon de venise* for soda glass. By the eighteenth, many more identifiable outputs enter the frame and by the nineteenth, and certainly the twentieth century, whether factory or studio glass, the manufacturers names and artists from most of these countries are known. Hence in the *Index* are references to a hundred or so outputs as well as many hundreds more references to patterns and artists. Here can be found Almeric Walter, Art Czechoslovakia or Austin's of Dublin, and on through the alphabet to Waterford or Webbs, Werner Werkstatte, Whitefriars or Paul Ysart. Yet despite the comprehensive nature of the coverage this work is not intended to be definitive. The whole point of this study is that it is not an A-Z of factories but rather an analysis of sales at auction over the last eight years. To ensure the work represents the market then it is entirely appropriate that our main focus reflects this by including multiple entries for the market heavyweights and increasingly less for outputs of less importance, who because of their lower values are more likely to appear on Ebay. Indeed not every output appears at auction. For example I could find no results for the Chance Brothers of Birmingham and I am certain that those collectors interested in the *Chippendale* range are also going to be disappointed, although I've included other examples of George Davidson's output. Nor could I find examples from Liskeard, Cornwall or Nazeing, Essex, but their average values are so low that they are an irrelevance and I am certain that the majority of readers will not be too much put out. Surprisingly also I have seen no sales of Michael Bang at auction, or Per Lutken for that matter but be assured that Holmeguaard is included as is Iittala through Timo Sarpaneva and Tappio Wikkala. And if Simon Gate at Orrefors is absent at least there is Edward Hald and others such as Vicke Lindstrand, even if the latter is only represented by a Kosta example. I am also surprised not to see Percy Thrower of Dartington but he isn't on everyone's lips like Geoffrey Baxter, whose ubiquitous presence reflects Whitefriar mania sweeping the country. And finally there were no sales that I could find for Ronald Stennet-Williams unless he has been unrecognised in which case a diligent reader may wish to point out that he is here after all! If he is not then there are many glass artists present who influenced his work. Glass of course, probably more than any other material is often irritatingly unmarked. There may be less missing examples than we thought. In fact I can assure the reader that there are very few omissions. Certainly I can think of none for whom I should apologise and refer the reader instead to the *Index* to check out the hundred or so artists and outputs that have been included, such as Etling and Kosta and Mdina and Sam Herman, John Ditchfield and Keith Murray whose work at its best is likely to make several hundreds of pounds at least when it appears at auction. Let us concentrate on these and the major figures and factories in the glass market.

The whole logic of a market approach to this price guide should now be explained further. In Part I, Section I, a glance through the pages will quickly reveal the outputs and the artists and the categories of glass that, on average perform better than others. For example here is the very best of Lalique, but not only here. A glance at the *Index* will show that there are at least sixty five examples of his work throughout the book. Lalique is one of the leading players at auction and the number of entries reflects his importance in the market. Here also is the very best of cameo glass and there are dozens more examples to follow but here one can check out the best of Thomas Webb, Daum, Gallé, Stevens & Williams and others. Also dominating this Section and continuing to other price ranges, is a category of glass that most of us wouldn't even bring to mind because we cannot always attach a name. This important category is silver mounted glass and there are at least twenty examples alone in this Section. When we do find names they more often than not attach to the silversmith and not the manufacturers, names such as Samson Mordan. But here also is Christopher Dresser and Gabriel Argy Rousseau and Tiffany and of course the very best of Bohemian ruby, to which we can rarely attach a factory. Many of these themes continue into the lower price ranges and they may be tracked through the *Index*. For example searching out Christopher Dresser shows that his lowest price was £500 on page 29. Here also in Section I is our first lustre at **82** and surprisingly over £1,500. the lustre trail can be followed by browsing pages and Sections. In Section II many themes move forward and new names appear. On page 15 we have our first Whitefriars and our first *Drunken Bricklayer* vase but there are about another ten of these vases throughout the book so that the reader can gauge the market. In all there must be about thirty cross references for Geoffrey Baxter precisely because this book reflects the market and the importance of Baxter in the market place. He is also discussed in the *Analyses*. Here also with his first entry at **117** is Sam Herman, from the United States, at a very good price but this is the top of his range. Here in Section II also is our first Venini at £920 hammer. See **122** and there are about a dozen further examples in all price ranges. I myself could hardly believe it when I saw the first Monart appearing so early at £800 hammer (**157**) but was even more surprised to see a ginger jar go to £750, but these were results from a special sale held at Lyon & Turnbull in Edinburgh in 2008. Another first in this Section is an Edvin Ohrstrom vase for Orrefors at **132** and this output has a dozen or so examples in later pages. A complete surprise is the silver mounted match tidy which fetched £646 at **265**! This is the first of our price guides where certain categories have been excluded from the main work but I have justified this in the *Introduction*. In these later Parts the whole price range is included and *Georgian Drinking Glasses* is the most comprehensive market survey of the subject ever attempted.

In more general market terms it is reasonable to suggest that, as in other categories of antiques the preoccupation with the twentieth century has subsided to some extent and prices have succumbed and settled at more sensible levels. The causes were the usual media hyperbole and fickle and insubstantial fashion. As a result fingers have been burnt. As the twentieth century turned into a new millennium, the market has continued to polarise across certain manufacturers, categories and types of glass. At least no glass collectors have appeared to go to the extreme of a Beswick collector who paid almost £3,500 for Beatrix Potter's *Duchess with Flowers* in 2005, but *Drunken Bricklayer* vases had gone up to about £1,200 and now and inevitably they average about £450 for the 13 inch vase, and I cannot see that being maintained. Rarity and/or quality are the key guidelines to collecting and speculation in areas that have no history of stability are to be avoided whatever the media report. The good thing about today's market, and the same applies to the retail sector, is that once more prices are keen and it is indeed a very good time to buy. And the upheavals and the turmoil of the last few years means we have lived through the experiences of market adjustments and can benefit from this knowledge and buy more wisely in the future. I hope that this book, with its 2,365 sales and market analyses from the last eight years will help.

Pitfalls in the market

It is certain that in most cases, investing in antiques is a safer bet than buying a car, an insurance policy, finding the cheapest railway ticket, contributing to a pension scheme or choosing your electricity, gas or telephone supplier. The marketing is rarely deliberately oblique and you will never face the onerous task of having to deal with a call centre. It is also nice to know that you are very unlikely ever to see dealers driving fast cars and living fast lifestyles: profit margins are too low.

However there are buying sources in which you cannot put your total trust. Rarely is there deliberate deception but there are reproductions and fakes about, and even genuine antiques that are misdescribed through a lack of knowledge on behalf of the dealer. Glass also lends itself to the deliberate concealment of restoration and repair. This is particularly the case with Georgian drinking glasses and the problems are aired in that Section. If you

are not an expert in your subject, and even experts can be deceived or mistaken, it is wise to buy from sources which give you consumer protection. Fine art fairs and dealers and auctions that are members of Trade associations are safer. Here you will always receive a receipt and the receipt should give not only a good description of the item but also its condition and an approximate date of manufacture. If buying from an auction check for a rescission clause in their conditions related to buying. This will guarantee the auction will rescind the sale and refund your money if within a certain time you are able to prove inaccuracy in the lot description. Rummers for example are a problem in all areas of the market place: most are reproductions. However if you are buying in a less controlled situation, ensure you get a receipt which includes the necessary information. If the vendor won't provide a receipt don't buy, unless you are the expert.

How to use this book

This book is an ideal browsing medium but it is recommended that both the *Introduction* and the *Section Analyses* are read at an early stage. A significant part of this work is the lot descriptions. These conclude with colour-coded market information, viz: *where the lot was sold, when the lot was sold* and *what the lot was sold for*. The prices quoted are the hammer price and the approximate buyer's price. (APB) This includes an additional 17.625% which is an average 15% buyer's premium plus the VAT on the premium. Auctions may charge more or less for the buyer's premium or the vendor's premium. Our **2008 Survey** showed that 50.2% of auctions charge a buyer's premium of 15% + VAT, 23% of auctions charge less and worryingly 26.4% more. Over a third of auctions, i.e. 36%, charge 17.5% + VAT, equal to 20.56%. The rates can be found in auction catalogues or by consulting the relevant auction. In addition, whilst every effort has been made by the Editor to check out the attributions, there exists the unlikely possibility of error. However, great care is taken and 'labelling' is in most cases accurate.

In some cases captions have been rationalised in order to solve editing requirements. Syntactical changes have been made and abbreviations used which did not occur in the original auction catalogue. And on occasions the Editor has used his discretion to omit descriptive detail which would be tedious and which would not materially influence the price. In all cases, the Editor has ensured that changes in meaning have not occurred and that the content of a caption remains true to the original version. Foreign spellings and name spellings also vary in the original catalogues. These remain but have been standardised in the *Index*.

Finally, the reader's attention is drawn to the *Glossary of Terms* and the *Index*. These are integral parts of this work. The *Index* has about 4,500 cross-references.

The Editor wishes to thank the dozens of auctions up and down the country who have supplied the sales information that appears in the main body of the book.

PART I: Decorative & Functional Glass c1830-2000
Section I: Over £1,000

'The simplicity of Dresser is unmistakable.....the rock crystal jug should have done better than £1,400.....Through mass production techniques Lalique succeeded in producing artistic glassware.....'

The first Part of this work is divided into eight Sections covering the price ranges from over a £1,000 to under £500. Here the upper end of the market is represented by a sample of 108 lots sold at auctions during the last eight years. Whereas at the upper end of the ceramics market we found that the dominant force was Chinese, here it is clear that Europe holds sway. Let us therefore look more closely at the types. Whilst at **1** the fine relief engraved panels depicting Alexander the Great defeating the Persians is outstanding, engraved glass that stands on its own only reappears at **29** where the association with damage in the Blitz to this claret jug seems to have trebled at least, its expected price. I cannot see this jug, in this condition, as worthy of a £3,175 price tag. However it is the first time that I have ever witnessed damage to a glass enhancing its value.

The best of silver mounted glass is bound to appear in the upper market and here there is ample evidence at **3, 5, 6, 17, 18, 19, 24, 26, 32, 33, 34, 43, 61, 66, 76, 78, 87, 90, 100, 106** and **108**, here listed because they are well worth study, representing almost 20% of the lots featured. Whilst a Samson Mordan & Co novelty pheasant at **3** exceeded expectations, Christopher Dresser at **5, 17** and (**32**) makes his mark and always courtesy of the famous silversmiths, Hukin & Heath. The simplicity of Dresser is unmistakable but one has to admire the claret jug at **24** by E H Stockwell. Not only are the silver mounts set as trailing oak branches with acorn clusters, but the body of the jug itself is formed as an acorn. Not overpriced are two Betjamann Patent silver tantali at **26** and **34**, the first having an association with Gracie Fields. Readers should note that it is always possible to date silver and that none of these pieces pre date the 1860s. In addition to the Dresser examples There is also a Fabergé jug at **43**, not to mention the caviar centrepiece at **33**, which seems to be well under priced. And again if I were to be pointing out good value, The Goldsmiths & Silversmiths 'rock crystal' claret jug at **76**, even though recently bought in 2007, should have done considerably better than £1,400 hammer.

Pate-de-verre appears at **10, 11** and **13** and again at **37**. See **Glossary**. Two of these examples are from Gabriel Argy Rousseau and two are by Almeric Walter. Expect to pay about £5,000 to buy into this technique but note also the £2,700 at **37**. Cameo glass is a time consuming art and readers should expect plenty of examples in this Section. See **2, 18, 22, 35, 55, 64, 71, 73, 74, 77, 89** and

95. Makers range from Thomas Webb at **2** to Daum, Gallé, Stevens & Williams and others with only a Stourbridge attribution as the maker is unknown. Note that cameo glass may be cut through with tools, that is literally carved, as in the example at **71**, or acid etched as with the Gallé example at **64.** There are several further examples of cameo work and other techniques in later Sections. See for example the cameo cranberry at **1328** and **1329** or the silver mounted cut glass decanter at **1326**, all on page 84.

It will be immediately evident on browsing these pages that Lalique plays a major part in our glass story and this will continue through the lower price ranges, even through to modern Lalique models of glass birds on page 113, where even here the price is a respectable £64. In this Section at **7** the highest price is £7,400 but £23,900 hammer was paid in 2004 at Christies, South Kensington for a vase '*Orange*', No. 964 in clear, frosted and black enamel, and prices under £20,000, but still in five figures, is not uncommon. Readers can view some of the best of Lalique at **7, 12, 15, 16, 20, 30, 31, 36, 38, 44, 47, 48, 49, 51, 52, 56, 57, 58, 68, 72, 75, 81, 86, 91, 92, 97, 99, 104** and **107**. I have provided the list of images to make the point that Lalique dominates the glass scene at auction and this domination will continue throughout the following price ranges until it tails off at the lower end of the market. Here Lalique examples provide a massive 28% of the lots in this Section. For a full list of pages which include Lalique see the **Index.**

Through mass production techniques Lalique succeeded in producing artistic glassware. But always his aim was to supplement the mass production with finishing techniques to make the pieces appear less manufactured. In the 1870s and in the north east of England, Sowerby turned the process of producing cheap pressed glass, which imitated blown moulded glass, into an art form, with finishing techniques, but he was aiming only at the aspiring classes of his age. Lalique developed mass production techniques with mould blown glass and hence aspired to much greater artistic achievements. Only later and in the 1920s did Lalique introduce new techniques for manufacturing virtually unlimited copies, including pressing, and even then the emphasis remained on art and industry combining to bring the decorative arts to every home at affordable prices.

Readers interested in lustres will see the highest priced examples beginning to appear at **70, 82, 98, 102** and may follow the market in later Sections.

Hammer: £64,000 - £4,000

19thC Bohemian vase/cover, relief engraved panels of a battle scene after Lebrun's painting depicting Alexander The Great defeating the Persians, 58cm total height. Wotton Auction Rooms, Wotton under Edge. Mar 08. HP: £64,000. ABP: £75,280.

Thomas Webb cameo double ground vase, by F Kretschman, c1888, 22.5cm, minute surface chips. Dreweatt Neate, Newbury. Nov 01. HP: £36,000. ABP: £42,345.

Victorian silver mounted glass novelty claret jug, by Samson Mordan & Co, London 1882, pheasant, 22cm high, a foot missing, matching spare glass body, Rd. mark for 1882. Sworders, Stansted Mountfitchet. Feb 07. HP: £22,500. ABP: £26,465.

Garniture of 3 pokals, mid 19thC, Bohemian flashed ruby glass, largest 64cm. Richard Winterton, Burton on Trent, Staffs. Feb 04. HP: £10,200. ABP: £11,997.

Dr Christopher Dresser (1834-1904), late Victorian glass claret jug, plated mounts, stamped 'Designed by Dr. C. DRESSER, 2045, Rd mark, by Hukin & Heath, 9.75in high, a.f. Diamond Mills & Co, Felixstowe. Mar 06. HP: £8,400. ABP: £9,880.

Pair of Russian silver & cut glass claret jugs by Khlebnikov, signed, dated 1916.. Cotswold Auction Company, Cirencester. Apr 08. HP: £8,200. ABP: £9,645.

Prices quoted are actual hammer prices (HP) and the Approximate Buyer's Price (ABP) includes an average premium of 15% + VAT.

Lalique vase 'Quatre groupes de lezards', moulded vertical bands of running lizards, engraved mark Lalique, 12.5in. Gorringes, Lewes. Jul 04. HP: £7,400. ABP: £8,704.

Otto Prutscher, set of six glasses designed for Wiener Werkstatte, c1910, amber glass casing, square cut stem, clear feet, 8.25in high. Gorringes, Lewes. Apr 05. HP: £6,800. ABP: £7,998.

Silver gilt mounted glass claret jug, John Figg, London 1875, base, applied masks, neck with female masks, handle with female figure & putto, etched trailing vines/masks, cartouches, strapwork, 41cm high, cased. Sworders, Stansted Mountfitchet. Nov 07. HP: £5,800. ABP: £6,822.

Gabriel Argy Rousseau 'Rayons de Soleil' pate-de-verre vase, red flowers on yellow stems, signed on body, etched France on base, 6in. Gorringes, Lewes. Jul 00. HP: £5,100. ABP: £5,998.

Almeric Walter pate-de-verre glass bowl/cover, c1925, incised A Walter Nancy, imp'd to base 'Marquise de Sevigne', paper label 'Sammlung Funke Kaiser', 6in high. Sotheby's, Billingshurst. Mar 00. HP: £4,800. ABP: £5,646.

Lalique vase, 'Sauterelles', Ref. 888, moulded crickets in green pigment, blue ground, early 20thC, etched mark R. Lalique, 11in. Gorringes, Lewes. Jul 04. HP: £4,600. ABP: £5,410.

Argy Rousseau pate-de-verre vase, 'Araignees et Ronces', spider in a web to each side & leaves, moulded signature, 4.5in. Gorringes, Lewes. Oct 04. HP: £4,600. ABP: £5,410.

Colotte Nancy Piece Unique cut-glass vase, 25.5cm high. Gorringes, Bexhill. Sep 04. HP: £4,500. ABP: £5,293.

Lalique 'Milan' frosted and polished amber/red glass vase, c1930, moulded with branches of serrated leaves, etched mark 'R. Lalique', 28cm high. Lyon & Turnbull, Edinburgh. Apr 08. HP: £4,400. ABP: £5,175.

Lalique 'Danseuses' opalescent glass vase, moulded with frieze of dancing figures and bands of waving foliage, etched stencil mark, 17.5cm high. Lyon & Turnbull, Edinburgh. Apr 08. HP: £4,200. ABP: £4,940.

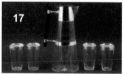

19thC silver mounted glass decanter, 4 beakers, designed by Dr Christopher Dresser, original leather case, Hukin & Heath, London 1882, jug 10in. Gorringes, Lewes. Oct 07. HP: £4,000. ABP: £4,705.

Silver metal mounted Daum glass ewer, signed in gilt, cross of Lorraine, 29.5cm high. Sworders, Stansted Mountfitchet. Feb 03. HP: £3,800. ABP: £4,469.

Russian cut glass Kovsh, silver mounts, prow in form of a helmeted warrior, 27cm long. Rosebery's, London. Mar 06. HP: £3,800. ABP: £4,469.

Lalique bowl, Sirene, No. 375, clear frosted/opalescent glass, moulded mark R Lalique, France, engraved No. 375, 36.4cm. Sworders, Stansted Mountfitchet. Sep 07. HP: £3,600. ABP: £4,234.

Peking glass vase, mark and period of Qianlong (1736-1795), egg yolk yellow, four character marks, 11.5cm. Sworders, Stansted Mountfitchet. Nov 04. HP: £3,500. ABP: £4,116.

Daum Nancy martele cameo glass vase in pale blue/green, carved dahlias, hammered ground, etched Daum Nancy underneath with separate Cross of Lorraine, 11.75in. Gorringes, Lewes. Dec 00. HP: £3,300. ABP: £3,881.

Early 20thC Baccarat suite of glassware, engraved and gilded: 3 pairs of decanters/stoppers, pair of confitures, covers and stands, water jug, pair of comports, 65 glasses. Gorringes, Lewes. Apr 01. HP: £3,200. ABP: £3,764.

19thC silver mounted glass claret jug, by E H Stockwell, London, 1883, silver mounts as trailing oak branches with acorn clusters, body as an acorn, 25.5cm. Sworders, Stansted Mountfitchet. Apr 06. HP: £3,200. ABP: £3,764.

The numbering system acts as a reader reference and links to the Analysis of each section.

Tiffany Favrille iridescent glass vase, c1900, 22.5cm high. Rupert Toovey & Co, Washington, Sussex. May 03. HP: £3,000. ABP: £3,528.

1930s Betjemanns patent silver tantalus, glass decanters, Charles Boyton & Son, 1930, 95oz gross, inscribed, given to Basil Dean OBE, by Gracie Fields. Gorringes, Lewes. Oct 02. HP: £2,900. ABP: £3,411.

Hammer: £3,800 - £2,400

Emile Galle cameo glass vase, c1900, overlaid with dark pink, etched with red currants/leaves, cameo signature, 46cm. Wintertons, Lichfield. Sep 03. HP: £2,900. ABP: £3,411.

Near pair of blue cased acid etched vases, poss. Daniel Pearce of Thomas Webb, with continuous bands of blue flowers, acanthus leaf ornament to bases, beaded ormolu mounts to top/bottom, 21in. Gorringes, Lewes. Sep 07. HP: £2,800. ABP: £3,293.

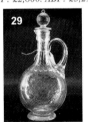

19thC claret jug, engraved, similar stopper, 9.25in high, extensively chipped in the Blitz. Canterbury Auction Galleries, Kent. Aug 01. HP: £2,700. ABP: £3,175.

Lalique opalescent glass Ceylan vase, etched R. LALIQUE FRANCE, No 905, 9.5in. Gorringes, Lewes. Oct 00. HP: £2,600. ABP: £3,058.

Lalique Mures vase by Rene Lalique, produced 1930-47, moulded in bass relief, stencilled R LALIQUE FRANCE, 7.5in. Byrne's, Chester. Mar 04. HP: £2,600. ABP: £3,058.

Victorian silver mounted glass claret jug, ebonised bar handle, Makers Hukin and Heath, Birmingham 1892, 16in. Gorringes, Lewes. Mar 03. HP: £2,600. ABP: £3,058.

Faberge overlaid blue, hobnail cut glass and gilt metal caviar dish centrepiece, hinged, acorn finial, serpent shaped feet, 18in. Amersham Auction Rooms, Bucks. May 02. HP: £2,400. ABP: £2,823.

Edwardian silver tantalus, by John George Betjemann and Ernest Edward Betjemann, London 1902, 3 square hobnail cut glass decanters, facet cut spherical stoppers, modern silver wine labels, monogrammed on frame, 36cm high. (10) Sworders, Stansted Mountfitchet. Nov 07. HP: £2,400. ABP: £2,823.

Hammer: £2,400 - £1,750

35

Daum, Nancy. Cameo glass ceiling light shade, 44cm dia. Rupert Toovey & Co, Washington, Sussex. Mar 03. HP: £2,400. ABP: £2,823.

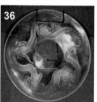

36

Large R. Lalique opalescent blue glass 'Coupe Calypso' dish, 15in. Academy Auctioneers, Ealing. Jul 99. HP: £2,300. ABP: £2,705.

37

Almeric Walter pate-de-verre chameleon mounted dish by Henri Berge, engraved A Walter Nancy, 6.75in. Gorringes, Lewes. Jun 00. HP: £2,300. ABP: £2,705.

38

Lalique iridescent amber glass bowl, moulded with fish, base with moulded R Lalique mark, 7in high. Tring Market Auctions, Herts. Jan 03. HP: £2,300. ABP: £2,705.

39

Set of ten Lobmeyr gilded and enamelled clear glass sundae dishes and stands. Rupert Toovey & Co, Washington, Sussex. Feb 03. HP: £2,200. ABP: £2,587.

40

Pair of 19thC Italian blue satin glass vases, 14.5in. Andrew Hartley, Ilkley. Dec 99. HP: £2,200. ABP: £2,587.

41

Pair of late 19thC Bohemian glass vases, 47.5cm, one base restored. Wintertons, Lichfield. May 02. HP: £2,100. ABP: £2,470.

> The illustrations are in descending price order. The price range is indicated at the top of each page.

42

Cut glass decanter/stopper, early 20thC, possibly Stevens & Williams, decorated with clear glass flower stems, star cut base, 47cm. Hampton & Littlewood, Exeter. Jul 04. HP: £2,100. ABP: £2,470.

43

Glass water jug, hinged silver lid, as a water lily leaf, Faberge mark, 20cm. Rosebery's, London. Mar 06. HP: £2,100. ABP: £2,470.

44

Lalique opalescent glass bowl, 'Perruches' pattern, band of birds on flowering branches, blue patina stencilled 'R LALIQUE, FRANCE', 9.5in wide. Hartleys, Ilkley. Apr 06. HP: £2,100. ABP: £2,470.

45

Late 19thC Bohemian ruby flash glass centre piece, 21in high. Gorringes, Bexhill. Feb 01. HP: £2,000. ABP: £2,352.

46

Pair of late 19thC Bohemian white overlaid, cranberry glass ewers, 23.5in. Amersham Auction Rooms, Bucks. Mar 03. HP: £2,000. ABP: £2,352.

47

Lalique vase 'Milan', Ref. 1025, moulded leaves/stalks stained in blue pigment, engraved mark R. Lalique, France, c1930-35, 11.25in. Gorringes, Lewes. Jul 04. HP: £2,000. ABP: £2,352.

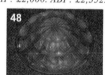

48

Pair of Lalique glass plafonniers, Acanthus moulded, inscribed 'R. Lalique, France', 17.5in. L. Taylor, Stoke. Jun 07. HP: £2,000. ABP: £2,352.

49

Lalique six figurines carafe, clear/sepia stained, moulded mark, 14in high. Gardiner Houlgate, Corsham. Apr 05. HP: £2,000. ABP: £2,352.

50

20thC suite, St Louis 'Thistle Gold' glasses: carafe, bowls, saucers, sherry glasses, wine glasses, martini glasses. (63) Rosebery's, London. Jun 08. HP: £1,900. ABP: £2,234.

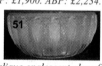

51

Lalique opalescent glass fruit bowl, moulded with continuous band of budgerigars amongst flowers, etched R. Lalique, France, 26cm dia. Eastbourne Auction Rooms, Sussex. Dec 05. HP: £1,900. ABP: £2,234.

52

Lalique clear/green tinted Milan vase engraved script R. Lalique France, No 1025, 11.25in. Gorringes, Lewes. Jul 01. HP: £1,800. ABP: £2,117.

53

Early 20thC multi coloured glass table centrepiece lamp, 23in high. Amersham Auction Rooms, Bucks. Jul 02. HP: £1,750. ABP: £2,058.

Pair of 19thC ruby flashed/ etched glass goblets, topographical scenes of South Africa, 34cm high. D M Nesbit & Co, Southsea. Sep 03. HP: £1,750. ABP: £2,058.

Daum Nancy cameo glass vase, band of yellow/brown toadstools, canary yellow ground, signed, 4in high. Andrew Hartley, Ilkley. Apr 04. HP: £1,750. ABP: £2,058.

Lalique Coquilles suite: dish, No. 3009, 12in dia, 6 dishes, No. 3012, 8in dia, 4 bowls, No. 3204, 5in dia. Sworders, Stansted Mountfitchet. Dec 01. HP: £1,700. ABP: £1,999.

Martins Pecheurs. Lalique blue stained glass vase. Mellors & Kirk, Nottingham. Feb 03. HP: £1,700. ABP: £1,999.

1930s Lalique opalescent moulded glass vase, marked 'R. Lalique, France', 19cm high. Lots Road Auctions, Chelsea. Oct 03. HP: £1,700. ABP: £1,999.

Lalique opalescent glass vase, 'Beliers' pattern, handles in form of rams, engraved 'R. Lalique, France', pattern No. 904 to base. 7.5in high. Canterbury Auction Galleries, Kent. Dec 03. HP: £1,700. ABP: £1,999.

19thC Bohemian ruby overlaid glass goblet/cover, continuously engraved, octagonal knopped stem, chipped rim, 19in. Gorringes, Lewes. Mar 04. HP: £1,700. ABP: £1,999.

Victorian silver mounted claret jug, finial capped lid and tall neck engraved with butterflies and foliage, body engraved with an anthropomorphic scene, 34.5cm high, maker's mark prob. Edward Charles Brown, London 1873. Bearne's, Exeter. Nov 07. HP: £1,700. ABP: £1,999.

Pair Bohemian opaque glass vases, late 19thC, painted floral borders, 40cm. Sworders, Stansted Mountfitchet. Jul 05. HP: £1,650. ABP: £1,940.

Hammer: £1,750 - £1,400

Stevens and Williams 'Dolce Relievo' cameo glass vase, c1885, 5in high. Biddle & Webb, Birmingham. Sep 01. HP: £1,550. ABP: £1,823.

Galle acid etched cameo glass vase, riverscape in russets/yellows, signature on the body, 8.75in. Gorringes, Lewes. Apr 01. HP: £1,500. ABP: £1,764.

Pair of late 19th/early 20thC Bohemian ruby flash glass trumpet vases, engraved with scene of stags in a woodland, stylised geometric borders, 16in. Gorringes, Lewes. Jul 08. HP: £1,500. ABP: £1,764.

Pair of George VI Art Deco silver mounted decanters and stoppers, stepped shoulders, Birmingham 1938, 10.75in. Gorringes, Lewes. Mar 04. HP: £1,500. ABP: £1,764.

Loetz small vase with petrol iridescence, pink ground, marked Loetz, Austria, 4.25in. Byrne's, Chester. Mar 04. HP: £1,450. ABP: £1,705.

Five Lalique 'Six Figurines No. 3400', clear and frosted glass goblets, engraved 'R. Lalique, France', 10cm, one goblet with damage, one with small rim bruise. Sworders, Stansted Mountfitchet. Jul 04. HP: £1,450. ABP: £1,705.

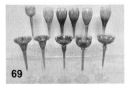

Eleven Bohemian Art Deco glasses with tall stems, bowls painted in crocus and similar floral manner, gilt highlights, 16cm high. Marilyn Swain Auctions, Grantham. May 05. HP: £1,450. ABP: £1,705.

Pair of Bohemian overlaid table lustres, white enamel panels with floral sprays reserved on a green ground, profuse gilt scrolling decoration, clear pendants/prism drops, 27cm high, 19thC, devoid three drops. Bearne's, Exeter. Nov 07. HP: £1,450. ABP: £1,705.

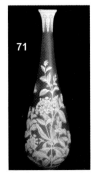

Stourbridge citron and white glass cameo vase carved in white relief with insects and flowers, 38cm high, c1880, minute bruise to foot rim. Dreweatt Neate, Newbury. Jun 03. HP: £1,400. ABP: £1,646.

Hammer: £1,400 - £1,200

Lalique frosted glass fish vase, moulded/etched, script marks R. Lalique France, 11in. Gorringes, Lewes. Sep 00. HP: £1,400. ABP: £1,646.

Daum cameo vase, mottled pink body overlaid in green, cameo mark, Daum, Nancy incorporating the Cross of Lorraine, 19in high. Clarke Gammon, Guildford. Sep 03. HP: £1,400. ABP: £1,646.

Gallé 'Cristallene' cameo glass bottle vase, amethyst overlay acid etched with a flower, leaves and tendrils, etched mark to underside, 'Cristallene, E. Galle, Nancy, Model a Decor Depose', 14in. Gorringes, Lewes. Jul 04. HP: £1,400. ABP: £1,646.

Lalique 'Cupe Calypso' bowl, etched mark, 30cm dia. Sworders, Stansted Mountfitchet. Apr 05. HP: £1,400. ABP: £1,646.

Edwardian silver mounted Stourbridge glass claret jug, Goldsmiths & Silversmiths Co, London 1908, deeply cut/engraved in rock crystal style, 31.5cm. Sworders, Stansted Mountfitchet. Nov 07. HP: £1,400. ABP: £1,646.

Stourbridge cameo glass vase, c1880, attrib. Thomas Webb. Richard.Winterton, Burton on Trent. Apr 08. HP: £1,400. ABP: £1,646.

> Categories or themes can be followed through the colour coded Index which contains over 4500 cross references.

Victorian cut glass claret jug, 10.5in high, Sheffield 1868, mark for Martin Hall & Co. Andrew Hartley, Ilkley. Sep 99. HP: £1,350. ABP: £1,587.

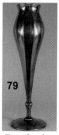

Tiffany Favrile glass vase. Woolley & Wallis, Salisbury. Sep 00. HP: £1,300. ABP: £1,529.

Victorian glass Dewars bulk whiskey container, marked Royal Warrant to Her Majesty the Queen, 30in high, slight chip to rim. Denhams, Warnham. Oct 03. HP: £1,300. ABP: £1,529.

Lalique glass vase, 'Saint Francois', pre-war, Ref 1055, moulded with birds/foliage, stencilled mark R. Lalique, France, 6.75in. Gorringes, Lewes. Jan 04. HP: £1,300. ABP: £1,529.

Pair of Victorian ruby/white overlay glass lustres, crenelated rim/opaline cartouches of flowers, drop-in white metal candle sconces, 12in high. Dee, Atkinson & Harrison, Driffield. Feb 05. HP: £1,300. ABP: £1,529.

Pair of late 19thC Chemist's glass display jars & covers, printed in colours, decorated in gilt with Royal Coat of Arms, worded 'Pure Drugs' and 'Toilet Articles', yellow ground, 26in high. Canterbury Auction Galleries, Kent. Dec 05. HP: £1,300. ABP: £1,529.

Pair of mid-19thC blue glass vases, cusped, turnover rims, hexagonal bodies gilded with figures and foliage, wrythen gilded knops, faceted bases, 12.75in, chips around bases. Gorringes, Lewes. Mar 06. HP: £1,300. ABP: £1,529.

Signed Loetz iridescent glass vase, dimpled globular shape, swirling bands of silver/blue iridescence on green glass ground, engraved Loetz, Austria, 11cm. Sworders, Stansted Mountfitchet. Sep 07. HP: £1,300. ABP: £1,529.

Lalique 'Avalon' vase, marks, R. Lalique France No. 986, 14.5cm high. Sworders, Stansted Mountfitchet. Feb 03. HP: £1,250. ABP: £1,470.

George VI silver mounted cut glass claret jug, ivory ball finial, maker Charles Boyton, 1937, 8.75in. Gorringes, Lewes. Apr 00. HP: £1,200. ABP: £1,411.

Pair of mid 19thC enamelled green glass table lustres, overlaid, gilded and floral painted with scalloped tops, 13in. Gorringes, Lewes. Oct 06. HP: £1,200. ABP: £1,411.

Daum martele opalescent cameo glass vase, overlaid in pink/magenta on a milky blue ground, etched 'Daum Nancy' to base, 13cm high. Rupert Toovey & Co, Washington, Sussex. Jun 03. HP: £1,200. ABP: £1,411.

19thC gilt bronze mounted cut-glass bowl, F & C Osler, cut with bevelled squares, hobnail decoration, parrot handles, stamped base, 11.5in. Gorringes, Lewes. Mar 03. HP: £1,200. ABP: £1,411.

Lalique opaque Avallon vase, moulded with birds/cherry blossom, etched R. Lalique France, No. 689, 5.75in. Gorringes, Lewes. Oct 05. HP: £1,200. ABP: £1,411.

Lalique 'St. Francois' vase, 11in high, marked to base R Lalique France. Kent Auction Galleries, Folkestone. Sep 06. HP: £1,200. ABP: £1,411.

Pair of 19thC Bohemian table lustres, portraits of girls alternating with oval floral panels, overlaid ground, gilded, prismatic clear glass lustre drops, 12.5in. Gorringes, Lewes. Dec 07. HP: £1,200. ABP: £1,411.

Pair Bohemian gilt overlay vases, alternate diamond cut overlay white glass & floral painted panels, 44cm. Thos Mawer & Son, Lincoln. Mar 04. HP: £1,150. ABP: £1,352.

Pair of Thomas Webb ruby cameo glass baluster vases, c1880, opaque overlay of flora and foliage, unmarked, 13cm. Richard Winterton, Burton on Trent. Jun 08. HP: £1,100. ABP: £1,293.

Pair of Edwardian brass mounted pink glass oil lamps, replaced glass dome shades, 18in. Gorringes, Lewes. Feb 01. HP: £1,100. ABP: £1,293.

Lalique clear/blue stained glass Saint Marc vase, ribbed body applied with doves, etched R. LALIQUE FRANCE, 6.5in, bruise on body. Gorringes, Lewes. Jan 02. HP: £1,100. ABP: £1,293.

Pair of Victorian table lustres, columns/tops with overlay gilt, coloured flower decoration, lustre drops, 30.5cm high. Sworders, Stansted Mountfitchet. Apr 05. HP: £1,100. ABP: £1,293.

Hammer: £1,200 - £1,050

Lalique 'Mesanges' frosted jardiniere, design 1927, oval vessel with 2 handles each as a finch, engraved R Lalique, France, 2 small chips to rim, 54.5cm. Sworders, Stansted Mountfitchet. Apr 05. HP: £1,100. ABP: £1,293.

Victorian silver gilt mounted glass claret jug, engraved with tall ship, Hermione, dated Feb 25 1868, star cut body, Sheffield 1864, 10in. Gorringes, Lewes. Sep 07. HP: £1,100. ABP: £1,293.

Lalique opalescent glass vase, moulded in the Actinia design with stylised waves, etched mark R Lalique, 9in high. Hartleys, Ilkley. Dec 07. HP: £1,100. ABP: £1,293.

Pair Victorian powder blue glass overlay table lustres, flared castellated lip & base decorated with gilt veined stylised leaves, facetted spear drops, 11.5in. Gorringes, Lewes. Apr 08. HP: £1,100. ABP: £1,293.

Art glass inkwell by Powell & Sons, 1907. Lawrences, Crewkerne. Oct 07. HP: £1,050. ABP: £1,235.

Lalique opalescent glass vase, embossed flower head & stem decoration, script signature, pattern No. 979, 22cm high. Great Western Auctions, Glasgow. Apr 00. HP: £1,050. ABP: £1,235.

Mid Victorian water jug with a pair of water goblets. Hamptons, Godalming. Mar 00. HP: £1,050. ABP: £1,235.

Victorian silver mounted glass claret jug, Sheffield 1869, Hy. Wilkinson & Co. Rosebery's, London. May 00. HP: £1,050. ABP: £1,235.

Opalescent glass plate decorated in relief with swirling nudes by Rene Lalique. Stride & Son, Chichester. Apr 02. HP: £1,050. ABP: £1,235.

19thC silver mounted claret jug, engraved with classical figures, horse drawn chariots, W & G Sissons, Sheffield 1869 10.5in. Gorringes, Lewes. Mar 04. HP: £1,050. ABP: £1,235.

PART I: Decorative & Functional Glass c1830-2000
Section II: £1,000-£500

'A drunken bricklayer vase fetched £1,000 hammer.....but those were heady days.....the Venini range is from about £3,000 downwards.....Glass prices were pushed to new heights at the Scottish Sale..... and none more so than Monart of Perth.....'

There are about a 176 lots in this Section and many follow the themes seen in **Section I**, but there are several new additions. In the previous Section there was a superb Peking vase at **21** and £3,500 hammer; eighteenth century obviously at this price but readers should be aware of its potential. Check out the **Index** for further examples and note the pair of blue bowls at **115** and a £1,000 hammer despite damage. Back on page 12 at **86** was a Lalique *Avalon* vase, at £1,250 hammer in 2003. Here at **91** is a further *Avalon* vase two years later for £1,200 hammer and at **120** a further example sold in 2007 for £950 hammer despite damage. Prices for quality are reliable whether in Essex, Sussex or Devon! Let us check out Lalique further by examining three sales of the *Formose* design at **125**, **146** and **275**. The latter sold in Leeds in 2000 for £520 hammer. Two years later and despite damage, **146** sold for £800 hammer and in 2005, **125** sold in Stoke-on-Trent for £900 hammer. These show the strength of the market in this price range.

In complete contrast, at **112** is our first Whitefriars and as to be expected in this price range a *Drunken Bricklayer* vase at a £1,000 hammer, but those were heady days! There are about a dozen examples of the 8 inch and the 13 inch vases in these pages and many examples of other Whitefriars such as *Banjo* vases. Check out this Section at **112, 149, 171, 174, 183, 193, 194, 195, 199, 214, 224** and **268**. The range was designed by Geoffrey Baxter in the 1960s to help the Company stave off bankruptcy by creating designs with popular appeal. Baxter would be astonished today to have seen these designs achieving almost cult status but of course this was yesterday, or in fact two or three years ago. Today at auction, prices for the 13 inch have slumped to about £300-£400 and the 8 inch can be had for about a £150. These are more sensible prices but I feel they still have a good way to go down yet. The earlier prices were on the back of a fashion frenzy and media hyperbole. Any thinking person can see by looking at this first page or anywhere in this Section that a drunken bricklayer vase should never appear in the same context as good Lalique or Gallé or Daum, where the manufacturing or mechanical input is restricted, and where the workers' hand in the production line performs the majority of the work on each vessel. Or even compare the English Stourbridge silver mounted cameo decanter at **249**. Such glass should be of decorative value only, unless of course it is uncommon or even rare and I can assure readers that Whitefriars glass of this period is quite common. Check out the whole of the Whitefriars market by referring to the **Index**.

At **117** is our first Sam Herman vase. (USA) This Scottish Sale in 2008 produced exceptional glass prices and at a £1,000 this is on the high side for this artist, but on the other hand this is the top end of his range. There aren't many sales in this country to establish much of a market but there are a few more lots in these pages. I like his work and if I had about a £1,000 to invest you can guess where my money wouldn't be going! At **122** is our first, and again a quite exceptional piece of Venini, and there are about a dozen examples in these pages. The Venini range is about £3,000 down to the lower end and I would expect this vase to date to the 1950s. Another new area for this Section is pharmacist's glass. See **119**. I have listed all of this glass under chemist' glass in the **Index** for those interested in this highly specialised area. At **128** is our first suite of glassware dating from the nineteenth century. It looks to be of good quality, is probably English lead crystal and decorated with gold. In the previous Section we saw our first lustres at £1,450 hammer (**70**) and further lustres at **82** and **102**. Here at **129, 137, 148, 181, 200, 201, 210, 219** and **235** are examples at the better end of the market, usually overlaid and enamelled and going no lower than about £600. The story of lustres can be followed down to about a £100 using the **Index**. The first Orrefors appears at **132** and this *Ariel* glass by Edvin Ohrstrom is top of the range. There are about ten examples in these pages.

The Scottish Sale at Lyon & Turnbull in Edinburgh in 2008 pushed some glass prices to new heights and none more so than Monart of Perth. At **157** and **169** are prices that would surprise even Monart collectors and I certainly would have expected these lots to fetch no more than half of their eventual hammer prices. Now Monart can go to about £4,000 hammer for table lamps and perhaps £1,500 for vases and even paperweights can fetch an awful lot of money. But I am certain that the ginger jar at **169** and £750 hammer is getting on for twice as much as the market would have expected. Monart has become a huge success story. Pieces that I would have sold twenty years ago for £30 or so are now fetching hundreds, and so they should. Salvador Ysart set up the concern in 1922 and his French experiences and his association with Gallé are well documented. Compare this output with Whitefriars. Check out all of the Monart in later Sections and follow also the Ysart and Vasart trails through the **Index**.

109

Near matching series of five Jewish glass jars, mid 19thC, deeply engraved with Menorah, angels, heraldic devices and script, sizes vary between 6 and 8in. Gorringes, Lewes. Jul 04. HP: £1,000. ABP: £1,176.

110

Victorian silver mounted claret jug, fruiting vine decoration and handle, similarly engraved glass body, London 1860, 11.5in. Gorringes, Lewes. Mar 04. HP: £1,000. ABP: £1,176.

111

Loetz-style baluster vase with lustrous iridescence in green with marvered grain-effect, 9.25in Gorringes, Lewes. Jun 03. HP: £1,000. ABP: £1,176.

112

Whitefriars tall Drunken Bricklayers vase, designed by Geoffrey Baxter, square, asymmetrical design, in an 'emerald' tone glass, 13in high. Halls Fine Art, Shrewsbury. Apr 05. HP: £1,000. ABP: £1,176.

113

Pair Victorian pink opaque glass vases with panel decoration of roses, 12in. Denhams, Warnham, Sussex. Jul 05. HP: £1,000. ABP: £1,176.

114

Modern Lalique glass vase, 'Bacchantes', modelled in relief with standing nudes, engraved marks to base rim, 9.5in. Gorringes, Lewes. Nov 05. HP: £1,000. ABP: £1,176.

115

Pair Peking blue glass bowls, engraved with birds/flowering plants, 4.25in, one rim a.f. Gorringes, Lewes. Dec 07. HP: £1,000. ABP: £1,176.

116

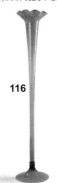

Art Nouveau vaseline glass lily vase, frilled rim, silvered collar, 176cm high. Lyon & Turnbull, Edinburgh. Apr 08. HP: £1,000. ABP: £1,176.

117

Sam Herman, blown glass vase, green, etched signature, 28cm high. Lyon & Turnbull, Edinburgh. Apr 08. HP: £980. ABP: £1,152.

Hammer: £1,000 - £900

118

Late 19thC WMF green glass decanter/claret jug, plated metal mounts in Art Nouveau manner, 15in high, marked rear of foot. Canterbury Auction Galleries, Kent. Apr 05. HP: £960. ABP: £1,129.

119

Pair of pharmacist's glass specie jars, 'Rhubarb' and 'Sulphur', printed/coloured royal arms marks, gilded glass covers, one jar with lifting decoration, thought to date to Queen Victoria's jubilee, 1887, 33in. high. Gorringes, Lewes. Dec 04. HP: £950. ABP: £1,117.

120

Lalique glass vase 'Avallon', clear blue-stained body moulded in deep relief, birds amongst branches, 14.5cm high, stencilled 'R. Lalique' to base, minor bruise to foot rim. Bearne's, Exeter. Nov 07. HP: £950. ABP: £1,117.

121

Silver mounted and etched glass claret jug, Birmingham, 1882. Great Western Auctions, Glasgow. Dec 07. HP: £940. ABP: £1,105.

122

Venini 'Pezzato' of oviform with flaring neck, clear body applied with irregular tesserae of red, green and blue, 22cm high, acid etched **** Murano ITALIA. Bearne's, Exeter. Jun 05. HP: £920. ABP: £1,082.

123

Keith Murray 'Cactus' glass vase for Stevens & Williams, c1935, engraved with cactus, etched facsimile signature, Royal Brierley, 14in. Gorringes, Lewes. Dec 03. HP: £900. ABP: £1,058.

124

Gallé cameo table lamp, pierced/gilded lid moulded with a flowerhead depicting wooded landscape in brown against a purple mountainous background, spreading foot, signed, 5.75in high. Andrew Hartley, Ilkley. Dec 04. HP: £900. ABP: £1,058.

125

Rene Lalique opalescent vase, Formose design, 7in, signed to base. Louis Taylor, Stoke on Trent. Mar 05. HP: £900. ABP: £1,058.

Hammer: £900 - £800

Lalique opalescent Laurier pattern vase with leaves and berries, engraved R.Lalique France in capitals, 7in. Gorringes, Bexhill. Mar 02. HP: £900. ABP: £1,058.

Emille Gallé cameo vase, dished rim, overlaid in green and etched with Dogwood, peach ground, 8.25in high. Andrew Hartley, Ilkley. Feb 06. HP: £900. ABP: £1,058.

Part suite of drinking glass-ware: 7 goblets, 11 wine glasses, 8 liqueurs, pair of ewers, with stoppers and jug, gilded with ribbons/festoons, glasses on faceted stems. Gorringes, Lewes. Mar 06. HP: £900. ABP: £1,058.

Pair 19thC Bohemian ruby glass & white overlaid table lustres, painted with medieval portrait bust medallions and flowers, gilded ground, hung with clear prismatic drops, 12in. Gorringes, Lewes. Oct 07. HP: £900. ABP: £1,058.

Blue overlaid glass vase, engraved with moorhen chick, 8in. Gorringes, Lewes. Jul 06. HP: £900. ABP: £1,058.

Daum cameo bowl, waved incurving rim, etched with flowering branches in red/green on a yellow staining to white ground, signed Daum Nancy France, 5.5in wide. Andrew Hartley, Ilkley. Feb 06. HP: £900. ABP: £1,058.

Orrefors Ariel glass vase designed by Edvin Ohrstrom, multi-layered interior with female figure amongst shapes and birds in blues, amber & greens, cased in clear, 19cm high, engraved Orrefors Areil nr 5840 Edvin Ohrstrom. Rosebery's, London. Mar 05. HP: £880. ABP: £1,035.

Lalique pale blue opalescent and frosted glass vase of 'Saint-Francois' design, exterior moulded in bold relief with birds on branches, 7in high x 6.75in dia, etched stencil mark to base 'R. Lalique, France', base rim with flake chip and 2 smaller chips. Canterbury Auction Galleries, Kent. Apr 07. HP: £880. ABP: £1,035.

Gallé cameo glass vase, river landscape at dusk, signed, c1900, 10.25in high. Andrew Hartley, Ilkley. Apr 04. HP: £860. ABP: £1,011.

Bohemian green tinted/gilt glass pedestal bowl, c1880, 28cm high. Wintertons Ltd, Lichfield. May 02. HP: £850. ABP: £999.

Pair 19thC Bohemian glass goblets, cranberry glass with white overlay, floral band, faceted stems, 20.5cm high. Sworders, Stansted Mountfitchet. Sep 03. HP: £850. ABP: £999.

Pair of Victorian lustre vases of trumpet form, blue cased glass cut with clear panels, gilded with foliate scrolling, fancy cut lustres, 11.5in high. Andrew Hartley, Ilkley. Apr 06. HP: £850. ABP: £999.

Lalique vase, 'Saint Marc', cat. ref. 10-934, patinated with rust pigment, symmetrical design of seated birds, introduced 1939, 6.75in. Gorringes, Lewes. Dec 06. HP: £850. ABP: £999.

George VI Art Deco silver mounted lockable cut glass decanter/stopper, key, Hukin & Heath, Birmingham 1937, 10in. Gorringes, Lewes. Jun 07. HP: £850. ABP: £999.

Victorian hobnail cut glass silver mounted claret jug, London 1891, 12in. Gorringes, Bexhill. Jul 02. HP: £840. ABP: £988.

Pair of 19thC Bohemian Lobmeyr style tapered green glass vases/covers, 15.5in. Gorringes, Lewes. Dec 00. HP: £800. ABP: £941.

Lalique blue stained frosted glass vase, stencilled R Lalique, France, 6.5in high. Andrew Hartley, Ilkley. Feb 01. HP: £800. ABP: £941.

Lalique opalescent Moissac vase, etched R. LALIQUE, FRANCE, 5.75in. Gorringes, Lewes. Jul 01. HP: £800. ABP: £941.

144

Glass, silver mounted claret jug, Edgar Finley and Hugh Taylor (H. Woodward and Co) London 1889, hinged lid with standing lion & vacant shield finial, plain glass body, star cut base, 28cm high. Halls Fine Art, Shrewsbury. Jun 08. HP: £800. ABP: £941.

145

Edwardian silver mounted glass claret jug with beaded borders, makers Goldsmith & Silversmiths Co. 1906, 11in. Gorringes, Lewes. Feb 01. HP: £800. ABP: £941.

146

Lalique frosted glass & blue stained Formose vase decorated with fan tail goldfish, moulded R. Lalique, 7in, chips to foot rim. Gorringes, Lewes. Jan 02. HP: £800. ABP: £941.

147

Laurier. Lalique opalescent glass vase, 17cm high, wheel cut mark R Lalique France, engraved No. 947. Mellors & Kirk, Nottingham. Apr 03. HP: £800. ABP: £941.

148

Pair Victorian lustres, frilled deeply dished rims painted with portrait/floral roundels, foliate gilded ground, 12in high. Andrew Hartley, Ilkley. Dec 04. HP: £800. ABP: £941.

149

Whitefriars tall Drunken Bricklayer vase designed by Geoffrey Baxter, 'emerald' toned glass, 13in high. Halls Fine Art, Shrewsbury. Mar 05. HP: £800. ABP: £941.

150

Suite of Bohemian amber flash table glass, c1900, decorated with landscape hunting scenes to incl: 12 goblets, 11 liquer goblets, 12 dishes and 12 plates. Rosebery's, London. Mar 05. HP: £800. ABP: £941.

151

Pair of Victorian glass, gilt metal & white marble cornucopia, each facetted vase issuing from a leaf, 26.5cm Dreweatt Neate, Donnington. Nov 02. HP: £800. ABP: £941.

152

Lalique 'Formos' bowl, 6.5in high, engraved R. Laliquue France 934. Kent Auction Galleries, Folkestone. Sep 06. HP: £800. ABP: £941.

Hammer: £800 - £760

153

Lalique eucalyptus pattern opalescent, blue stained vase, decorated with leaves, moulded 'R Lalique' mark, 6.75in. Gorringes, Lewes. Feb 06. HP: £800. ABP: £941.

154

Pair 19thC Bohemian glass goblets, overlaid and gilded bowls with castellated rims, faceted and gilded stems, 12in. Gorringes, Lewes. Feb 07. HP: £800. ABP: £941.

The numbering system acts as a reader reference as well as linking to the Analysis of each section.

155

Daum cameo vase, green & lilac overlay acid-etched with leafy shrubs, orange & lilac ground, engraved mark Daum, Nancy, 7.5in. Gorringes, Lewes. Dec 07. HP: £800. ABP: £941.

156

Lalique vase, 'Laurier', moulded with leaves/berries, blue staining, etched mark to base, 7in. Gorringes, Lewes. Nov 05. HP: £800. ABP: £941.

157

Monart, glass decanter with stopper, shape VI+ SC 395, orange and green glass with aventurine inclusions, paper label, 21cm high. (2) Lyon & Turnbull, Edinburgh. Apr 08. HP: £800. ABP: £941.

158

Lalique Marguerites frosted cased white glass vase, blue enamelling, No. 922, stencilled mark 'R Lalique France, 9in high. Tring Market Auctions, Herts. Jul 04. HP: £780. ABP: £917.

159

Victorian cut glass claret jug, 11in high, Birmingham 1896, maker Elkington & Co. Andrew Hartley, Ilkley. Dec 03. HP: £775. ABP: £911.

160

19thC Bohemian white overlay ruby tinted glass vase, 8 medallions, 10.25in high, gilt on stem and footrim rubbed. Canterbury Auction Galleries, Kent. Apr 04. HP: £760. ABP: £893.

Hammer: £760 - £700

Early 20thC Loetz yellow & iridescent blue vase, signed to base: Loetz Austria, 5.5in high. Maxwells, Wilmslow. Sep 02. HP: £760. ABP: £893.

Christopher Dresser glass claret jug, silver plated mounts. Rosebery's, London. Nov 00. HP: £750. ABP: £882.

Conical decanter with ribbed glass body, Heath & Middleton, Rd. No. 179916, dated Birmingham 1891, 8.5in high. Gorringes, Bexhill. Sep 03. HP: £750. ABP: £882.

Victorian glass gin urn and cover, engraved 'Holland & Co. Ltd Celebrated Sweet Gin', carved ivory finial to tap, 63cm high. Rosebery's, London. Jun 04. HP: £750. ABP: £882.

Loetz-style vase of globe and shaft form, lustrous iridescence in green and marvered grain effect, 7.5in high. Gorringes, Lewes. Jun 03. HP: £750. ABP: £882.

Lalique smoked glass vase, 'Belieri', engraved signature to base, R.Lalique, cat. ref. 904, 9.5in. Gorringes, Lewes. Apr 06. HP: £750. ABP: £882.

> The illustrations are in descending price order. The price range is indicated at the top of each page.

George V silver mounted glass claret jug, embossed with grapes/vine leaf, maskhead spout, cover with lion and shield finial, Elkington and Co, Birmingham 1916, 28cm high. Wingetts Auctioneers, Wrexham. Nov 07. HP: £750. ABP: £882.

Lalique, 'Palissy' frosted glass vase, moulded with shells, moulded mark 'R. Lalique', 17cm high. Lyon & Turnbull, Edinburgh. Apr 08. HP: £750. ABP: £882.

Monart glass ginger jar and cover, shape Z, red mottled glass with amethyst/aventurine, inclusions to rim, paper label, 26.5cm high. (2) Lyon & Turnbull, Edinburgh. Apr 08. HP: £750. ABP: £882.

Lalique moulded opaque ceiling bowl, 1930s, 12in dia. Halls Fine Art, Shrewsbury. Apr 03. HP: £740. ABP: £870.

Whitefriars 'Banjo' vase, designed by Geoffrey Baxter, bluish grey colour, unmarked, 32cm high. Hampton & Littlewood, Exeter. Jul 04. HP: £740. ABP: £870.

Lalique vase in 'Chevaux' pattern, stencilled mark to base. Great Western Auctions, Glasgow. May 05. HP: £740. ABP: £870.

Late 19thC Galle silver mounted green fruit bowl, enamelled floral decoration, design mirrored in silver rim, engraved signature in Japanese taste to underside, 8.75in. Gorringes, Lewes. Oct 07. HP: £740. ABP: £870.

'Drunken Bricklayer' glass vase, designed by Geoffrey Baxter, late 1960s, 13in high, original label, smoky brown colour. Biddle & Webb, Birmingham. Apr 04. HP: £720. ABP: £846.

Hukin & Heath 1883 silver mounted glass claret jug, 8.5in. Gorringes, Lewes. Apr 02. HP: £720. ABP: £846.

19thC Bohemian ruby glass octagonal jar, steeple cover, slice cut body, raised panels, conforming knop to stem, 16in high. Canterbury Auction Galleries, Kent. Dec 05. HP: £720. ABP: £846.

Lalique 'Laurier' pattern clear/opalescent vase, traces of blue staining to the leaves, engraved 'Lalique' to underside and R Lalique' to side, 17.5cm high. Sworders, Stansted Mountfitchet. Jul 04. HP: £700. ABP: £823.

Victorian cameo glass bowl decorated with convolvulus, green ground, possibly Webb, 5in. Gorringes, Lewes. Jun 00. HP: £700. ABP: £823.

Victorian silver mounted glass claret jug, 1888. Gorringes, Lewes. Sep 00. HP: £700. ABP: £823.

Lalique glass plaffonier, etched mark R Lalique, 17.5in wide. Andrew Hartley, Ilkley. Oct 01. HP: £700. ABP: £823.

Pair of Victorian blue/gilt cut class table lustres, 12.5in high, gilding rubbed, 1 drop broken. Sworders, Stansted Mountfitchet. Apr 01. HP: £700. ABP: £823.

Cameo glass vase, engraved to base Daum, Nancy with cross of Lorraine, 18.5cm. Sworders, Stansted Mountfitchet. Feb 03. HP: £700. ABP: £823.

Whitefriars kingfisher blue Drunken Bricklayer vase, designed by Geoffrey Baxter, 13.5in. Gorringes, Lewes. Sep 04. HP: £700. ABP: £823.

Victorian silver mounted claret jug, lion and shield thumb-piece, mask and floral decoration, body cut with stars on lemon squeezer base, maker I.F. London 1860, 10.25in. Gorringes, Lewes. Mar 04. HP: £700. ABP: £823.

Lalique opalescent glass vase, relief moulded in the 'Poppies' pattern with flower-heads on tall stalks, signed R Lalique, 5.75in high. Andrew Hartley, Ilkley. Feb 05. HP: £700. ABP: £823.

John Heath & John Middle-ton, Edwardian shouldered and chamfered glass box decanter, facet cut stopper, applied silver collars and a looped wire clasp to silver plated padlock, Birmingham 1907, 10.5in high. Amersham Auction Rooms, Bucks. Feb 08. HP: £700. ABP: £823.

Hammer: £700

Glass claret jug, Hukin & Heath, Birmingham, 1919, silver mount, lid and handle, 20cm high. Sworders, Stansted Mountfitchet. Feb 05. HP: £700. ABP: £823.

19thC Bohemian ruby over-lay glass tazza, alternating hatched and painted panels of summer flowers, all over gilding, opaline panel with a female portrait, 11in high. Dee, Atkinson & Harrison, Driffield. Feb 05. HP: £700. ABP: £823.

Loetz silver overlaid irides-cent glass vase, sinuous plant form, engraved silver flowers & leaves, iridescent green glass ground, unsigned, 8.75in. Gorringes, Lewes. Jun 05. HP: £700. ABP: £823.

19thC Bohemian glass ale set: jug & 6 tankards, amber glass, blue glass handles, cast pewter covers inset with an antler carving, bodies painted with dancing figures, German verse, jug 15.75in. Gorringes, Lewes. Nov 05. HP: £700. ABP: £823.

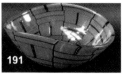

Ercole Barovier, for Barovier & Toso, Murano, a Tessere Ambra bowl, originally designed 1957, c1975-, 12.5cm, engraved marks to base. Rosebery's, London. Mar 05. HP: £700. ABP: £823.

Han Dynasty type bottle vase, lobed neck with loop handles to shoulders, 32cm. Sworders, Stansted Mountfitchet. Feb 06. HP: £700. ABP: £823.

Lalique vase, 'Druide', cat. ref. 937, opalescent and moulded with berries, pre-war, engraved mark, 7in. Gorringes, Lewes. Oct 06. HP: £700. ABP: £823.

Geoffrey Baxter for White-friars, glass 'Banjo' vase, orange colour, 32cm high. Lyon & Turnbull, Edinburgh. Apr 08. HP: £700. ABP: £823.

Whitefriars tall Drunken Bricklayer vase, designed by Geoffrey Baxter, emerald toned glass burst surface bubble, 13in high. Halls Fine Art, Shrewsbury. Jul 05. HP: £700. ABP: £823.

196

Daum cameo and enamelled bowl, river scene with trees, green ground, enamelled mark Daum Nancy with a cross of Lorraine, 5in wide. Andrew Hartley, Ilkley. Aug 03. HP: £680. ABP: £799.

197

Daum Cameo glass vase, early 20thC, etched/enamelled with a yellow iris in bud and bloom, cameo mark, Daum Nancy & Cross of Lorraine, 19cm high. Rosebery's, London. Sep 04. HP: £680. ABP: £799.

198

Late 19thC silver mounted glass claret jug, by H Woodward & Co, Birmingham 1880, mounts embossed with wheat husks surrounding vacant oval cartouches, stook finial, glass body with hobnob cut panels, 28cm high. Sworders, Stansted Mountfitchet. Nov 07. HP: £680. ABP: £799.

199

Geoffrey Baxter for Whitefriars, glass 'Banjo' vase, orange colour, 32cm high. Lyon & Turnbull, Edinburgh. Apr 08. HP: £680. ABP: £799.

200

Pair Victorian pink opaque glass lustres, bellied bowls with waved rims, painted and gilded with floral panels, clear glass icicle lustre drops, knopped stem, 15in high, glass domes, ebonised bases. Hartleys, Ilkley. Apr 08. HP: £680. ABP: £799.

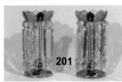

201

Pair 19thC trumpet shaped lustres overlaid in blue and cut back, painted in leaf designs in gilt, faceted drops, 11in high. Maxwells, Wilmslow. Sep 04. HP: £670. ABP: £788.

> Categories or themes can be followed through the colour coded Index which contains over 4500 cross references.

202

Suite of ten Edwardian silver mounted glass match strikers, Faudel Phillips & Sons, London 1903, and 4 London 1904, 4.5cm and 5.25cm high. (10) Sworders, Stansted Mountfitchet. Feb 05. HP: £660. ABP: £776.

203

Pair of swag/bead engraved glass decanters, scene of a horse and cart crossing a bridge, silver gilt necks with silver gilt vine handled cork stoppers, London 1909, 30cm. Rosebery's, London. Mar 06. HP: £660. ABP: £776.

204

Lalique milky blue stained Roger pattern glass box/cover, moulded Lalique mark, 5.25in dia. Gorringes, Lewes. Jul 00. HP: £650. ABP: £764.

205

WMF green glass decanter, pewter mounts, 38cm. Locke & England, Leamington Spa. Feb 03. HP: £650. ABP: £764.

206

Moser type blue glass brass mounted casket, late 19thC, enamelled and enriched in gilt, 13cm wide. Rosebery's, London. Mar 04. HP: £650. ABP: £764.

207

Lalique vase, 'Spirales', cat. ref. 1060, moulded design of raised spirals, etched mark R.Lalique, c1935, 6.5in. Gorringes, Lewes. Jul 04. HP: £650. ABP: £764.

208

Victorian silver/parcel gilt mounted cut glass claret jug, pierced thumb piece and star cut body W & G Sissons, Sheffield 1864, 9in. Gorringes, Lewes. Apr 07. HP: £650. ABP: £764.

209

19thC silver mounted claret jug, clear glass body cut with a lattice design, 30cm high, Hirons, Plante & Co., Birmingham 1864. Bearne's, Exeter. Nov 07. HP: £650. ABP: £764.

210

Pair 19thC overlay glass opaque table lustres, approx 14in high. Kent Auction Galleries, Folkestone. Mar 08. HP: £650. ABP: £764.

211

Lalique blue tinted glass vase, 'Espalion', also known as 'Fougeres', with moulded R Lalique, cat. ref. 996, 7in. Gorringes, Lewes. Mar 06. HP: £650. ABP: £764.

212

Daum glass vase, enamel & gilt decoration, green ground, silver coloured metal base, 9.5cm high. Charterhouse Auctioneers, Sherborne. Apr 08. HP: £650. ABP: £764.

213

Muller Freres Luneville cameo glass vase, signed, 26cm high. Cheffins, Cambridge. Nov 99. HP: £640. ABP: £752.

Late 1960s 'Drunken Brick-layer' glass vase, designed by Geoffrey Baxter, 13in high, smoky pewter colour. *Biddle & Webb, Birmingham. Apr 04. HP: £630. ABP: £741.*

20thC silver mounted glass decanter, Birmingham 1939, key lock, 22.5cm. *Sworders, Stansted Mountfitchet. Apr 05. HP: £620. ABP: £729.*

'Zanfirico' glass vase, in the manner of Paolo Venini, first designed c1954, internally decorated with blue/white zanfirico threads, ground pontil to base, three line acid etched mark, 38cm high. *Rosebery's, London. Mar 06. HP: £620. ABP: £729.*

Set of 12 Continental white metal Art Nouveau style wine goblets and tray, late 20thC, goblets decorated trailing vine leaves and initials MR, tray with vine leaf border, 46cm long, 111oz, 800 mark. (13) *Rosebery's, London. Mar 08. HP: £620. ABP: £729.*

Gallé cameo glass vase, green flower/foliage decoration, pink ground, signed Gallé, 17cm high. *Charterhouse Auctioneers, Sherborne. Apr 08. HP: £620. ABP: £729.*

Pair late 19thC lustre glass vases, hung with prism drops and lozenges, c1870/80, 25.5cm high. *Cheffins, Cambridge. Dec 00. HP: £600. ABP: £705.*

Prices quoted are actual hammer prices (HP) and the Approximate Buyer's Price (ABP) includes an average premium of 15% + VAT.

Gabriel Argy Rousseau pate-de-verre vase, signed on body and etched 11960 on base, 6.5in, extensive cracks to body. *Gorringes, Lewes. Jul 00. HP: £600. ABP: £705.*

Lalique opalescent glass vase, moulded in relief, 'Laurier' pattern of leaves and berries, marked R Lalique, France, 7in high. *Andrew Hartley, Ilkley. Apr 02. HP: £600. ABP: £705.*

Hammer: £630 - £600

Late Victorian ruby tinted glass epergne, c1900, 51cm high. *Wintertons Ltd, Lichfield. Mar 03. HP: £600. ABP: £705.*

Lalique clear/frosted glass Meandres vase decorated with wavy lines, stencilled R.Lalique France mark, 7in. *Gorringes, Bexhill. Mar 02. HP: £600. ABP: £705.*

Whitefriars Kingfisher blue glass Banjo vase designed by Geoffrey Baxter (1967-1973), 32cm high. *Clevedon Salerooms, Bristol. Jun 05. HP: £600. ABP: £705.*

Lalique opalescent glass vase, 'Rampillon', pre-war, cat. ref. 991, moulded lozenges and blue-stained foliage, stencilled mark R. Lalique, France, 5in. *Gorringes, Lewes. Jun 05. HP: £600. ABP: £705.*

R Lalique clear and frosted glass ceiling bowl. *Gorringes, Bexhill. Jun 05. HP: £600. ABP: £705.*

Emille Gallé cameo vase, overlaid in brown and etched with Dogwood, pink ground, signed Galle, 9.5in high *Andrew Hartley, Ilkley. Feb 06. HP: £600. ABP: £705.*

Lalique 'Libellules' opalescent glass box and cover, (Marcilhac No 51) designed 1921, underside of the cover moulded with 3 dragonflies, moulded mark Lalique, 17cm dia. *Rosebery's, London. Mar 06. HP: £600. ABP: £705.*

Art Nouveau glass decanter, silver mount and stopper, London 1902, maker's mark 'JTH/JHM' with engraved star burst to the foot of the decanter, 10.5in high. *Halls Fine Art, Shrewsbury. Mar 06. HP: £600. ABP: £705.*

Edward VII hobnail cut glass claret jug, silver mounts, hinged cover with flame finial, round star cut base, London 1901, 11.5in high. *Ewbank, Send, Surrey. Dec 06. HP: £600. ABP: £705.*

Glass Prices **21**

Hammer: £600 - £580

Four Edwardian ships decanters and stoppers, ring cut. Cheffins, Cambridge. Apr 05. HP: £600. ABP: £705.

Victorian silver mounted cut and etched glass claret jug, cherub finial and engraved detailing, A. Rhodes & Barker, Sheffield, 1879, 11.5in. Gorringes, Lewes. Apr 07. HP: £600. ABP: £705.

Lalique Coqs et Plumes vase, etched R.Lalique, France, 6.25in. Gorringes, Lewes. Sep 07. HP: £600. ABP: £705.

Mid-19thC Bohemian green glass vase, painted with oval panel of scholar surrounded by overlaid floral panels, gilded ground, 15in. Gorringes, Lewes. Dec 07. HP: £600. ABP: £705.

Pair of Victorian green glass lustre vases, 10.25in high. Andrew Hartley, Ilkley. Oct 01. HP: £580. ABP: £682.

Edwardian cut glass claret jug, silver shaped rim and hinged lid with thumb piece, body with alternate hob nail and diamond cut panels, 10.25in high, Birmingham 1906. Andrew Hartley, Ilkley. Aug 00. HP: £580. ABP: £682.

Lalique frosted/blue stained glass Boutons D'Or vase, stencilled LALIQUE, 5.75in. Gorringes, Lewes. Sep 02. HP: £580. ABP: £682.

> The numbering system acts as a reader reference as well as linking to the Analysis of each section.

Lalique Ormeaux glass vase, design of press moulded leaves, c1930, moulded mark R Lalique, 6.5in. Gorringes, Lewes. Mar 03. HP: £580. ABP: £682.

WMF Ikora crystal glass vase, red rim, green/yellow swirling flattened body, 14.5in high. Andrew Hartley, Ilkley. Jun 03. HP: £580. ABP: £682.

Pair of Victorian epergne. Tring Market Auctions, Herts. Oct 04. HP: £580. ABP: £682.

Lalique blue opalescent and frosted glass vase of 'Saint-Francois' design, exterior moulded in bold relief with ten birds on branches, 7in high, etched stencil mark to base 'R. Lalique, France', bruise to base rim extending 0.375in. Canterbury Auction Galleries, Kent. Feb 07. HP: £580. ABP: £682.

French silver mounted claret jug, late 19thC, cut glass body, 950 standard, 30.5cm high. Sworders, Stansted Mountfitchet. Nov 04. HP: £580. ABP: £682.

Edwardian cut glass claret jug, fluted domed lid with foliate finial, mask spout, and leaf moulded scroll loop handle, strawberry/diamond cut bottle with stars, 11.5in high, Sheffield 1904. Andrew Hartley, Ilkley. Feb 05. HP: £580. ABP: £682.

Whitefriars textured, waisted vase in kingfisher blue, 32cm high. Bearne's, Exeter. Jun 05. HP: £580. ABP: £682.

Lalique frosted glass fruit bowl, moulded with bands of flowerheads, moulded mark 'R. Lalique, France', 10in dia. Canterbury Auction Galleries, Kent. Dec 03. HP: £580. ABP: £682.

Pair of Victorian cased glass vases, painted with panel of exotic birds/flowers within white/green panels, gilded green ground, 11.25in high. Hartleys, Ilkley. Oct 07. HP: £580. ABP: £682.

Art glass bowl, blue with yellow veining, everted neck-rim with blue border, three blue glass toes, unsigned, 7in. Gorringes, Lewes. Dec 07. HP: £580. ABP: £682.

Muller Freres cameo glass vase, clear glass overlaid in blue, acid-etched, landscape scene, cameo mark, 26.5cm high. Lyon & Turnbull, Edinburgh. Apr 08. HP: £580. ABP: £682.

249

Silver mounted Stourbridge cameo glass decanter, aqua-marine body decorated with white overlay flowers and leaves, London 1887 maker CS F? 9in high. Kent Auction Galleries, Folkestone. Mar 08. HP: £570. ABP: £670.

250

Daum jug with silver gilt mounts. Sworders, Stansted Mountfitchet. May 00. HP: £560. ABP: £658.

251

Set of 10 Lalique wine glasses, stems decorated with angels, signed Lalique France. Denhams, Warnham. Dec 03. HP: £560. ABP: £658.

252

Extensive suite of Stourbridge table glass to include: Claret jug 12in high, pair of decanters 12in high, 12 wine glasses 7in high, bowl 10in dia, 12 bowls 5in dia, 12 liqueur glasses 5in, 12 wine glasses 6in high, 12 port glasses, 6in high, and 12 sherry glasses 5.5in. Ewbank, Send, Surrey. Dec 06. HP: £560. ABP: £658.

253

Lalique turquoise blue opal-escent/frosted glass vase, exterior moulded in relief, 'Oleron' design of numerous fish, 3.25in high, engraved mark 'R. Lalique, France', No. 1008 to base. Canterbury Auction Galleries, Kent. Feb 07. HP: £560. ABP: £658.

254

Lalique Rampillon pattern opalescent glass vase, with pre-war signature, 5in. Gorringes, Lewes. Jul 08. HP: £550. ABP: £646.

255

Lalique opalescent glass powder box, 'Tokio', cat. ref. 50, cover moulded with a stylised chrysanthemum, moulded/engraved marks, 6.75in. Gorringes, Lewes. Jul 04. HP: £550. ABP: £646.

256

Gallé cameo glass vase, amethyst overlay acid-etched with irises, script signature in cameo relief, 6in. Gorringes, Lewes. Jul 04. HP: £550. ABP: £646.

257

Schneider large bullet shape Art Glass bowl, purple shaded bands with orange, 12in dia. Golding Young & Co, Grantham. Feb 06. HP: £550. ABP: £646.

Hammer: £570 - £550

258

Webb 50-piece suite of Wellington pattern cut glass, for 12: champagnes, clarets, wines and ports plus a pair of decanters. Gorringes, Lewes. Apr 00. HP: £550. ABP: £646.

259

Sam Herman blown glass vase, etched signature, 40.5cm high. Lyon & Turnbull, Edinburgh. Apr 08. HP: £550. ABP: £646.

260

Almeric Walter pate-sur-pate shaped dish, signed Walter, Nancy, 4.5in long. Clarke Gammon, Guildford. Dec 02. HP: £550. ABP: £646.

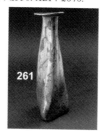

261

Loetz iridescent glass posy vase, of triangular section with inset engraved silver leaves against the iridescent blue ground, unsigned, 7.5in. Gorringes, Lewes. Jun 05. HP: £550. ABP: £646.

262

Two pairs of Bohemian enamelled goblets, one pink glass, other green, enamelled with bright leaf scrolls and gilding, knopped stems, 5.25in. Gorringes, Lewes. Apr 04. HP: £550. ABP: £646.

263

Victorian silver-gilt topped glass claret jug. Gorringes, Bexhill. Dec 04. HP: £550. ABP: £646.

264

Lalique vase, 'Esterel', cat. ref. 941, moulded leaves stained with blue pigment throughout, moulded mark, c1930, 6in. Gorringes, Lewes. Jul 04. HP: £550. ABP: £646.

265

Edwardian silver mounted ribbed glass match tidy, London 1910, 5in high. Gorringes, Lewes. Mar 04. HP: £550. ABP: £646.

266

Pair of Varnish & Co pale green silver cased pedestal glass bowls or sweetmeat dishes, 14.5cm high, each set with patent inset disc, c1850. Dreweatt Neate, Newbury. Jun 02. HP: £550. ABP: £646.

Victorian decanter stand, Greek key, vitruvian scroll borders and beaded bun feet, 2 glass bottles cut with swags & diamond banding, 9in wide, Birmingham 1864, maker William Goss, stand 23ozs 8dwts. Hartleys, Ilkley. Feb 05. HP: £550. ABP: £646.

Whitefriars tangerine glass Banjo vase, designed by Geoffrey Baxter, c1967, 12.5in. Gorringes, Lewes. Mar 05. HP: £550. ABP: £646.

Victorian opaque black glass vase, painted with a girl at a pond with ducks in a heart-shaped panel, leaf-scroll borders in white enamel, 32.5in. Gorringes, Lewes. Apr 05. HP: £550. ABP: £646.

Art Nouveau cameo glass biscuit barrel, acid etched with sinuous plants in amethyst, frosted ground, silver plated mount, handle and cover, 5.5in. Gorringes, Lewes. Dec 06. HP: £550. ABP: £646.

Lalique opalescent glass bowl, 'Tournon', c1935, cat. ref. 401, moulded mark R. Lalique, France, 11.75in. Gorringes, Lewes. Apr 05. HP: £550. ABP: £646.

Victorian green and vaseline glass epergne with 4 vases and 3 hanging baskets. Gorringes, Lewes. Jun 01. HP: £550. ABP: £646.

> The illustrations are in descending price order. The price range is indicated at the top of each page.

English white overlaid ruby glass pedestal dish, c1860, 20cm. Sworders, Stansted Mountfitchet. Mar 04. HP: £540. ABP: £635.

R. Lalique 'peruches' dish in clear and opalescent glass, raised fish decoration, marks to underside, 11.75in dia. Biddle & Webb, Birmingham. Apr 04. HP: £530. ABP: £623.

Lalique 'formose' pale opalescent glass vase. Phillips, Leeds. Mar 00. HP: £520. ABP: £611.

George V claret jug. body with sliced cuttings and etched ribbon/floral swag ornament, 11.25in high, by H W, Sheffield, 1910. Canterbury Auction Galleries, Kent. Apr 05. HP: £520. ABP: £611.

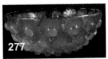

Lalique pale blue opalescent fruit bowl, exterior moulded in bold relief with 3 tiers of peacock feather eyes, 9.25in dia x 3.75in high, engraved mark 'R. Lalique, France' to interior of bowl. Canterbury Auction Galleries, Kent. Feb 07. HP: £520. ABP: £611.

Victorian silver mounted glass claret jug, by Aldwinkle and Slater, London 1883, pierced thumbpiece, glass body with elongated neck, engraved with crest to cover, 24cm high. Sworders, Stansted Mountfitchet. Nov 07. HP: £520. ABP: £611.

Glass and silver mounted decanter/stopper, Birmingham 1903, designed as a glass life belt with rope decoration and star cut base, 21.5cm high. Halls Fine Art, Shrewsbury. Apr 08. HP: £520. ABP: £611.

Pair of 19thC French opaline glass vases, applied enamelled roundels of 18thC style ladies in Neo Classical gilt borders, 84cm high. Locke & England, Leamington Spa. Mar 08. HP: £520. ABP: £611.

Victorian Moser style ruby glass casket. Sworders, Stansted Mountfitchet. May 00. HP: £520. ABP: £611.

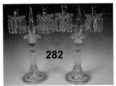

Pair of twin branch glass candelabrum, silver plated sconces, drip trays with prism lustres, 37.5cm high. Sworders, Stansted Mountfitchet. Sep 03. HP: £520. ABP: £611.

Pair of Bohemian blue/white overlaid tapering vases, gilt scroll decoration, 19thC, 10in high. Clarke Gammon, Guildford. Jul 04. HP: £520. ABP: £611.

Lalique 'Coquilles' opalised lamp shade of four moulded shells, stencil signed to a central reserve 'R Lalique, France', plated frame, shade 21cm dia. Dockree's, Manchester. May 00. HP: £510. ABP: £599.

'If the Haida School vase....could be attributed to....Freidrick Egermann then £500 is a snip.....should you really consider buying the Murano millefiori at £50 a piece?.....better to have bought the Gallé cameo or the Argy Rousseau bowl.....rather than the mixed lot of Whitefriars.....'

Despite going under £500 there have been some bargains at auctions in recent years. Both the French art nouveau vase at **287** and the Orrefors Graal vase at **301** are cases in point. I would include the Lalique *Domramy* vase at **296** if it were not chipped. And for those with more classical taste, and certainly those who are in the process of collecting the fine accoutrements of dining, what better than the Victorian silver mounted claret jug at **300,** as handsome a piece of glass as one will see, and yet its purpose is primarily function. And then at **298** is the Haida School cut glass vase which will date from the 1930s. This Bohemian region is famous for its glass which is highly collected. It is a specialist area but if this could be attributed to say a name like Freidrick Egermann in particular, or even an output, then at only £500 hammer it is a snip. It's all about knowledge! For the same figure you could have bought the twelve items of Murano millefiori at **289**, with added premium, at just under £50 a piece. This would have been a mistake, when for the same money you could have bought just one worthwhile object, which would stand a much better chance of increasing its equity in the future. For example you could have bought the Gallé cameo vase at **307** or the Monart at **309** or **311**, or for that matter, if Murano is your thing better to seek something of the quality of the pair of Murano vases at **306**. Try to avoid buying at the lower end of the market and if necessary be prepared to save until the better pieces appear.

At **322** is our first John Ditchfield, a living glassmaker working from the Glassform Studio in Lancashire. Note this piece is signed and uniquely numbered as is all of his latest output although some earlier pieces had only a paper label. This piece at £450 hammer is at the top of his range. further examples can be found on pages 40, 49, 65 and 67, the latter unusually not signed.

Functional glass tableware continues to impress as excellent value for money. At **326** and **327** are two fine silver mounted claret jugs and at **356** is a fine pair of Regency style candelabra. See also the glass jug at **342** and the candlesticks at **343**. At **328** is our first example, so named of the aesthetic movement. These vases are not to everyone's liking, but in this case there are collectors for fish related glass also. Note the £500 paid for a fishing related goblet at **349**. When you view the three pieces of Whitefriars at **357**, along with one other piece of unidentified glass, at £470 including premium, and even removing serendipity from the argument, it must be clear to most of us that this is a long way from a sensible

buy. Compare at the same price several fine pieces of Gallé cameo at **363**, **367** and **372** or the Argy Rousseau bowl at **370**, or even the pair of cut glass sweetmeats at **361**. In my opinion such lots exemplify what not to buy, unless of course, they go for a song!

At **383** is a very nice Lalique *Ormeaux* vase at just under £450 including premium. There is some scuffing to the foot but this is still a good buy, when in the same year an *Ormeaux* vase sold at auction for £682 including premium. See **238**. Interested readers can also check out a bowl in the same pattern at **611** which, even chipped did well in 2008 at £258.

There are some astonishing pieces of glass continuing to appear in this Section, not least a range of silver mounted claret jugs. See **397, 398, 399** and **416** etc. The example by Rupert Favell at **416** is of a particularly pleasing and unusual form and a further example of his style can be found at **771**. Readers should note that this decanter has a not uncommon white bloom on the inner surface and I can assure readers before they even try that no amount of treatment will remove it. In fact this is not a deposit as such that might be removed with treatment but rather the result of water residues being left in the decanter and the acids in the water actually attack and eat into the surface of the glass. This may only be removed by skimming the surface with hydrofluoric acid, not a task that can be tackled by collectors or dealers but a service that is quite economically available through a specialised glass restorer.

There are many more themes beginning to appear in this Section and the whole point about there being so many images, descriptions and prices is that the reader can follow their own trail by either browsing the pages or working from the *Index*. And where readers might have a problem understanding the terminology, then most of this is covered in the *Glossary of Terms*. For example by browsing ahead I have noted the rather surprising early appearance of Henry Greener pressed glass on page 40 at over £300. Some readers will be aware of the heady days of yesteryear when a £1,000 would exchange hands for a Sowerby table centre nursery set. Today we should, quite rightly be more interested in the quite superb Albert Mazoyer enamelled glass vase on page 39, (**531**) which fetched a very modest price when it sold at Rosebery's in London in 2004 for a mere £280 hammer. At 34cms in height, a commanding piece of glass, this can only increase in value and I wished that I owned it now, having paid less than £300 only four year ago.

Hammer: £500 - £480

285

Lalique frosted glass vase with mistletoe, 7in high, moulded mark R. Lalique to base. Canterbury Auction Galleries, Kent. Jun 01. HP: £500. ABP: £588.

286

19thC Bohemian ruby glass 2 branch candelabra with icicle drop, faceted stem/foot, 23.5in. Gorringes, Lewes. Oct 00. HP: £500. ABP: £588.

287

French Art Nouveau, c1900, glass vase decorated with poppies, graduated blue to clear ground, 26cm high. Bonham's, Bath. Nov 01. HP: £500. ABP: £588.

288

Lalique frosted/blue stained glass vase, Oursins, 7.25in. Gorringes, Lewes. Dec 04. HP: £500. ABP: £588.

289

Twelve items of millefiori glass, Murano, 20thC, tallest 42cm. (12) Sworders, Stansted Mountfitchet. Jul 05. HP: £500. ABP: £588.

290

Pair of Edwardian silver mounted cut glass decanters/ stoppers, retailed by Asprey & Co, Birmingham 1910, 12in. Gorringes, Lewes. Mar 04. HP: £500. ABP: £588.

291

Gallé cameo glass vase with mauve leaves and flowers on a yellow ground, cameo signature, 7.75in. Gorringes, Bexhill. Mar 02. HP: £500. ABP: £588.

292

Pair of late 19thC two-tier cut glass lustres, scalloped bands suspending prism drops, 42cm high, chips. Dreweatt Neate, Donnington. Nov 02. HP: £500. ABP: £588.

293

Lalique suite of table glass, plain bowls, moulded grape pattern knopped stems, plain footrims: 8-6in wine goblets, 6-4.75in champagne bowls (one chipped), 6-5.25in wine glasses, 6-4.75in dessert wine glasses, plain urn pattern decanter, 9in, moulded stopper for same. Engraved 'Lalique, France' to bases. Canterbury Auction Galleries, Kent. Apr 07. HP: £500. ABP: £588.

294

Cut smoke glass double seal, French, 19thC, 3.5cm dia, circular matrix, engraved with crest of a bearded male head, castle turret to top, top of seal with hatch cut matrix, 10cm high. Rosebery's, London. Dec 05. HP: £500. ABP: £588.

295

Lalique opalescent glass vase, moulded in 'Lierres' pattern with a band of hares, foliate ground with blue patina, etched 'R Lalique France, No.942', 6.5in high. Andrew Hartley, Ilkley. Apr 06. HP: £500. ABP: £588.

296

Lalique pale blue opalescent/ frosted glass vase, 'Domramy' design, moulded in bold relief with thistles/leaves, 8.25in high, footrim with engraved mark 'R. Lalique, France' & No. 979, rim with chip 18 x 8mm. Canterbury Auction Galleries, Kent. Apr 07. HP: £500. ABP: £588.

297

Victorian silver mounted cut glass claret jug, by Edgar Finley & Hugh Taylor, Birmingham 1883, fruiting vine knop, scrolling foliate decoration above spreading cut body, chips to base, 31.5cm. Sworders, Stansted Mountfitchet. Nov 07. HP: £500. ABP: £588.

298

Haida School cut glass vase, decorated with yellow/black grid enclosing concave roundels, 34cm high. Lyon & Turnbull, Edinburgh. Apr 08. HP: £500. ABP: £588.

299

Waterford cut glass terrestrial globe. Rosebery's, London. Oct 01. HP: £490. ABP: £576.

300

Victorian silver mounted claret jug, diamond/ratchet cut decoration, by H. T. Brockwell, London 1884, 26cm high. Ambrose, Loughton. May 00. HP: £480. ABP: £564.

301

Orrefors tinted glass graal vase, internally decorated with black fish, etched on base, Orrefors Graal NV 244A Edward Hald, 5.5in. Gorringes, Lewes. Jun 00. HP: £480. ABP: £564.

302

Lalique frosted/stained blue Nefliers vase, etched R. Lalique, France in script, 5.5in. Gorringes, Lewes. Jun 00. HP: £480. ABP: £564.

303

19thC Bohemian ruby overlaid goblet/cover, engraved with hunting scenes, grapes & vine leaves, 11.75in, chips, and a similar tapering vase, 10.25in, repaired. Gorringes, Lewes. Dec 04. HP: £480. ABP: £564.

304

Gallé cameo glass vase, amber tinted body overlaid with amethyst glass acid-etched with large flowerhead and foliate branches, signed in cameo 'Gallé', 5.5in high. Fellows & Sons, Birmingham. Jul 03. HP: £480. ABP: £564.

Categories or themes can be followed through the colour coded Index which contains over 4500 cross references.

305

Pair 19thC Bohemian white overlay/blue glass lustre vases, shaped/cut rims, decorated in gilt, leaf pattern ornament, plain cut prismatic drops, 12.5in high, one repaired/gilt rubbed, lacking wires to hang lustres. Canterbury Auction Galleries, Kent. Apr 05. HP: £480. ABP: £564.

306

Pair Millefiori covered glass vases, octagonal trumpet and bellied form, conforming stoppers, 12cm. Locke & England, Leamington Spa. Jul 05. HP: £480. ABP: £564.

307

Gallé cameo glass vase, pink overlay, acid-etched with plants, cameo signature, 5in. Gorringes, Lewes. Dec 07. HP: £480. ABP: £564.

308

Victorian glass/silver mounted claret jug, in Neo-Classical manner with anthemions and other motifs, maker's mark indistinct, London 1866, glass cracked, 31cm. Locke & England, Leamington Spa. Mar 08. HP: £480. ABP: £564.

309

Two Monart, early tapering glass vases, shape S, early tapering glass, blue glass with bubble inclusions, 16cm high (£280) and another 15.5cm high (£200). Lyon & Turnbull, Edinburgh. Apr 08. HP: £480. ABP: £564.

310

Tiffany Favrile glass vase & dish, vase 05158 engraved, 8.5cm, dish 'LCT' engraved 13cm, both early 20thC. Woolley & Wallis, Salisbury. Sep 00. HP: £470. ABP: £552.

311

Monart vase in pink, green & aventurine. Great Western Auctions, Glasgow. Dec 05. HP: £470. ABP: £552.

Hammer: £480 - £460

312

Victorian silver mounted glass liqueur jug, style of Christopher Dresser, maker's Hukin & Heath, Birmingham 1886, retailed by Clark of Old Bond St., 6.5in. Gorringes, Lewes. Feb 01. HP: £460. ABP: £541.

313

Pantin enamelled glass vase, c1900, clear glass form with applied enamels of dragon-flies amongst wild flowers, highlighted within gilt piped borders, 40cm tall, painted factory marks to underside. Rosebery's, London. Mar 05. HP: £460. ABP: £541.

314

Lalique opalescent glass dish, waved rim, moulded in relief, Companules pattern, etched mark R Lalique France, 12.5in wide. Andrew Hartley, Ilkley. Aug 05. HP: £460. ABP: £541.

315

Silver mounted cut glass claret jug, London 1868, body cut with stars, silver collar and lip, engraved with stylised gothic motifs, maker 'ECB' within a trefoil, 20cm high. Rosebery's, London. Dec 05. HP: £460. ABP: £541.

316

19thC Bohemian overlaid centrepiece, gilt leaf design, white overlay/green ground, 12in high. Gorringes, Lewes. Feb 06. HP: £460. ABP: £541.

317

Victorian silver mounted cut glass claret jug, maker H. Woodward & Co. Birmingham 1878, 10.5in. Gorringes, Lewes. Jun 06. HP: £460. ABP: £541.

318

Lalique pale blue opalescent glass fruit bowl, 'Lys' design, exterior/feet modelled in form of 4 flowerheads, 9.5in x 5in high, engraved 'R. Lalique, France' to base, chip to rim & a flowerhead. Canterbury Auction Galleries, Kent. Apr 07. HP: £460. ABP: £541.

319

Victorian cut glass claret jug, ball finial on domed lid, neck embossed cartouche flowers and scrolls, body with drape festoons on hobnail/diamond cut ground, 9in high, Birmingham 1894, maker's mark P & C. Hartleys, Ilkley. Oct 07. HP: £460. ABP: £541.

Clutha glass vase. Great Western Auctions, Glasgow. Oct 05. HP: £460. ABP: £541.

Heavy pair 19thC cut glass Masonic firing glasses, engraved with Masonic symbols, solid baluster bases, 5.75in high. Wallis & Wallis, Lewes. May 02. HP: £450. ABP: £529.

Green glass table lamp by John Ditchfield, bell shaped shade, signed, No. 8844, 25.5in high. Andrew Hartley, Ilkley. Feb 03. HP: £450. ABP: £529.

Hannah Walton, group of 4 glass finger bowls, painted in enamels with swimming fish, crabs, lobsters & mermaids, signed monogram, 11.5cm dia. Lyon & Turnbull, Edinburgh. Apr 08. HP: £450. ABP: £529.

Art Deco pink glass jardiniere by Muller Freres, depicting a boar hunt in high relief, moulded base, signed, 8.75in high. Hartleys, Ilkley. Oct 06. HP: £450. ABP: £529.

19thC silver-mounted claret jug, John Grinsell & Son, Birmingham, 1878, body cut with a broad band of hobnail decoration, foliate engraved/embossed mount, Roman Corinthian finial, 28cm high. Henry Adams, Chichester. Jan 03. HP: £450. ABP: £529.

Early 20thC silver mounted glass claret jug, by Mappin & Web, 1911, bead borders, 27.5cm high. Sworders, Stansted Mountfitchet. Feb 06. HP: £450. ABP: £529.

Victorian etched glass claret jug, silver mounts, applied lion/shield finial, crested, London 1865, 26.5cm high. Charterhouse Auctioneers, Sherborne. Feb 08. HP: £450. ABP: £529.

Pair of Aesthetic Movement white enamel/iridescent glass vases, one decorated with 2 leaping fish, leaves & dragonfly, other similarly decorated one fish, 28cm high. Locke & England, Leamington Spa. May 08. HP: £450. ABP: £529.

Millefiori ink bottle/stopper set with pink, white/yellow concentric canes, probably early 20thC, 14cm, bruise to side of stopper. Woolley & Wallis, Salisbury. Sep 00. HP: £440. ABP: £517.

Modern glass hundi lamp, floral wheel engraved decoration, gilt metal mounts, 32cm high, with a smaller similar example, 27cm high. (2) Rosebery's, London. Jun 08. HP: £440. ABP: £517.

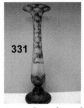

Bohemian ruby coloured etched glass vase decorated a wooded landscape, running stags/deer's, base with grape vines, 47cm. Boldon Auction Galleries, Tyne & Wear. Sep 04. HP: £440. ABP: £517.

Moser glass jug, ruby coloured glass enamelled with oak leaves/acorns, amber glass handle, marked in enamel, Moser, No. 801, D180, 4.5in. Gorringes, Lewes. Dec 04. HP: £440. ABP: £517.

Lalique clear glass Poissons dish, signed Lalique, France, 14in. Gorringes, Lewes. Apr 02. HP: £440. ABP: £517.

Loetz dimpled glass posy vase, petrol-blue/green iridescence, 4.5in. Gorringes, Lewes. Mar 04. HP: £440. ABP: £517.

Pair of Bohemian flashed glass vases, splayed rims, bodies decorated with stags within a landscape, 21cm high. Gorringes, Bexhill. Dec 05. HP: £440. ABP: £517.

> Prices quoted are actual hammer prices (HP) and the Approximate Buyer's Price (ABP) includes an average premium of 15% + VAT.

Two 19thC Bohemian red flashed and gilt decorated decanters/stoppers, ten sided bodies, triple ringed necks, gilt leaf scroll ornament, 8in high, slightly chipped and gilt rubbed. Canterbury Auction Galleries, Kent. Jun 07. HP: £440. ABP: £517.

Sam Herman blown glass vase, broad everted rim, etched signature, 33cm high. Lyon & Turnbull, Edinburgh. Apr 08. HP: £440. ABP: £517.

Lalique clear glass/turquoise stained Dampiere vase, etched R. Lalique, France, 5in. Gorringes, Lewes. Jun 00. HP: £420. ABP: £494.

Whitefriars orange Banjo vase designed by Geoffrey Baxter, 32cm high. Woolley & Wallis, Salisbury. Jun 00. HP: £420. ABP: £494.

Loetz blue green iridescent glass triform bowl, dimpled body, wavy line decoration, 5ins Gorringes, Bexhill. Mar 02. HP: £420. ABP: £494.

Pair of Victorian cased/flash cut lustres, petal rim foot, facet cut clear lustre droppers, 9.25in high. Fieldings, West Hagley, Worcs. Jun 05. HP: £420. ABP: £494.

Victorian glass jug, c1880, neck with a frilly ribbon tied cord, engraved with a giraffe & bird amidst foliage with a palm tree and a spider in its web, 21.5cm high. Sworders, Stansted Mountfitchet. Jul 05. HP: £420. ABP: £494.

Pair Edwardian glass candle-sticks, tulip shaped candle holders, drip-tray crystal drops, beaded ormolu foot, 10in high. Dee, Atkinson & Harrison, Driffield. Feb 06. HP: £420. ABP: £494.

Loetz a silver mounted vase c1900, pale amber ground washed in an even green and purple iridescence, mounts cast as trailing flowers, 16.5cm high. Rosebery's, London. Mar 06. HP: £420. ABP: £494.

Pair of Victorian green glass lustres, 12in. Denhams, Warnham, Sussex. Mar 06. HP: £420. ABP: £494.

Victorian silver cut glass claret jug, Birmingham 1900, 9.75in. Gorringes, Lewes. Jun 06. HP: £420. ABP: £494.

Set of five amethyst glass pharmacy bottles, early 19thC, remains of gilt labels, three cracked. (5) Sworders, Stansted Mountfitchet. Apr 06. HP: £420. ABP: £494.

French glass bowl, gilded decoration of floral swags, scrolls, lattice work, central figure of winged cherub, 12.5in dia. Brightwells, Leominster. Sep 06. HP: £420. ABP: £494.

Hammer: £420 - £410

Victorian glass goblet, fishing related, engraved with a gentleman wearing top hat, fishing from a riverbank, waisted, hollow stem, 9in. Gorringes, Lewes. Feb 07. HP: £420. ABP: £494.

Three Whitefriars cinnamon glass vases, 'Nuts and Bolts', Ref. 9668, 10.5in, 'Shoulder' vase, Ref. 9678, 9.75in and a 'Pyramid' vase, Ref. 9674, 7in, factory labels beneath, Geoffrey Baxter designs, c1967. Gorringes, Lewes. Apr 07. HP: £420. ABP: £494.

Gallé cameo glass vase, claret overlay acid-etched with leafy plants, cameo signature, 10.5in, neck-rim chipped. Gorringes, Lewes. Dec 07. HP: £420. ABP: £494.

Monart, three glass vases: flaring vase, shape GC with swirling blue glass body, 16cm high, shouldered ovoid vase, shape HF, with pale blue mottled glass body, 17.5cm high, and a smaller tapering vase, shape RA, in a similar colourway, 13cm high. (3) Lyon & Turnbull, Edinburgh. Apr 08. HP: £420. ABP: £494.

Late 19thC Bohemian flash ruby glass baluster vase, with white overlay cut into gothic arches, with gilt decoration, on circular foot, 11.5in. Gorringes, Lewes. Apr 08. HP: £420. ABP: £494.

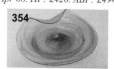

Clutha glass dish designed by Christopher Dresser, fold-over rim to one side, and pink, green and white swirl inclusions, late 19thC, 8in wide, acid etched mark. Hartleys, Ilkley. Apr 08. HP: £420. ABP: £494.

Late Victorian vaseline glass oil lamp, ribbed body, later blue/white decorated shade, base 29cm high. Sworders, Stansted Mountfitchet. Jul 04. HP: £415. ABP: £488.

Pair of early 20thC moulded and frosted glass three light candelabra, 'Regency' manner, cut pinnacle finial, shaped branches with reeded sconces hung cut prismatic drops, columns moulded with classical females, 24in high. Canterbury Auction Galleries, Kent. Feb 06. HP: £410. ABP: £482.

Hammer: £400

Three pieces of mid 20thC Whitefriars orange moulded glassware incl: 'Drunken bricklayer' vase, 2 others & a bottle shaped grey glass vase, 21.5 x 11.5cm. Locke & England, Leamington Spa. Sep 04. HP: £400. ABP: £470.

Monart vase, mottled green with black/aventurine inclusions at the neck, paper label beneath, now on Oriental stand, 12in. Gorringes, Lewes. Oct 04. HP: £400. ABP: £470.

Gilded and clear glass ewer probably French, c1860, 33cm high, also a matching pair of goblets. (3) Hampton & Littlewood, Exeter. Jul 04. HP: £400. ABP: £470.

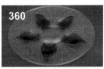

Lalique glass dish with green petal and cut decoration, signed Lalique, France, 12in. Gorringes, Lewes. Apr 02. HP: £400. ABP: £470.

Pair of cut glass sweetmeat jars and covers, c1900, 26cm. (4) Sworders, Stansted Mountfitchet. Feb 05. HP: £400. ABP: £470.

Pair of Victorian cut glass table lustres, 10in. Gorringes, Bexhill. Mar 02. HP: £400. ABP: £470.

Gallé cameo glass vase, amber tinted body overlaid with amethyst glass acid-etched snowdrops & foliage, signed in cameo 'Gallé', 4in high. Fellows & Sons, Birmingham. Jul 03. HP: £400. ABP: £470.

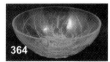

Lalique 'Graines D'Asperges No. 1' bowl, cat. ref. 3220, opalescent glass press-moulded with design of twigs and berries, c1935, moulded mark R Lalique, France, engraved 3220, 9.5in. Gorringes, Lewes. Jun 03. HP: £400. ABP: £470.

Pair Victorian overlaid glass jugs, one clear glass, other ruby, overlaid with opaque white leaves, gilded veins, ruby jug handle repaired, 10.75in. Gorringes, Lewes. Mar 05. HP: £400. ABP: £470.

Burr walnut veneered/metal bound Tantalus, 3 crystal decanters each with facet cut stopper. Locke & England, Leamington Spa. Nov 06. HP: £400. ABP: £470.

Gallé glass vase overlaid in amethyst tone with trailing foliage, berries and tendrils against a green and purple shaded ground, signed, 9.75in high. Halls Fine Art, Shrewsbury. Jul 05. HP: £400. ABP: £470.

Victorian Bohemian green glass & white/gilt enamelled vase of club form, 15in. Denhams, Warnham, Sussex. Jul 05. HP: £400. ABP: £470.

Pair of Bohemian glass vases, 10in high. Kivell & Sons, Bude. Dec 05. HP: £400. ABP: £470.

Early 20thC Argy Rousseau glass bowl, mauve/green ground, moulded with berries and leaves, impressed G. ARGY ROUSSEAU, 4in dia. Diamond Mills & Co, Felixstowe. Mar 06. HP: £400. ABP: £470.

Pair of Bohemian overlaid glass table lustres, painted with flowers against opaque white ground, clear glass lustre drops, 10.25in. Gorringes, Lewes. Feb 07. HP: £400. ABP: £470.

Gallé cameo glass vase, early 20thC, flattened ovoid form, floral decorated, with mauve over amber, 13.5cm. Sworders, Stansted Mountfitchet. Feb 07. HP: £400. ABP: £470.

Late Victorian silver mounted star engraved glass claret jug Gorringes, Bexhill. Mar 02. HP: £400. ABP: £470.

Two Whitefriars glass vases, 'Nuts and Bolts', Ref. 9668, one in pewter, other cinnamon, factory labels, a Geoffrey Baxter design, c1967, 10.5in. Gorringes, Lewes. Apr 07. HP: £400. ABP: £470.

Lalique plate, 'Poissons', Ref. 3056, pre-war, opalescent glass, etched mark, 11.75in. Gorringes, Lewes. Apr 07. HP: £400. ABP: £470.

Pair Vaseline glass comports, tops as oval frilled flower heads, twisted stem, 8.5in high. Hartleys, Ilkley. Apr 08. HP: £400. ABP: £470.

377

Edwardian cruet set: 6 square cut glass bottles, 3 with silver tops, stand with turned handle, 6.5in wide, Sheffield 1901. Hartleys, Ilkley. Oct 07. HP: £400. ABP: £470.

378

Pair Loetz 'Candia Papillon' iridescent glass vases, c1900, amber ground with silvery blue/purple iridescence, 35cm high. Rosebery's, London. Mar 08. HP: £400. ABP: £470.

379

Auguste Jean glass vase, rim with dripping collar, in gilt/coloured enamels with Japanese motifs, embellished with applied trailing tendrils, apparently unmarked, 33cm. Lyon & Turnbull, Edinburgh. Apr 08. HP: £400. ABP: £470.

380

Victorian Art Nouveau Vaseline glass lamp shade, wavy edge/stylized trailing foliate decoration, 23cm. Locke & England, Leamington Spa. May 05. HP: £395. ABP: £464.

381

19thC pink glass claret jug, poss. Webb's Burmese, gilded with leaves, plated handle & cover, 10.5in. Gorringes, Lewes. Jul 03. HP: £390. ABP: £458.

382

Loetz iridescent green glass bowl streaked with undulating waves, 7.75in dia. Gorringes, Lewes. Oct 02. HP: £380. ABP: £446.

383

Lalique frosted and moulded glass vase, 'Ormeaux' pattern, moulded in relief, 6.5in high, engraved 'R. Lalique, France', pattern No. 984, scuffed to footrim. Canterbury Auction Galleries, Kent. Aug 03. HP: £380. ABP: £446.

The numbering system acts as a reader reference as well as linking to the Analysis of each section.

384

R. Lalique glass bowl, stylised lily flowers heads terminating in 4 feet, etched 'R. Lalique France No.382'. Biddle & Webb, Birmingham. Feb 04. HP: £380. ABP: £446.

385

Lalique opalescent glass bowl, 'Coquilles', cat. ref. 3204, 1930s, 5.25in. Gorringes, Lewes. Jul 04. HP: £380. ABP: £446.

386

Whitefriars pewter glass banjo vase, moulded with geometric patterns, 12.25in. Gorringes, Lewes. Jul 08. HP: £380. ABP: £446.

Hammer: £400 - £380

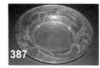

387

Lalique bowl, Coupe Gazelles, moulded with design of antelopes/leaf laurels, lightly stained in red, moulded mark R.Lalique, engraved France, 11.5in. Gorringes, Lewes. Mar 03. HP: £380. ABP: £446.

388

Set of four Edwardian etched glass ceiling light shades, floral decoration, shaded pink ground, gilt metal fittings, 7in. Gorringes, Lewes. Jul 06. HP: £380. ABP: £446.

389

Lalique pink stained clear/frosted glass Tournai vase, rim chips, moulded R.Lalique mark, 4.75in. Gorringes, Bexhill. Mar 02. HP: £380. ABP: £446.

390

Pair of George V silver and enamel cut glass vases, hobnail cut decoration on cornflower blue enamel/silver bases, maker HM, Birmingham 1926, 9in. Gorringes, Lewes. Sep 05. HP: £380. ABP: £446.

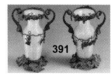

391

Pair of pale yellow & white spiralled glass vases, exteriors ribbed to give a chequered effect, ornate fruiting vine & scrolling gilt metal frames, 6.25in high overall. Tring Market Auctions, Herts. Jan 04. HP: £380. ABP: £446.

392

Claret jug/glass set, c1870: flash cut and gilt decorated claret jug and six pedestal glasses. (8) Sworders, Stansted Mountfitchet. Nov 05. HP: £380. ABP: £446.

393

19thC glass epergne, glass trumpet and 3 pendant vases, blue-tinted glass, frill rims, 19in high. Gorringes, Lewes. Nov 05. HP: £380. ABP: £446.

394

Daum Nancy glass vase, decorated with thistle sprays, gold signature to base. Great Western Auctions, Glasgow. Sep 06. HP: £380. ABP: £446.

395

Early 19thC ormolu mounted cut glass candelabrum, foliate scroll branches/lustre drops, 16in. Gorringes, Lewes. Apr 07. HP: £380. ABP: £446.

396

Pair of 19thC Bohemian ruby glass vases, gilded with leaf scrolls, 12in. Gorringes, Lewes. Dec 07. HP: £380. ABP: £446.

Hammer: £370 - £360

19thC silver/cut glass claret jug. Warren & Wignall, Leyland. Mar 04. HP: £370. ABP: £435.

Late Victorian silver mounted/ cut glass claret jug, 22.5cm high, maker's John Grinsell & Sons, Birmingham 1897. Bearne's, Exeter. Jun 05. HP: £370. ABP: £435.

Edwardian silver claret jug, by H. Atkin, Sheffield 1904, cut glass body with repouss, decorated mounts, 27cm high. Sworders, Stansted Mountfitchet. Apr 06. HP: £370. ABP: £435.

R Lalique, France, opalised glass charger, 'Poissons', spiral form with multiplicity of swimming fish, signed stencil mark in capital letters, 12in. Dockree's, Manchester. May 00. HP: £360. ABP: £423.

Cameo glass bowl with fuchsias, blue ground, 5in. Gorringes, Lewes. Jun 00. HP: £360. ABP: £423.

Pair of Victorian pink glass table lustres, enamel painted floral swags, prism drops, 14.5in. Gorringes, Lewes. Mar 01. HP: £360. ABP: £423.

Early 20thC novelty, coloured glass table lamp: bulb holders, shades fashioned as bunches of grapes, 16in high. Amersham Auction Rooms. Jun 03. HP: £360. ABP: £423.

> The illustrations are in descending price order. The price range is indicated at the top of each page.

Early 20thC Gallé glass vase, tones of pink, acid etched & carved with stylised leaves & berries, signature, star mark, 9.5in high. Amersham Auction Rooms, Bucks. Aug 03. HP: £360. ABP: £423.

Venini Murano glass vase, c1989, clear cased with green/red vertical stripes, 28cm high, label, engraved to underside 'Venini 89'. Rosebery's, London. Sep 04. HP: £360. ABP: £423.

19thC Bohemian overlaid glass vase, engraved with horses in fenced paddock, background overlaid in amber (reduced) 11.75in. Gorringes, Lewes. Jul 03. HP: £360. ABP: £423.

19thC Bohemian cranberry glass pedestal bowl, panels alternating white hobnail enamel, old damage to top of stem now riveted, 30.5cm high. Marilyn Swain Auctions, Grantham. May 05. HP: £360. ABP: £423.

Waterhouse, Dublin, burr & simulated walnut tantalus 'Betjemann's Patent', reeded bail handle and brass hinged locking cover, set of 3 facet and hobnail cut decanters, 34 x 41cm. Locke & England, Leamington Spa. Jul 05. HP: £360. ABP: £423.

Loetz art glass vase, 7.25in. Gorringes, Lewes. Apr 04. HP: £360. ABP: £423.

Venetian glass bowl, cut/gilt decorated with cherub within broad foliate and trellis star cut band, 32cm dia. Locke & England, Leamington Spa. Feb 06. HP: £360. ABP: £423.

Silver mounted cut glass claret jug, Russian c1900, cut with strawberry diamonds and flutes, plain silver collar, retailers mark 'Shanks and Co.' to cover, base AF, 29.5cm high. Rosebery's, London. Dec 05. HP: £360. ABP: £423.

Large early 20thC Val St Lambert cameo glass vase, high shouldered ovoid body, compressed double gourd neck. Fieldings, Stourbridge. Feb 06. HP: £360. ABP: £423.

Emile Gallé cameo vase, shallow circular form, dished and flared rim, overlaid in purple and etched with 'Soliflores Clematites', yellow ground, signed Gallé, 5.75in high. Andrew Hartley, Ilkley. Feb 06. HP: £360. ABP: £423.

Victorian milk glass ewer, mid 19thC, brass mounted gadrooned rim and foliate scroll handle terminating in a mask, 31cm high max. Rosebery's, London. May 06. HP: £360. ABP: £423.

415

Trio of Victorian turquoise opaline vases, lily of the valley and butterfly decoration. Cotswold Auction Company, Gloucester. Aug 07. HP: £360. ABP: £423.

416

Victorian silver mounted clear glass claret jug engraved 'THI 1896', hinged lid with openwork thumb-piece, glass discoloured, London 1883 by Rupert Favell, 18.5cm high. Dreweatt Neate, Donnington. Nov 04. HP: £350. ABP: £411.

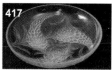

417

Lalique opalescent glass bowl, 'Veronique', cat. ref. 397, floral design, moulded mark R. Lalique, France, 8.5in. Gorringes, Lewes. Jul 04. HP: £350. ABP: £411.

418

Birmingham 1914, pair of cut glass columnar candle-sticks with rectangular silver tops and sconces. Thos Mawer & Son, Lincoln. Mar 04. HP: £350. ABP: £411.

419

Pair of Baccarat glass table lustres, 19thC, prismatic drops, bulbous cut stems, stepped bases. Sworders, Stansted Mountfitchet. Feb 05. HP: £350. ABP: £411.

420

Late 19th/early 20thC Stour-bridge crystal cameo vase, poss. Thomas Webb, cased in cranberry over clear crystal and cut back with a wild flower design below a foliate and lattice collar, clear ground detailed with a fine hatched pattern, 6.25in high. Fieldings, Stourbridge. Apr 05. HP: £350. ABP: £411.

421

Monart glass vase, paper label to base. Great Western Auctions, Glasgow. Jun 05. HP: £350. ABP: £411.

422

Silver mounted glass claret jug, by Walker and Hall, Chester 1907, silver mount with a pierced thumbpiece, monogrammed, 26cm high. Sworders, Stansted Mountfitchet. Apr 06. HP: £350. ABP: £411.

423

Pair of Bohemian ruby over-lay bottles, red/gilt stylised leaves, clear acid etched and gilt scrolling ground, 16cm high, one with matching stopper, 19thC. Bearne's, Exeter. Nov 07. HP: £350. ABP: £411.

424

Lalique bowl, moulded in 'Roscoff' pattern with fish and bubbles, signed 'Lalique France'. Hartleys, Ilkley. Dec 06. HP: £350. ABP: £411.

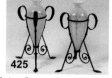

425

Pair of vases, Powell style vaseline glass amphora shape vases mounted on Benson style frames, 35cm high. Charterhouse Auctioneers, Sherborne. Nov 07. HP: £350. ABP: £411.

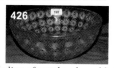

426

Lalique frosted and moulded glass bowl, concave flower head design with black centres, engraved signature 'Lalique, France', 25cm. Reeman Dansie, Colchester. Apr 06. HP: £350. ABP: £411.

427

Victorian etched glass and silver plate mounted claret jug, lion surmount. Great Western Auctions, Glasgow. Dec 07. HP: £350. ABP: £411.

428

Poissons No 1, Lalique opal-escent glass dish, moulded with a shoal of fish, 30cm, etched R Lalique France. Mellors & Kirk, Nottingham. Sep 03. HP: £340. ABP: £399.

429

Legras cameo glass bottle shaped vase, frosted pink ground overlaid in pink and decorated with fruiting vine, cameo mark 'Legras' 40.5cm high. Rosebery's, London. Sep 04. HP: £340. ABP: £399.

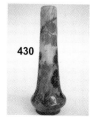

430

Daum cameo glass vase, early 20thC, opalescent yellow ground, overlaid in autumnal colours, etched with leaves/berries, cameo mark 'Daum' Nancy & Cross of Lorraine, 21.5cm. Rosebery's, London. Sep 04. HP: £340. ABP: £399.

431

Contemporary glass vase, designed by Gianni Versace, made by Venini, clear glass with blue cased panels with turquoise yellow and red murrines design, 25cm high, engraved marks Venini Gianni Versace 1998/57. Rosebery's, London. Sep 04. HP: £340. ABP: £399.

432

Venini Murano glass vase, 'Scotsasi' Tartan pattern, clear glass, banding in amber, red, white and blue, 22cm high, label, engraved 'Venini Italia' A.D.S. Rosebery's, London. Sep 04. HP: £340. ABP: £399.

Hammer: £340 - £320

Pair of Lalique milky blue glass coquilles plates, 8in. Gorringes, Lewes. Dec 00. HP: £340. ABP: £399.

Pair of 19thC Bohemian goblets, flashed ruby glass with painted, cut and gilded decoration, stems repaired, 8in. Gorringes, Lewes. Dec 04. HP: £340. ABP: £399.

Pair of glass table lustres, knopped stems, 10in. Gorringes, Lewes. Jun 05. HP: £340. ABP: £399.

Victorian blue glass epergne, tall central vase, 3 smaller vases, undulating rims, 21.75in. Gorringes, Lewes. Jun 05. HP: £340. ABP: £399.

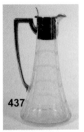

Cut glass claret jug, silver mounts Sheffield 1909, 27cm high. Charterhouse Auctioneers, Sherborne. Feb 06. HP: £340. ABP: £399.

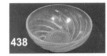

Lalique opalescent glass fruit bowl, 'Poissons', pre-war, cat. ref. 3211, concentric fish design, moulded mark R. Lalique, 9.5in. Gorringes, Lewes. Jun 05. HP: £340. ABP: £399.

Pair of Victorian blue-over-laid glass table lustres, with pendant clear glass lustre drops, 10in. Gorringes, Lewes. Sep 05. HP: £340. ABP: £399.

Modern silver mounted novelty glass liqueur jug, spout/cover in the form of a cockatoo head, claw feet, maker E&J, London 1956, 6.25in. Gorringes, Lewes. Oct 05. HP: £340. ABP: £399.

Victorian epergne, 3 trumpets centred by a large trumpet, 3 hanging baskets (supports missing), 4 rims to trumpet bowl, baskets overlaid pink/cream, 20in. Dee, Atkinson & Harrison, Driffield. Jul 08. HP: £340. ABP: £399.

Pair Edwardian glass storm lanterns, wheel cut with band of foliage, panelled stem, stepped square base, 15in high. Andrew Hartley, Ilkley. Apr 06. HP: £340. ABP: £399.

Orrefors Graal glass vase by Edward Hald, green/black fish inclusion, etched mark to base, No. 569L, 7.5in. Gorringes, Lewes. Jul 06. HP: £340. ABP: £399.

Monart vase in mottled pink, purple and aventurine. Great Western Auctions, Glasgow. Aug 06. HP: £340. ABP: £399.

Victorian cut glass claret jug, hinged lid with lion thumb piece, 11.5in high. Andrew Hartley, Ilkley. Apr 01. HP: £330. ABP: £388.

Claret jug of bulbous clear glass form. Tring Market Auctions, Herts. Oct 04. HP: £330. ABP: £388.

Lalique frosted glass bowl, moulded in 'Chiens No.1', leaping dogs amongst blue stained foliage, 9.5in wide, moulded R. Lalique mark. Hartleys, Ilkley. Jun 07. HP: £330. ABP: £388.

Michael Harris, cased glass bottle vase, pale irridescent surface with trailing and gilt inclusions above pale blue, white and green opaque marbling, signed, 8.25in high. Andrew Hartley, Ilkley. Dec 99. HP: £320. ABP: £376.

Substantial Etling stylised trefoil opalised glass vase, as three fish on faceted shaped base, signed in relief on the base 'Etling, France, 123'. Dockree's, Manchester. May 00. HP: £320. ABP: £376.

Victorian Burmese glass 'Clerks Fairy Light' with pink and yellow crimped rim, 6in. Gorringes, Lewes. Jul 00. HP: £320. ABP: £376.

Lalique amber glass volubilis dish, etched R. LALIQUE, FRANCE, 8.5in. Gorringes, Lewes. Feb 01. HP: £320. ABP: £376.

Pair of Victorian clear glass lustres, prismatic drops, 30cm high. (5 drops missing) Sworders, Stansted Mount-fitchet. Mar 03. HP: £320. ABP: £376.

453

Coquilles.Lalique opalescent glass plate, 30cm dia, wheel cut mark R Lalique France, engraved No. 3009. Mellors & Kirk, Nottingham. Apr 03. HP: £320. ABP: £376.

454

Set of 6 George V glass tots, silver holders, decorated in relief, by James Dixon & Sons, Sheffield 1991, lined box. Hobbs Parker, Ashford, Kent. Sep 04. HP: £320. ABP: £376.

Categories or themes can be followed through the colour coded Index which contains over 4500 cross references.

455

Venini Murano glass vase attributed to Alessandro Mendini, c1988, clear cased with vertical lines in turquoise, red and blue, 39.5cm high, label and engraved Venini 80 to underside. Rosebery's, London. Sep 04. HP: £320. ABP: £376.

456

Pair of Bohemian gilt decorated glass vases, raised panels within a foliate decorated ground, 19thC, 35cm high. (2) Rosebery's, London. Sep 04. HP: £320. ABP: £376.

457

Pair of George V cut glass claret jugs/stoppers, silver collars, facetted bell shape form, Birmingham 1918, 8.25in. Gorringes, Lewes. Mar 04. HP: £320. ABP: £376.

458

Lalique frosted glass plaffonier moulded with a radiating leaf design, etched mark R.Lalique France 12in. dia. Gorringes, Lewes. Mar 03. HP: £320. ABP: £376.

459

Part service of pedestal glass: four sizes of facet cut glasses, 12 water goblets, 2 similar sizes of 7 wine glasses and 11 sherry glasses. (37) Sworders, Stansted Mountfitchet. Feb 05. HP: £320. ABP: £376.

460

Part service of pedestal glass: four sizes of facet cut glasses, 12 water goblets, 10 wine glasses, 16 smaller wine glasses and 6 sherry glasses. (42) Sworders, Stansted Mountfitchet. Feb 05. HP: £320. ABP: £376.

461

Large glass goblet and cover, Bohemian 19th/20thC, domed cover, bowl decorated with a huntsman & hound pursuing a stag, 48cm high. Rosebery's, London. Jun 05. HP: £320. ABP: £376.

Hammer: £320

462

Pair clear glass table lustres, 19thC, prismatic drops, 16.5cm. Sworders, Stansted Mountfitchet. Feb 05. HP: £320. ABP: £376.

463

Victorian white overlay toilet water bottle, hand painted floral sprays and trailing gilt flora, crimped umbrella stopper, 11in high. Dee, Atkinson & Harrison, Driffield. Feb 05. HP: £320. ABP: £376.

464

Pair of Bohemian opaque glass overlay bottles, late 19thC, tulip-shaped stoppers, scrolling gilt leaf flowers and painted floral panels, one damaged, 24cm. Sworders, Stansted Mountfitchet. Jul 05. HP: £320. ABP: £376.

465

Silver-mounted cameo glass vase, inverted baluster shape, two-tone green glass, acid-etched with leaves, base mounted with continuous silver band of engraved leaves, 5in. Gorringes, Lewes. Jun 05. HP: £320. ABP: £376.

466

Three ruby glass salts on silver-gilt quadripartite stands with pied de biche, LONDON 1900 BY GEORGE FOX. Dreweatt Neate, Donnington. Nov 02. HP: £320. ABP: £376.

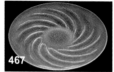

467

Rene Lalique Poissons No. 2 opalescent/clear glass plate, moulded with a design of spiralling fish, relief signature, 32cm dia. Charterhouse Auctioneers, Sherborne. Oct 06. HP: £320. ABP: £376.

468

Bohemian ruby overlaid glass vase cut with figure drinking seated on grape-vine, octagonal star-cut base, 17.5cm high. Rosebery's, London. Apr 07. HP: £320. ABP: £376.

469

Pair 20thC American green glass vases, foliate scroll white metal overlay, 17cm high. (2) Rosebery's, London. Mar 08. HP: £320. ABP: £376.

470

Timo Sarpaneva for IItala, Finland, clear glass 'Orkidea' (orchid) vase, designed 1954, engraved signature to base, 28cm high. Lyon & Turnbull, Edinburgh. Apr 08. HP: £320. ABP: £376.

Hammer: £320 - £300

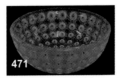

Lalique glass bowl, 'Nemours' pattern, signed Lalique Paris, 10in dia. Bourne End Auction Rooms, Bourne End. Oct 07. HP: £320. ABP: £376.

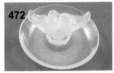

R.Lalique Deux Colombes opalescent glass ashtray, modelled with two pigeons, stencilled mark R.Lalique, 4in. Gorringes, Lewes. Apr 08. HP: £320. ABP: £376.

Pair of Continental lobbed glass pedestal sweet dishes, decorated in enamels with 'Court' figures within gilt cartouches, 18cm dia. and a matching dish, 21cm dia. Trembath Welch, Great Dunmow. Nov 99. HP: £310. ABP: £364.

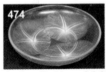

Lalique milky blue volubilis dish, etched R. LALIQUE, FRANCE, 8.5in. Gorringes, Lewes. Dec 00. HP: £310. ABP: £364.

Pair of Victorian Bohemian amber cased glass sweet jars and covers, engraved with hunting scenes, 11.75in high. Sworders, Stansted Mountfitchet. Jul 01. HP: £310. ABP: £364.

Tiffany sterling silver mounted cut glass vase, 6.75in. Louis Taylor, Stoke. Sep 03. HP: £310. ABP: £364.

Venetian harlequin set of ice cream bowls, early 20thC, aventurine/latticino decoration, clear glass cherub head handles, 10cm dia. Sworders, Stansted Mountfitchet. Jul 04. HP: £310. ABP: £364.

Victorian cameo glass vase decorated with pink flowers, 3in. Gorringes, Lewes. Jun 00. HP: £300. ABP: £352.

Victorian vaseline glass vase, crimped form, stylised floral decoration, 6in. Gorringes, Lewes. Jul 00. HP: £300. ABP: £352.

Austrian art nouveau plate mounted iridescent glass liquer jug, 9in. Gorringes, Lewes. Jun 00. HP: £300. ABP: £352.

Late 19thC silver mounted amethyst glass lobed decanter, Sheffield 1899, 11in. Gorringes, Lewes. Jun 00. HP: £300. ABP: £352.

Lalique milky blue glass poisson bowl, moulded R Lalique mark, etched France No 3211, 9.5in. Gorringes, Lewes. Jul 00. HP: £300. ABP: £352.

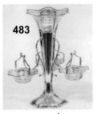

Epergne, central trumpet, lobed pierced rim, applied scrolling arms supporting 3 similar pierced baskets, 10.5in high, Birmingham 1913. Andrew Hartley, Ilkley. Oct 03. HP: £300. ABP: £352.

Pair of Loetz style iridescent glass vases, green ground, waved pattern in gold/purple iridescence, 21.5cm high. Rosebery's, London. Sep 04. HP: £300. ABP: £352.

Rock crystal snuff bottle, 19thC, carved deeply on one side with a longtail bird on peony, reverse with pine and bamboo, 6.5cm. Sworders, Stansted Mountfitchet. Nov 04. HP: £300. ABP: £352.

Set of six rococo style wine glasses, bowls each engraved and gilded with a building, figures & wildfowl, hollow ruby baluster stems with prunts, 7in. Gorringes, Lewes. Jan 04. HP: £300. ABP: £352.

Set of 6 Victorian glass rummers, fluted bowls, square bases, 5in. Gorringes, Lewes. Jul 04. HP: £300. ABP: £352.

Gallé cameo glass posy vase, acid-etched with leaves, ochre ground, relief mark, 4in. Gorringes, Lewes. Mar 04. HP: £300. ABP: £352.

Large Irish rock crystal glass pedestal fruit bowl, 19thC, finely cut with foliate/fruit, flute moulded ground, 29.5cm dia. Rosebery's, London. Dec 04. HP: £300. ABP: £352.

Pair of French mid 19thC bronze/opaline glass ewers, painted with flowers, foliate cast mounts, stoppers lacking, 11.5in. Gorringes, Lewes. Apr 03. HP: £300. ABP: £352.

491

Victorian cut glass biscuit box with plated mounts. Gorringes, Lewes. Apr 03. HP: £300. ABP: £352.

492

19thC Bohemian amethyst overlaid glass vase, cut and gilded panels, 17in and pair of Victorian cut, clear glass table lustres, 8in. Gorringes, Lewes. Apr 02. HP: £300. ABP: £352.

> Prices quoted are actual hammer prices (HP) and the Approximate Buyer's Price (ABP) includes an average premium of 15% + VAT.

493

Orivit art nouveau pewter mounted claret jug, overlaid green/white glass fluted body, foliate cast mounts, 12.25 in. Gorringes, Lewes. Jun 03. HP: £300. ABP: £352.

494

Italian ruby tinted glass goblet, enamelled in colours and gilt with merchants on a harbour side with ships to background, 17.5in high. Canterbury Auction Galleries, Kent. Apr 05. HP: £300. ABP: £352.

495

Loetz glass vase, stylised violet design in low relief against an iridescent orange ground, engraved mark Loetz, Austria, 6.75in, small chip to side. Gorringes, Lewes. Apr 05. HP: £300. ABP: £352.

496

Gallé cameo glass vase, acid-etched with a plum coloured hibiscus design, moulded mark in cameo, 9.5in, chip to neck-rim. Gorringes, Lewes. Jun 05. HP: £300. ABP: £352.

497

Pair of hallmarked silver and clear glass decanters, fruiting vine and plume cut shoulders, silver collars, triform spout, possibly Webbs. 9in high, Birmingham 1905. S/D. Fieldings, West Hagley, Worcs. Jun 05. HP: £300. ABP: £352.

498

Edwardian silver mounted claret jug, Joseph Gloster & Sons, Birmingham 1905, collar, cover and handle plain over a decoratively cut clear glass body, 18.75cm high. Cheffins, Cambridge. Apr 05. HP: £300. ABP: £352.

Hammer: £300

499

Victorian Vaseline epergne. Stroud Auctions, Stroud. Aug 05. HP: £300. ABP: £352.

500

Green glass vase, probably Monart, mottled effects in various shades of green and aventurine, 15in. Gorringes, Lewes. Jun 05. HP: £300. ABP: £352.

501

Late 19thC Bohemian engraved, ruby tinted covered glass jar, 12.125in high. Mervyn Carey, Tenterden. Sep 03. HP: £300. ABP: £352.

502

Monart ware glass bowl. Gorringes, Bexhill. Oct 05. HP: £300. ABP: £352.

503

Edwardian glass claret jug, silver mounts, Birmingham 1901, 24cm. Charterhouse Auctioneers, Sherborne. Feb 06. HP: £300. ABP: £352.

504

Pair of early 19thC ormolu and cut glass posy vases, 7in. Gorringes, Lewes. Apr 06. HP: £300. ABP: £352.

505

Peking green glass bulbous vase. Gorringes, Bexhill. Oct 05. HP: £300. ABP: £352.

506

Early 19thC cut glass and ormolu mounted casket with diamond cut foot and ormolu rococo shell and scroll base, 15cm. Reeman Dansie, Colchester. Apr 06. HP: £300. ABP: £352.

507

George VI silver mounted cut glass claret jug, inverted tapering form, Walker and Hall, Sheffield 1939, 11in. Gorringes, Lewes. Oct 06. HP: £300. ABP: £352.

508

Victorian glass centrepiece, twin-sconces issuing from central bulbous stem, lustre drops pendant from each, 19in high. Gorringes, Lewes. Jun 06. HP: £300. ABP: £352.

Hammer: £300 - £280

Miniature cameo glass jardiniere, acid etched with leaves & fruit, acid etched signature of Gallé, 2.5in. Gorringes, Lewes. Oct 06. HP: £300. ABP: £352.

Pair of Walsh and Walsh 'Brocade' ware vases, yellow-tinted glass with 'vaseline' floral detail, 6in dia. Gorringes, Lewes. Jun 06. HP: £300. ABP: £352.

Schneider 'Le Verre Francais' cameo glass pitcher. Great Western Auctions, Glasgow. Oct 06. HP: £300. ABP: £352.

Lalique dish, 'Poissons No. 1', cat. ref. 3056, pre-war, vivid opalescent, stencilled mark, 11.75in. Gorringes, Lewes. Dec 06. HP: £300. ABP: £352.

Two from a set of 3 Continental graduated decanters, silver mounts depicting figures in pastoral scenes & figural tops. Great Western Auctions, Glasgow. May 07. HP: £300. ABP: £352.

Poissons R Lalique bowl (fish with bubbles) embossed R Lalique etched France 3212, 8in dia. Kent Auction Galleries, Folkestone. Feb 07. HP: £300. ABP: £352.

Silver plate & cut glass centrepiece epergne. Great Western Auctions, Glasgow. May 07. HP: £300. ABP: £352.

Lalique, 'Medicis' pattern moulded & frosted glass tray, etched mark 'R. Lalique, France No. 280', 15cm wide. Lyon & Turnbull, Edinburgh. Apr 08. HP: £300. ABP: £352.

Lalique opalescent glass 404 pattern bowl, base engraved Lalique France, 25cm dia. Charterhouse Auctioneers, Sherborne. Apr 08. HP: £300. ABP: £352.

German silver claret jug, clear glass body with fluted bulbous base, hinged lid embossed/chased with monogram, pierced neck with laurel swags in relief, early 20thC, 17in high. Hartleys, Ilkley. Aug 06. HP: £290. ABP: £341.

Three dark emerald green glass flasks, all mid 19thC, all with related stoppers, 19cm approx. Woolley & Wallis, Salisbury. Sep 00. HP: £290. ABP: £341.

Pair of 19thC turquoise opaque glass lustre vases, edges decorated in white opaque glass, 9.75in high. Canterbury Auction Galleries, Kent. Aug 02. HP: £290. ABP: £341.

Lalique iridescent bowl decorated with fish, impressed marks to base. Biddle & Webb, Birmingham. Apr 04. HP: £290. ABP: £341.

Bohemian ruby glass vase, tulip form, foliate gilded, hob nail cut and floral enamel decorated, pedestal foot, 35cm. Locke & England, Leamington Spa. May 05. HP: £290. ABP: £341.

Pair of Victorian green glass lidded vases, pointed finials, painted with a gentleman in 16thC dress, 18in high. Hartleys, Ilkley. Oct 06. HP: £290. ABP: £341.

R. Lalique, 'Poissons' No.1. 3056, opalescent plate, post war, face moulded with spiral fish pattern, moulded mark 'R.Lalique', 31.4cm dia. Rosebery's, London. Mar 08. HP: £290. ABP: £341.

Art Nouveau cameo glass bottle vase by M. Drogy, decorated with Japanese anemones and dragonflies in red, etched orange ground, 16in. Gorringes, Lewes. Apr 08. HP: £290. ABP: £341.

The numbering system acts as a reader reference as well as linking to the Analysis of each section.

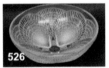

Lalique milky blue 'coquilles' bowl etched R. LALIQUE FRANCE, No 3201, 8.25in. Gorringes, Lewes. Oct 00. HP: £280. ABP: £329.

Orrefors Sven Palnqvist vase, tinted blue, yellow and green with bubble inclusions, base inscribed Orrefors Kraka Nr 322 Sven Palnqvist, 30cm high. Charterhouse Auctioneers, Sherborne. Jun 08. HP: £280. ABP: £329.

528

Lalique blue stained glass cigarette holder, stylised star decoration, moulded R Lalique mark, 3in. Gorringes, Lewes. Jul 00. HP: £280. ABP: £329.

529

Lalique Actinia plate, stencilled mark R. Lalique, France, 1927-47, 11in, original retailers label. Gorringes, Lewes. Mar 03. HP: £280. ABP: £329.

530

Pair Victorian amber glass lustres, waisted stem, chip/gadroon form decoration, diamond cut lustres, facet cut spreading foot, 42cm high, one lustre missing. Thos Mawer & Son, Lincoln. Sep 04. HP: £280. ABP: £329.

531

Albert Mazoyer enamelled glass vase, c1930, painted in blues/black with flowerheads & branches, 34cm high, black painted mark, A Mazoyer, France. Rosebery's, London. Sep 04. HP: £280. ABP: £329.

532

Pair of Victorian ruby glass lustres, 14in. Dee, Atkinson & Harrison, Driffield. Apr 06. HP: £280. ABP: £329.

533

Monart glass globe and shaft vase mottled in red, black and aventurine, 10in, label missing. Gorringes, Lewes. Apr 02. HP: £280. ABP: £329.

534

Claret jug, glass wrythen fluted body mounted with a plain silver collar, handle & cover by the Alexander Clark Manufacturing Company, Birmingham 1915, 24cm high. Cheffins, Cambridge. Feb 05. HP: £280. ABP: £329.

535

Pair of 19thC Bohemian mugs, ruby-overlaid and engraved with wildlife and fruiting vines, covers with pewter mounts, 6in. Gorringes, Lewes. Mar 05. HP: £280. ABP: £329.

536

Verlys opaque glass bowl, moulded with carp amongst bubbling waves, mounted with a metal mount and handle, 35.5cm. Sworders, Stansted Mountfitchet. Apr 05. HP: £280. ABP: £329.

537

Late Victorian silver mounted cut glass claret jug, angular handle, maker John Grinsell & Sons, London, 1898, 9.75in. Gorringes, Lewes. Feb 06. HP: £280. ABP: £329.

Hammer: £280 - £270

538

Sam Herman blow glass vases, etched signature, 12cm high and another SAM HERMAN vase, etched signature, 14cm high. Lyon & Turnbull, Edinburgh. Apr 08. HP: £280. ABP: £329.

539

Whitefriars, glass Drunken Bricklayer vase, pattern 9673, pewter coloured, 21.5cm. Locke & England, Leamington Spa. Nov 05. HP: £280. ABP: £329.

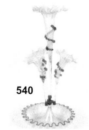
540

19thC vaseline glass epergne, large trumpet surrounded by three smaller trumpets, leaf moulded rims, trailed green glass decoration, bowl base with frilled rim edged in green, sd, 23.5in high. Fellows & Sons, Hockley, Birmingham. Oct 03. HP: £280. ABP: £329.

541

Mdina 'Cut Ice' glass vase, designed by Michael Harris, c1970, internal blue, brown/green swirling cased in clear, signed 'Michael Harris Mdina Glass Malta' to underside, 22cm high. Rosebery's, London. Mar 08. HP: £280. ABP: £329.

542

Lalique opalescent glass Actinia pattern plate, etched R LALIQUE FRANCE, 27cm. Charterhouse Auctioneers, Sherborne. Apr 07. HP: £280. ABP: £329.

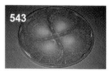
543

Lalique opalescent glass dish, moulded in Coquilles pattern with four shells, 11.75in wide, etched mark, No.3009. Hartleys, Ilkley. Aug 06. HP: £280. ABP: £329.

544

19thC Bristol blue glass bowl, 22cm high. Sworders, Stansted Mountfitchet. Jun 03. HP: £270. ABP: £317.

545

Bohemian white overlay comport, 2nd half 19thC, Gothic taste, emerald green ground, gilt embellishment, 24cm high. Hampton & Littlewood, Exeter. Jul 04. HP: £270. ABP: £317.

546

Pair Loetz style vases, green glass decorated with applications in blue/purple iridescence, pontil marks to undersides, 25cm high. Rosebery's, London. Sep 04. HP: £270. ABP: £317.

Hammer: £270 - £260

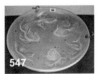

Sabino opalescent glass light-bowl, fish design, moulded mark, 37cm dia. Great Western Auctions, Glasgow. Apr 08. HP: £270. ABP: £317.

Set of 16 Stephens & Williams amethyst coloured cut wine and sherry glasses, etched marks. Sworders, Stansted Mountfitchet. Dec 02. HP: £260. ABP: £305.

Amethyst glass jack-in-the-pulpit vase by John Ditch-field, signed, No. 5912, 18.25in high. Andrew Hartley, Ilkley. Feb 03. HP: £260. ABP: £305.

Greener & Co. Marquis of Lorne pattern butter dish, brown, olive green and white marbled glass, clear Greener 1st mark to lid, unclear mark and reg. diamond to base. Boldon Auction Galleries, Tyne & Wear. Jun 04. HP: £260. ABP: £305.

Pair of cut glass preserve pots, 19thC, lambrequin white metal mounts, 13cm. Sworders, Stansted Mountfitchet. Feb 06. HP: £260. ABP: £305.

Art Nouveau glass vase, flared incurving top, waved rim, applied with green glass trailing stylised foliage, poss. by James Parnell, 9.25in high. Andrew Hartley, Ilkley. Aug 04. HP: £260. ABP: £305.

Whitefriars Kingfisher mobile phone 9668 vase, by Geoffrey Baxter, 26.7cm high, indigo. Rosebery's, London. Sep 04. HP: £260. ABP: £305.

> The illustrations are in descending price order. The price range is indicated at the top of each page.

Venini Murano glass decanter, turquoise body and neck, yellow bulbous waist & stopper, c1983, 36cm high, label and engraved Venini, Italia 83 to underside. Rosebery's, London. Sep 04. HP: £260. ABP: £305.

Daum cameo glass posy vase, acid-etched with naturalistic flowers/leaves in green, red & amber, etched mark Daum, Nancy, Cross of Lorraine, 3.75in, chips around base. Gorringes, Lewes. Apr 03. HP: £260. ABP: £305.

Set six amethyst shaded glass posy vases attributed to Moser, floral decoration, 4in. Gorringes, Lewes. Feb 06. HP: £260. ABP: £305.

Loetz style vase with Jack-in-the-Pulpit top, purple trails on a yellow lustre ground, 7in high. Andrew Hartley, Ilkley. Apr 06. HP: £260. ABP: £305.

Silver plated framed tantalus, 3 full cut original bottles No. 1, 2 & 3, 'As Presentation to the Mayor & Mayoress of Haslingden Alderman & Mfs. Raaron Holt, April 7th 1899' by Walker & Hall 'The Only Holdfast' No. 16328/2. Kent Auction Galleries, Folkestone. Sep 06. HP: £260. ABP: £305.

Gallé Cameo glass vase, flowers/foliage in dark red overlaid on amber glass body, 9cm. Charterhouse Auctioneers, Sherborne. Oct 06. HP: £260. ABP: £305.

John Ditchfield iridescent glass table lamp, mushroom form, tones of purple, blue and green, signed, 24.5in high. Hartleys, Ilkley. Dec 06. HP: £260. ABP: £305.

Bohemian green glass vase, 19thC, painted with a panel of a young woman wearing a scarf, gilt highlights, 34cm. Sworders, Stansted Mountfitchet. Feb 07. HP: £260. ABP: £305.

Contemporary Murano glass vase, possibly by Missoni, clear glass with red/blue/green diagonally striped coloured design, 37cm high, unsigned. Rosebery's, London. Mar 05. HP: £260. ABP: £305.

Part wine service: 8 large glasses, 3 medium wines, 4 small wines and 3 cordial glasses, faceted bowls wheel cut with fruiting vines. (20) Hartleys, Ilkley. Feb 08. HP: £260. ABP: £305.

Josef Hofmann for Moser (attrib.) facetted glass jar and cover, corresponding knop handle, amethyst glass, 16cm high & smoked glass facetted bowl, 17.5cm dia. (2) Lyon & Turnbull, Edinburgh. Apr 08. HP: £260. ABP: £305.

Pair clear glass table lustres, flared castellated bowls, 10 prismatic drops, faceted stem/base with zigzag cut border, 12.5in high. Hartleys, Ilkley. Apr 08. HP: £260. ABP: £305.

PART I: Decorative & Functional Glass c1830-2000
Section IV: £250-£100

'My tongue is firmly in my cheek when I suggest you seek façon de venise.....Kosta can go up to £1,200 at least.....Keith Murray averages about £300.....give me Walsh-Walsh any day for the same money.....or you would be better off buying Timo Sarpaneva for £300.....'

Whilst the best of Tiffany can go to five figures, our examples start on page 9 at **25** and can be found also at **79, 310, 476,** here at **566** and at **829,** but a glass window does make £2,000 hammer at **1838** on page 114, although this later Section will contain its own analysis. Similarly Venetian glass, when early, or even façon de venise, that is, European but in the style of Venice, and sixteenth or seventeenth century, can be worth a great deal of money. See **2011.** More modestly Venetian glass here commences with a fine pair of nineteenth century goblets, very modestly priced at under £300. Note the small feet indicating their lateness. In Georgian and earlier drinking glasses the feet are much wider and when placed together would always touch first. In this pair it is evident that the bowls will make the first contact. These nevertheless, are cheap enough to sell on at less than £300 and should make £500 at least. Check out the *Index* for later examples and if you study the subject carefully, and in particular the early period, then you could, with a considerable degree of luck, find a bargain that everyone else has missed. My tongue is firmly in my cheek! At **593** we have our first Kosta at £240 hammer and there is a further example at **724** in this Section on page 49, and then the story can be followed in later pages. Kosta can go up to £1,200 hammer at least, and at this price is worth every penny. Perhaps more glass collectors should consider its future investment potential because it is so reasonably priced that it can only go up in value.This story continues on pages 61, 72, 78 and 107.

At **596** is our first Keith Murray, normally of Wedgwood and pottery fame. Here about £300 is pretty average and the top end of the Murray market in glass appears on page 15 at **123** and £900 hammer. He bottoms out at about £130 hammer where for me at least his work has absolutely no appeal. Incidentally neither would I pay over a £1,000 for the Cactus vase. Give me the opportunity to buy Walsh-Walsh any day. Our first example occurred on page 38 at £300 hammer and here at **571** an art deco decanter set reached £250 plus premium. See also **605, 792** and **1253.** At **626** is a Schneider art glass vase at £220 hammer, but back at **257** on page 25 a good art glass bowl did much better at £550 hammer and a cameo glass pitcher at **511** I think, was under priced at £300 hammer. Charles Schneider can be followed further at **682** with 'Le Verre Francais' and then at **701** etc. Use the *Index.* Here at **652** is a wonderful piece of Burmese which was very modestly priced in **2002** at

£200 hammer. Back at **381** a Webb's Burmese made £390 hammer and at **450,** £320 hammer. The lower end of the Queen's Burmese glass market is represented at £80 hammer at **983.** Those readers wishing to follow Thomas Webb have almost twenty further examples in these pages, starting with the incredible cameo double gourd vase at **2,** which fetched over £42,000.

I was surprised to see Edward Moore of the Tyne Flint Glassworks, South Shields, appearing so early in these pages at **675,** where a brown and white pressed glass malachite vase fetched £190 hammer. Of course, this lot did sell at Boldon Auction Galleries only a couple of miles away from South Shields and this is a regional price. The same happens in Stourbridge.

Whilst Whitefriars vies with Lalique for the most entries it is not all about Geoffrey Baxter, although he appears again at **679** and everywhere else for that matter. See also other Whitefriars at **694** and **699** and expect Whitefriars to appear in the paperweights. Millefiore inkwells don't appear often at auction and when they do they will fetch at least as much as a good Stourbridge paperweight. See **687.** I wouldn't have expected Gabriel Argy Rousseau to appear so far down the pecking order but here is a pate de verre 1920s glass ashtray at **691,** so there is hope for us all if we cannot afford the very best of pate de verre. I skirted around the Sabino at **547** in the last Section but there is a fine example at **714** and a bowl in the Sabino manner at **732.** Readers may follow on through the *Index.* More interesting is the *Finlandia* vase by Timo Sarpaneva at **731.** Timo first appeared at **470** and £320 hammer and can be seen again at **1002** at £80. Unfortunately, there are no more examples. The French art glass pitcher by G de Feuvre at **738** is quite intriguing in that it explores exactly what Salvador Ysart was about at Monart and indicates his French pedigree. This pitcher is worth more than a £188! At **796** is a Legras vase for £130 hammer but this was a few years ago. Check out the cameo bottle at **429** and what at first seemed a cheap Legras cameo at **994** except that it has been damaged and restuck. Don't underestimate Legras. His lamps can go over £2,000 and his cameo vases over £500. Finally at **851** we have our first Mary Gregory and I include about a dozen further examples in later pages. This was never of any serious quality, but now it has been so much copied and reproduced that it is almost worthless, except that at Boldon Auction Galleries in 2005, a Victorian jug did fetch a reasonable £80, but I think those days are past! See **1406.**

Hammer: £250 - £240

Tiffany & Co opalescent green glass jar/cover, brass metal leafage cut overlay cover, brass inner liner, impressed 'Tiffany Studios New York', 16.5cm high. Locke & England, Leamington Spa. May 03. HP: £250. ABP: £294.

Late Victorian silver 3 bottle tantalus, threaded frame on a trefoil base, 13.5in high. Tring Market Auctions, Herts. Mar 03. HP: £250. ABP: £294.

Pair glass hall candle vases, 'storm' shades, engraved/etched with foliate sprays, two tier base, 39cm high. Hampton & Littlewood, Exeter. Jul 04. HP: £250. ABP: £294.

Pair of late 19thC Venetian goblets, blue/white & aventurine, clear glass stems with moulded hollow knops, 7in. Gorringes, Lewes. Mar 03. HP: £250. ABP: £294.

Modern Murano glass dish, 19.5in. Gorringes, Lewes. Jun 05. HP: £250. ABP: £294.

Art Deco decanter set designed by Clyne Farquharson for John Walsh Walsh c1936, decanter/stopper with set of 6 footed liqueurs, leaf pattern, signed/dated for 1940, decanter 10.5in. Fieldings, Stourbridge. Nov 05. HP: £250. ABP: £294.

Pair of drunken bricklayer vases by Geoffrey Baxter for Whitefriars Glass, tangerine colour, shape No 9673 produced between 1969-74, 21cm high. Rosebery's, London. Mar 06. HP: £250. ABP: £294.

> Categories or themes can be followed through the colour coded Index which contains over 4500 cross references.

1920s moulded/tinted glass dish decorated with hounds and ivy, bird border, signed in two places 'R Lalique' and 'Lalique', 21cm. Reeman Dansie, Colchester. Apr 06. HP: £250. ABP: £294.

Whitefriars emerald green ribbed wave tumbler vase, c1930, designed by Marriot Powell, paper label, 38cm high. Rosebery's, London. Apr 07. HP: £250. ABP: £294.

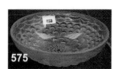

Pressed opaline glass bowl decorated with birds. Great Western Auctions, Glasgow. Nov 07. HP: £250. ABP: £294.

Large 19thC Bohemian glass goblet/cover, ten-sided bowl engraved with a stag, deer and woodland, ruby-overlaid ground, knopped stem, ten-sided foot, cover with spiral rim & acorn finial, 20.25in. Gorringes, Lewes. Dec 07. HP: £250. ABP: £294.

Bohemian flared glass beaker, 2nd half 19thC, 11.5cm. Woolley & Wallis, Salisbury. Sep 00. HP: £240. ABP: £282.

Daum Nancy etched cameo glass bowl, acid etched mark on side, painted initials BJ underneath, 2in, tiny rim chip. Gorringes, Lewes. Apr 01. HP: £240. ABP: £282.

19thC Bohemian ruby flash glass vase engraved with alternating floral and animal panels, faceted lobed foot, 7.5in. Gorringes, Lewes. Apr 01. HP: £240. ABP: £282.

Venini Murano glass decanter, c1983, claret/turquoise body, claret coloured stopper, 33.5cm high, Venini labels and engraved 'Venini Italia' 83 to underside. Rosebery's, London. Sep 04. HP: £240. ABP: £282.

Whitefriars Drunken Bricklayer glass vase, kingfisher blue, designed by G. Baxter, 8in. Gorringes, Lewes. Dec 04. HP: £240. ABP: £282.

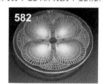

Lalique opalescent plate 'Coquilles', etched R Lalique France No. 3011, 9.25in. Gorringes, Lewes. Jun 05. HP: £240. ABP: £282.

Pair of Continental cased glass trumpet vases, green overlaid panels, gilt cloud fret ground, 10.75in, one rim repaired. Gorringes, Lewes. Oct 02. HP: £240. ABP: £282.

Victorian ebonised tantalus, 3 cut glass decanters, 2 silver labels, 16in. Gorringes, Lewes. Dec 06. HP: £240. ABP: £282.

Pair of Victorian blue glass table lustres, cusped rims, gilding/enamelled garlands, knopped stems, clear glass lustre drops, 14.5in. *Gorringes, Lewes. Feb 06. HP: £240. ABP: £282.*

Venetian glass bottle, labelled Venini, Murano, striped in smoke glass/opaque white, spire stopper, 18.5in. *Gorringes, Lewes. Jun 05. HP: £240. ABP: £282.*

Gray Stan glass vase, goblet shape. *Great Western Auctions, Glasgow. Apr 06. HP: £240. ABP: £282.*

Pair of Victorian cut glass vases and covers, hob nail cut decoration, flattened lid, square bases, 9.5in. *Gorringes, Lewes. Apr 08. HP: £240. ABP: £282.*

Lalique frosted glass bird vase, post-war, two nesting birds, wings raised, engraved mark Lalique, France, 8.5in. *Gorringes, Lewes. Jul 03. HP: £240. ABP: £282.*

19thC cut-glass oval basket, Georgian manner, silvery metal handle by Tiffany & Co, body with slice, panel & hobnail cuttings, 8 x 4.5 x 11in high, handle stamped 'Tiffany & Co, Makers'. *Canterbury Auction Galleries, Kent. Dec 05. HP: £240. ABP: £282.*

Keith Murray green glass vase for Stevens & Williams, broad foot-rim, facsimile signature, 10in. *Gorringes, Lewes. Mar 06. HP: £240. ABP: £282.*

Set of four 19thC cut glass decanter bottles, faceted stoppers, star cut bases, 24cm high. *Sworders, Stansted Mountfitchet. Jul 03. HP: £230. ABP: £270.*

Lalique opalescent glass cake plate, moulded in relief to underside, radiating fern design, stencilled sand blasted mark, 28cm dia. *Cheffins, Cambridge. Feb 05. HP: £240. ABP: £282.*

Gallé acid etched cameo glass vase, shades of mauve, floral decoration, 2.75in. *Gorringes, Lewes. Dec 06. HP: £240. ABP: £282.*

Lalique Poissons No. 1 clear and opalescent glass bowl, moulded with design of swirling fish, base etched R LALIQUE FRANCE, 24cm dia. *Charterhouse Auctioneers, Sherborne. Apr 08. HP: £240. ABP: £282.*

Lalique bowl decorated with roundels in a swirled pattern, marks to base. *Biddle & Webb, Birmingham. Apr 04. HP: £230. ABP: £270.*

19thC tôle peinte glasses stand, 3 decanters, 30cm dia. *Sworders, Stansted Mountfitchet. Feb 05. HP: £240. ABP: £282.*

Kosta 1590 vase. *Great Western Auctions, Glasgow. Mar 06. HP: £240. ABP: £282.*

R. Lalique Feuilles blue glass oval trinket dish, modelled with leaves, etched script R.Lalique, 7in. *Gorringes, Lewes. Apr 08. HP: £240. ABP: £282.*

Pair of late Victorian clear glass decanters, silver mounts, twin pouring spouts, clear glass stoppers, London 1894, 12in high. *Tring Market Auctions, Herts. Jul 04. HP: £230. ABP: £270.*

Elkington & Co silver plated claret jug, lid with lion rampant thumbpiece, collar with cavorting cherubs, hobnail cut glass body, 11in. *Gorringes, Lewes. Jan 05. HP: £240. ABP: £282.*

Monart glass vase. *Great Western Auctions, Glasgow. Mar 06. HP: £240. ABP: £282.*

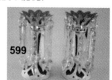

Pair of late 19thC Bohemian overlaid green glass table lustres, flared castellated rims, circular feet with gilt foliate decoration, facetted spear drops, 10in. (a.f.) *Gorringes, Lewes. Apr 08. HP: £240. ABP: £282.*

Oak/brass bound miniature tantalus by E.Rimmel-London, three cut glass decanters & stoppers. 22cm long x 18cm high. *Rosebery's, London. Dec 04. HP: £230. ABP: £270.*

Hammer: £230 - £220

Late 19thC John Walsh Walsh vaseline posy bowl, spherical body, triform rim, stylised Art Nouveau foliate motif in vaseline over pale citron ground, 5in high. Fieldings, West Hagley, Worcs. Jun 05. HP: £230. ABP: £270.

Set 6 French harlequin hock glasses, green, lime green, blue, pink & purple, shallow overlaid bowl with diamond cutting, clear glass faceted tapering stem, star cut foot, 8in high, green decanter to match, mallet form, 15.75in high. (7) Hartleys, Ilkley. Aug 06. HP: £230. ABP: £270.

Pair Victorian silver mounted oil/vinegar ewers, London 1875 by Stephen Smith. Great Western Auctions, Glasgow. Mar 08. HP: £230. ABP: £270.

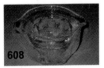

Set of 8 clear glass rinsers, double lip to rim, panelled sides wheel cut with fruiting vines, start cut base, 19thC, 6in wide. Hartleys, Ilkley. Aug 06. HP: £230. ABP: £270.

Pair of Victorian hand-decorated lustres. Orpington Salerooms, Kent. Nov 05. HP: £225. ABP: £264.

Glass inkwell set with three receivers, faceted coloured and clear glass covers. Gorringes, Lewes. Apr 01. HP: £220. ABP: £258.

R. Lalique Ormeaux frosted glass bowl, moulded with bands of leaves, stencilled mark, chipped, with a small similar bowl, 6.25in. Gorringes, Lewes. Jul 08. HP: £220. ABP: £258.

Gallé cameo vase, c1900, pale yellow ground in purple, decorated with wisteria, cameo signature, 14.5cm high. Rosebery's, London. Sep 04. HP: £220. ABP: £258.

Gunnel Nyman for Nuuta-jarvi-Notsjo, free blown crystal glass vase, air inclusions, engraved factory mark Notsjo '54', 18cm high, signature. Rosebery's, London. Sep 04. HP: £220. ABP: £258.

Pair of Victorian glass table lustres, faceted stems and prismatic drops, 9.75in. Gorringes, Lewes. Dec 04. HP: £220. ABP: £258.

Mid 19thC gilt brass mounted glass trumpet vase table centre, wheel engraved foliate decoration, fluted tapered shaft and alabaster pan on claw feet, 25in. Gorringes, Lewes. Dec 04. HP: £220. ABP: £258.

Pair of Venetian glass goblets. Gorringes, Bexhill. Dec 04. HP: £220. ABP: £258.

Gallé cameo glass posy vase, ruby overlaid/carved with sunflowers, leaves, script signature 'Gallé', 2.5in. Gorringes, Lewes. Jul 04. HP: £220. ABP: £258.

Victorian green glass jug, 6in, 21 various drinking glasses with coloured bowls and a Venetian drinking glass with swan stem, 6.25in. Gorringes, Lewes. Apr 03. HP: £220. ABP: £258.

Art Nouveau iridescent green glass jardiniere painted continuously with sinuous foliage, 11in. Gorringes, Lewes. Apr 02. HP: £220. ABP: £258.

Lalique 'Volubilis' No. 383 bowl, opalescent, moulded to underside with 3 flowerheads, stalks forming 3 feet, etched mark, 21.5cm. Sworders, Stansted Mountfitchet. Apr 05. HP: £220. ABP: £258.

French glass/bronze wine cistern, glass font cut and engraved with grapes/vine leaves, lacquered bronze stem, spigot tap, glass cover, 19in. Gorringes, Lewes. Apr 03. HP: £220. ABP: £258.

Set of 7 Lalique Poully pattern tot glasses, green tinted frieze of leaping fish, stencilled R. LALIQUE, 2.75in. Gorringes, Lewes. Oct 02. HP: £220. ABP: £258.

Early 20thC gilt metal mounted cut glass claret jug, decorated with fruiting vines, 28cm high. Sworders, Stansted Mountfitchet. Apr 05. HP: £220. ABP: £258.

Opaque glass ceiling lampshade. Great Western Auctions, Glasgow. Jan 06. HP: £220. ABP: £258.

625

Late 19thC Loetz iridescent green glass vase, moulded and dimpled decoration, Art Nouveau pewter mounts, twin handles, 25cm. Reeman Dansie, Colchester. Apr 06. HP: £220. ABP: £258.

626

Schneider 'Art' glass vase, decorated in orange, rose & cream with swirling cloud forms, 7.5in high, engraved mark to footrim. Canterbury Auction Galleries, Kent. Apr 06. HP: £220. ABP: £258.

627

Extensive part suite of Edwardian glasses, c1900, Pall Mall design: 2 decanters/stoppers, 2 jugs & 57 various glasses. (61) Sworders, Stansted Mountfitchet. Feb 07. HP: £220. ABP: £258.

628

Cut glass silver topped claret jug by '?D & EM', approx 7in, maker's mark worn, plain polished handle, square pouring spout, h/m Birmingham 1898. A F Brock & Co Ltd, Stockport. May 07. HP: £220. ABP: £258.

629

Lalique opalescent glass 'Dahlias' pattern bowl, moulded R Lalique, etched France No 3210. Great Western Auctions, Glasgow. Feb 08. HP: £220. ABP: £258.

630

Christopher Dresser influenced silver mounted glass claret jug, bell shape vessel, Birmingham 1901, 25cm. Charterhouse Auctioneers, Sherborne. Feb 08. HP: £220. ABP: £258.

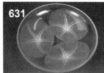

631

R Lalique, 'Volubilis' No 383 pattern, clear, frosted and opalescent bowl, c1930, moulded with sea anemones, tinted opalescent ground, etched mark 'R Lalique France', No 383, 21.5cm dia. Rosebery's, London. Mar 08. HP: £220. ABP: £258.

> Prices quoted are actual hammer prices (HP) and the Approximate Buyer's Price (ABP) includes an average premium of 15% + VAT.

632

World Fair 1939, six glass tumblers, commemorating the World Fair, New York, 1939, with motifs depicting various pavilions, 13.5cm high. Lyon & Turnbull, Edinburgh. Apr 08. HP: £220. ABP: £258.

633

Whitefriars Kingfisher blue glass textured hoop vase designed by Geoffrey Baxter (1967-1973), 29cm high. Clevedon Salerooms, Bristol. Jun 05. HP: £210. ABP: £247.

Hammer: £220 - £200

634

Edwardian glass gin pig decanter with silver snout. Bristol Auction Rooms. Nov 01. HP: £210. ABP: £247.

635

Late 19thC clear glass vase, exterior enamelled in colours with fish and various leaves, 3 stump feet,7in high, surface of enamelling slightly rubbed. Canterbury Auction Galleries, Kent. Aug 02. HP: £210. ABP: £247.

636

Lalique opalescent glass bowl, moulded in Coquilles design, 8in wide, etched 'R. Lalique France No.3201'. Hartleys, Ilkley. Apr 08. HP: £210. ABP: £247.

637

Daum Cameo glass vase, early 20thC, opalescent white ground overlaid in autumnal colours, etched rose boughs & leaves, engraved mark and Cross of Lorraine, 21cm high. Rosebery's, London. Sep 04. HP: £210. ABP: £247.

638

Edwardian Staniforth's patent silver plated tantalus frame with 3 cut glass spirit decanters. (1f) Denhams, Warnham, Sussex. Jun 06. HP: £210. ABP: £247.

639

Art Deco clear/black glass decanter/stopper, waisted stepped form, with 5 conforming glasses, associated burr wood/chrome tray. Locke & England, Leamington Spa. Jul 06. HP: £210. ABP: £247.

640

Continental silver mounted claret jug, hinged cover with thumb piece, marked 800, cut glass body, 29cm high. Lambert & Foster, Tenterden. Mar 08. HP: £210. ABP: £247.

641

Venini 'Fazzoletto' vase, designed by Paolo Venini c1955, alternate blue/white latticino vertical bands, 3 line acid mark 'Venini Murano Italy', to underside, 10.5cm high. Rosebery's, London. Mar 08. HP: £210. ABP: £247.

642

Whitefriars kingfisher drunken bricklayer vase, by Geoffrey Baxter. Great Western Auctions, Glasgow. Sep 06. HP: £205. ABP: £241.

643

Pair Victorian glass sweetmeat bowls, turn-over rims/cut detail, pedestal bases, 7.75in. Gorringes, Lewes. Mar 06. HP: £200. ABP: £235.

Set of 3 Lalique milky blue glass tumblers with swimming fish bases and a pair of taller glasses with leaves. Gorringes, Lewes. Sep 00. HP: £200. ABP: £235.

German Art Nouveau green iridescent glass inkwell, brass and copper mounts. Gorringes, Lewes. Oct 04. HP: £200. ABP: £235.

Engraved silver overlay amber glass vase, Bohemian 19thC, body with 3 engraved panels depicting horses, set within Gothic silver overlay borders, later white metal collar. Rosebery's, London. Sep 04. HP: £200. ABP: £235.

Silver/tortoishell mounted cut glass inkwell, Birmingham 1909, hinged cover inlaid with ribbon tied scrolls, with a second silver mounted cut glass inkwell, London 1910. Rosebery's, London. Sep 04. HP: £200. ABP: £235.

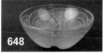

Lalique opalescent bowl, 'Coquilles No.2', cat.ref 3201, etched signature R Lalique, 8.25in. Gorringes, Lewes. Mar 06. HP: £200. ABP: £235.

Set of six Victorian rummers, conical bowls engraved with grapes and vine leaves, on square 'lemon-squeezer' bases, 5in. Gorringes, Lewes. Jul 04. HP: £200. ABP: £235.

Pair of Bohemian ruby flash trumpet vases, facetted stems, petal shaped rims, scrolling decoration 13in. Gorringes, Lewes. Mar 04. HP: £200. ABP: £235.

Collection of Irish glass finger bowls, 19thC, faceted body, star cut bases, possibly Waterford, varying heights & diameters, with 2 Edwardian cut glass decanters. (12). Rosebery's, London. Jun 08. HP: £200. ABP: £235.

Victorian Burmese glass bowl enamelled with ivy leaves, 2.5in. Gorringes, Bexhill. Mar 02. HP: £200. ABP: £235.

Venini Murano glass hand-kerchief vase, c1984, topaz blue exterior with milky blue interior, 33cm high, engraved Venini Italian 1984 to under-side. Rosebery's, London. Mar 05. HP: £200. ABP: £235.

Mould blown Persian glass vessel, 10thC, 2 other vessels, two glass bangles with spiral twist applied borders and other fragments, 9.75cm max. Rosebery's, London. Mar 05. HP: £200. ABP: £235.

Four mid 19thC cut glass urn-shaped rummers with diamond bands, square plinth bases, 14.5cm high. Dreweatt Neate, Donnington. Nov 02. HP: £200. ABP: £235.

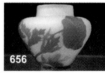

Small Gallé glass vase, c1910, 7cm high. Sworders, Stansted Mountfitchet. Apr 05. HP: £200. ABP: £235.

The numbering system acts as a reader reference as well as linking to the Analysis of each section.

Monart glass vase, mottled in crimson/darker shades, raised pontil beneath, label missing, 8.5in. Gorringes, Lewes. Jun 05. HP: £200. ABP: £235.

Pair cut glass lustre candle-sticks, English 19thC, each with a shaped sconce, mount supporting drops, urn shaped stem, (one AF) 23cm high. Rosebery's, London. Jun 05. HP: £200. ABP: £235.

Monart glass vase. Great Western Auctions, Glasgow. Jun 05. HP: £200. ABP: £235.

Art Nouveau rectangular glass bowl, gilt-metal mount in the form of a nude maiden and sunset background, 8in. Gorringes, Lewes. Jun 05. HP: £200. ABP: £235.

Pair of silver Georgian style gadroon edge coasters, Birm-ingham 1966, glass claret jug and matching decanter. (4) Rosebery's, London. Mar 06. HP: £200. ABP: £235.

Pair of 19thC Stourbridge glass sideboard ornaments, conical with multi-coloured decoration, 11in. Gorringes, Lewes. Jul 06. HP: £200. ABP: £235.

19thC 'Bristol' blue glass decanter, silver plated mount and stopper (14in), a plated cruet set with blue glass condiments and 3 coloured wine glasses. Gorringes, Lewes. Oct 06. HP: £200. ABP: £235.

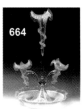

Victorian vaseline and glass epergne, with three branches, 55cm. Sworders, Stansted Mountfitchet. Apr 06. HP: £200. ABP: £235.

Art Nouveau WMF style green glass bowl, pierced pewter mount, 3 scrolled supports, 10in. Denhams, Warnham, Sussex. Sep 05. HP: £200. ABP: £235.

Set of 12 clear/green hock glasses, c1930, each bowl engraved with a coronet and wheat sheaves, facet cut and knopped stems, circular foot, 18.2cm. (12) Sworders, Stansted Mountfitchet. Feb 07. HP: £200. ABP: £235.

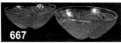

Two Lalique pale blue opalescent small bowls, exteriors moulded in relief, 'Coquilles' design, each of four shells, 5.25in dia x 2.25in high, one engraved mark 'R. Lalique, France' to interior of bowl. Canterbury Auction Galleries, Kent. Feb 07. HP: £200. ABP: £235.

19thC etched glass rummer commemorating Lord Nelson, with a portrait bust and line of ships inscribed 'Nelson, October 21st 1805', 5.5in. Gorringes, Lewes. Apr 08. HP: £200. ABP: £235.

Regency design cut glass ormolu mounted bowl, with dolphin feet, castellated top, 9.5in. Gorringes, Lewes. Apr 08. HP: £200. ABP: £235.

Lalique glass decanter, five matching glasses, tray, signed R. Lalique, France. Gorringes, Lewes. Jul 01. HP: £190. ABP: £223.

Webb's 'cameo fleur' vase, late 19thC, clear body overlaid with transparent green glass, acid-etched, stylized tulips and leaves in rounded relief with wheel-cut detail, textured ground, signed on edge of foot and underside of base 'Webb', 20.5cm high. Rosebery's, London. Jun 08. HP: £190. ABP: £223.

Loetz Persian iridescent swan necked glass vase, 10in high. Gorringes, Bexhill. Jun 03. HP: £190. ABP: £223.

Sven Palmquist Orrefors glass vase. Gorringes, Bexhill. Sep 04. HP: £190. ABP: £223.

Hammer: £200 - £190

Late Victorian tantalus. Tring Market Auctions, Herts. Oct 04. HP: £190. ABP: £223.

Edward Moore vase, chained swan pattern in unusual white and brown opaque mix glass, 17cm. Boldon Auction Galleries, Tyne & Wear. Sep 04. HP: £190. ABP: £223.

Lalique vase 'Mossi', 1950s, frosted form, rows of large clear nodules 20cm, Lalique France. Boldon Auction Galleries, Tyne & Wear. Sep 04. HP: £190. ABP: £223.

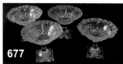

Set 4 Regency design glass tazzae, deeply cut, pedestal stems, stepped square bases, 6in dia. Gorringes, Lewes. Jul 04. HP: £190. ABP: £223.

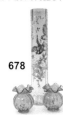

Large Victorian ruby glass cylindrical vase, decorated with painted birds and a pair of round ruby glass vases, pinched rims, 4.5in, 17.5in. Gorringes, Lewes. Mar 04. HP: £190. ABP: £223.

Pair of Whitefriars drunken bricklayer vases, designed by Geoffrey Baxter, textured tangerine coloured glass, 8in, c1967. Gorringes, Lewes. Mar 04. HP: £190. ABP: £223.

Lalique opalescent glass Coquilles plate, pre-war, cat ref. 3012, engraved R.Lalique, France. Gorringes, Lewes. Mar 04. HP: £190. ABP: £223.

Two Chinese inside painted glass snuff bottles, one with Japanese boys playing football, signed Zhou Shao Yuan and dated 1909, other with scribes, signed Ye Zhongson, dated 1924, stoppers both 3in. Gorringes, Lewes. Mar 03. HP: £190. ABP: £223.

Charles Schneider 'Le Verre Francais' cameo glass vase, acid etched, 3 birds perched on foliage in tortoiseshell glass, frosted ground, Art Deco style, c1925, engraved mark, 7in. Gorringes, Lewes. Mar 03. HP: £190. ABP: £223.

19thC ormolu mounted circular diamond cut glass bowl on 3 claw feet, 8in dia. Gorringes, Lewes. Jul 01. HP: £190. ABP: £223.

Hammer: £190 - £180

Monart glass vase. Orpington Salerooms, Kent. Nov 05. HP: £190. ABP: £223.

Three small items of Daum glass, ribbed, gilt decoration, 11cm jug. (3) Sworders, Stansted Mountfitchet. Nov 05. HP: £190. ABP: £223.

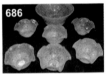

Vasart dessert service: large bowl and 6 dishes. Great Western Auctions, Glasgow. Jun 06. HP: £190. ABP: £223.

Stourbridge glass inkwell, domed stopper & base inset millefiore flowers in pinks, blues and yellows, 5.75in high. Hartleys, Ilkley. Jun 07. HP: £190. ABP: £223.

Monart footed bowl in green, purple/aventurine inclusions, paper label to base, 29cm dia, some scratches. Great Western Auctions, Glasgow. Dec 07. HP: £190. ABP: £223.

Two 19thC overlaid glass centrepieces, 12.25in & 9.25in. Gorringes, Lewes. Apr 04. HP: £190. ABP: £223.

Whitefriars glass 'hoop' vase, textured smokey grey body, typical stepped decoration, 30cm high. Locke & England, Leamington Spa. Jan 08. HP: £190. ABP: £223.

Gabriel Argy-Rousseau pâte de verre glass ashtray, 1920s, moulded as a snake biting a seated leopard, yellow and blue glass, signed, chips, 16.5 x 9.5cm. Sworders, Stansted Mountfitchet. Nov 07. HP: £190. ABP: £223.

Whitefriars cinnamon hoops vase designed by Geoffrey Baxter. Great Western Auctions, Glasgow. Feb 08. HP: £190. ABP: £223.

Victorian etched glass claret ewer, silver plated mount. Denhams, Warnham, Sussex. Aug 07. HP: £190. ABP: £223.

Whitefriars ruby coloured wave ribbed tumbler vase, designed c1930 by Marriot Powell, produced to 1960s, one of largest produced, 37cm high. Rosebery's, London. Mar 08. HP: £190. ABP: £223.

Gallé cameo glass vase with purple flowers, 2.5in, bruised, small chip. Gorringes, Lewes. Jul 00. HP: £180. ABP: £211.

Continental 19thC ruby glass vase/cover, faceted tapering shape, jewelled/embossed metal base, 13in. Gorringes, Lewes. Jan 04. HP: £180. ABP: £211.

> The illustrations are in descending price order. The price range is indicated at the top of each page.

Lalique decanter, 'Boules', 1935-40, clear glass with moulded stopper, 8.25in. Gorringes, Lewes. Jul 04. HP: £180. ABP: £211.

Early 20thC cut glass table lamp, baluster stem, 14in. Gorringes, Bexhill. Mar 02. HP: £180. ABP: £211.

Powell clear glass vase, flared crinoline rim decorated green glass cabochons, 17cm high. Cheffins, Cambridge. Apr 05. HP: £180. ABP: £211.

Lalique glass ice pail, three raised bands of trailing grapevine design heightened with blue, etched mark, 13cm high. Cheffins, Cambridge. Apr 05. HP: £180. ABP: £211.

Schneider green glass vase, signed to base. Gorringes, Bexhill. Jul 05. HP: £180. ABP: £211.

Monart glass dish. Great Western Auctions, Glasgow. Nov 05. HP: £180. ABP: £211.

Two Amberina wine decanters, one with wrythen body, large Amberina jug, clear glass handle and smaller wrythen Amberina jug. (4) Dee, Atkinson & Harrison, Driffield. Feb 06. HP: £180. ABP: £211.

Silver/glass liqueur decanter, as a penguin, possibly by Aspreys & Co, clear twisted glass body, applied black glass fins, head crafted in silver, glass eye, impressed marks to head, 26cm high. (AF) Rosebery's, London. Mar 06. HP: £180. ABP: £211.

Victorian Bristol blue decanter/stopper, facet cut neck, thumb cut body, with four other pieces of Bristol blue glass: water jug, claret jug, sugar bowl and vase. (5) Rosebery's, London. Mar 06. HP: £180. ABP: £211.

Pair of Victorian opaque glass trumpet shaped vases, gilt and red applied jewel decoration, spreading feet,2 jewels chipped, gilt rubbed to 1 vase, 14in. Denhams, Warnham, Sussex. Jun 06. HP: £180. ABP: £211.

Lalique vase in Laurier pattern. Great Western Auctions, Glasgow. Aug 06. HP: £180. ABP: £211.

Daum orange glass bowl, aventurine inclusions, signed Daum, Nancy. Great Western Auctions, Glasgow. Jun 07. HP: £180. ABP: £211.

Art Nouveau Loetz style lidded bowl, flat hinged brass lid incised with stylised foliage & white metal flower heads, pink tapering lustre bowl, 6in wide. Hartleys, Ilkley. Oct 07. HP: £180. ABP: £211.

Set of six small Lalique glasses, approx 2.25in tall, bases stamped. A F Brock & Co Ltd, Stockport. Aug 07. HP: £180. ABP: £211.

Monart mottled yellow and pink glass vase. Great Western Auctions, Glasgow. Dec 07. HP: £180. ABP: £211.

French art nouveau period green iridescent moulded glass vase within gilt metal cast iris panels, 8.75in high. af. Tring Market Auctions, Herts. May 02. HP: £175. ABP: £205.

19thC Bristol Blue, three decanters, various shapes, 2 covered vases & 2 tankards. (7) Kent Auction Galleries, Folkestone. Mar 06. HP: £175. ABP: £205.

Sabino blue glass vase depicting parrots. Great Western Auctions, Glasgow. Oct 06. HP: £175. ABP: £205.

Hammer: £180 - £170

Val Saint Lambert glass vase engraved with a male and female dancing, 10.5in high. Tring Market Auctions, Herts. Nov 02. HP: £170. ABP: £199.

Amber glass vase by John Ditchfield, purple trailing & iridescent surface, unsigned, 10.5in high. Andrew Hartley, Ilkley. Feb 03. HP: £170. ABP: £199.

Green glass vase by John Ditchfield, signed, numbered 5810, 10.25in high. Andrew Hartley, Ilkley. Feb 03. HP: £170. ABP: £199.

Edvin Ohrstrom for Orrefors, Ariel glass bowl, claret coloured design cased in clear, 19cm dia, engraved 'Orrefors' Ariel 1711E Edvin Ohrstrom. Rosebery's, London. Sep 04. HP: £170. ABP: £199.

Pair of Victorian cut glass table lustres, crosshatch cut tops, baluster stems and a circular foot, cut glass drops, 33cm Rosebery's, London. Dec 04. HP: £170. ABP: £199.

Loetz style iridescent green glass vase, violet splashes, hand-blown with pinched body, 7in. Gorringes, Lewes. Jul 03. HP: £170. ABP: £199.

Art Deco glass liqueur set: faceted conical decanter with stopper (6.25in) and six tots, flashed black glass cubes & engraved leaves, glass tray. Gorringes, Lewes. Jan 05. HP: £170. ABP: £199.

Four various large glasses, mid 19thC, bowls engraved with flowers, three initialled, tallest 19.5cm. Sworders, Stansted Mountfitchet. Jul 05. HP: £170. ABP: £199.

Lalique frosted glass box and cover with floral top, etched Lalique France in script, 5.5in dia. Gorringes, Bexhill. Mar 02. HP: £170. ABP: £199.

Swedish clear glass vase, poss. designed by Stromberg for Kosta Boda Paper label, from Rastgarth House, Winchester, 21cm. Sworders, Stansted Mountfitchet. Apr 05. HP: £170. ABP: £199.

Hammer: £170 - £160

Gallé Leveille glass vase, c1890, Chinese inspiration, sides applied with a pair of lion masks, straw coloured glass, drizzled decoration, mottled inclusion of red, green and gold, engraved mark 'leveille' Paris, 21cm high. Rosebery's, London. Mar 05. HP: £170. ABP: £199.

Late 19th/early 20thC iridescent glass vase by Loetz, triform compressed panels, petrol tone looped pattern over pale green ground, 6in high. Fieldings, West Hagley, Worcs. Jun 05. HP: £170. ABP: £199.

Lalique glass decanter, French early 20thC, scalloped moulded rim, inset stoppe, acid etched mark to base, stopper chipped, 16.5cm high. Rosebery's, London. Dec 05. HP: £170. ABP: £199.

Emille Gallé cameo glass vase, c1900, frosted ground overlaid in purple and etched with catkins, cameo mark Gallé, 20cm high. Rosebery's, London. Mar 06. HP: £170. ABP: £199.

Two Vaseline glass shades. Great Western Auctions, Glasgow. Dec 05. HP: £170. ABP: £199.

Lalique glass bowl 'Nonnettes' No. 398, clear & opalescent bowl, moulded mark R. Lalique France, dia 21.8cm. Rosebery's, London. Mar 06. HP: £170. ABP: £199.

Finlandia glass vase by Timo Sarpaneva, c1960s, slate grey glass body, moulded to represent ice, engraved mark Timo Sarpaneva to underside, 23cm high. Rosebery's, London. Mar 06. HP: £170. ABP: £199.

Pale blue opalescent glass shallow bowl, 'Sabino' manner, plated/copper mounts, crenulated rim, exterior moulded in relief with panels of scroll ornament, bowl 10.5in dia, 6 stump feet, stepped boss pattern side handles. Canterbury Auction Galleries, Kent. Apr 06. HP: £170. ABP: £199.

Coloured glass vase, red, blue & green stripes, 12.5in. Gorringes, Lewes. Mar 06. HP: £170. ABP: £199.

Orrefors Graal glass vase, decorated with fish, base engraved Orrefors Graal No. 1085M Edward Hald, (a.f.) 12cm high. Charterhouse Auctioneers, Sherborne. Apr 08. HP: £170. ABP: £199.

Art Nouveau style dish & matching glass vase, green glass peacock feather design in clear glass. Great Western Auctions, Glasgow. Mar 08. HP: £162. ABP: £190.

Two peacock carnival glass dishes in iridescence on blue base glass, prob. Northwood, 23cm. Lambert & Foster, Tenterden. Sep 02. HP: £160. ABP: £188.

> Categories or themes can be followed through the colour coded Index which contains over 4500 cross references.

Late 19thC Bohemian glass vase, overlaid in blue, cut with ovals and star devices, 10in. Gorringes, Lewes. Dec 03. HP: £160. ABP: £188.

French Art glass pitcher signed G. de Feuvre, c1910, acid etched green to orange shading, signature to base, 7in. Gorringes, Lewes. Jan 04. HP: £160. ABP: £188.

Loetz glass bowl, possibly by Michael Powolny, blue ground with white spiral design, 3 white glass ball feet, 21cm dia. Rosebery's, London. Sep 04. HP: £160. ABP: £188.

Oiva Toika for Nuutajavi-Notsjo, red/green specked glass vase, white ground, 16.5cm high, engraved signature to underside. Rosebery's, London. Sep 04. HP: £160. ABP: £188.

Whitefriars tangerine Cello vase, by Geoffrey Baxter, 7in high. Dee, Atkinson & Harrison, Driffield. Jul 08. HP: £160. ABP: £188.

Pair 19thC gilded ruby glass vases, applied white hand painted female head/shoulders portraits, crenulated rims, 10in high. Dee, Atkinson & Harrison, Driffield. Mar 04. HP: £160. ABP: £188.

Pair of Webb cut/enamelled glass vases, English 19thC, faceted waisted neck, enamelled with dragon flies among bull rushes/flowers, 9.5in high. Rosebery's, London. Dec 04. HP: £160. ABP: £188.

Suite Georgian-style square based drinking glasses: 10 ale glasses, 10 champagne glasses & 10 cordial glasses, lightly engraved bowls. *Gorringes, Lewes. Apr 02. HP: £160. ABP: £188.*

Late 19th/early 20thC claret jug, gilt metal mounts, as a cockatoo, 10.25in high, glass body cracked. *Canterbury Auction Galleries, Kent. Apr 05. HP: £160. ABP: £188.*

Part suite, Whitefriars glacier pattern glassware designed in 1969 by Geoffrey Baxter: decanter, jug, 11 tumblers, 4 beakers & 3 goblets. *Sworders, Stansted Mountfitchet. Apr 05. HP: £160. ABP: £188.*

Collection of 18 various apothecary bottles and jars, 19thC, largest 24cm high. *Gorringes, Bexhill. Jun 05. HP: £160. ABP: £188.*

20thC Pekin cameo glass jar/ cover, green overlay etched and cut with birds amongst lotus, white ground, 16.5cm high. (2) *Cheffins, Cambridge. Apr 05. HP: £160. ABP: £188.*

Pair of late 19thC Bohemian green glass vases, gilded white overlay, 7in, and a similar decanter, 11.75in. *Gorringes, Lewes. Apr 04. HP: £160. ABP: £188.*

Murano glass inkwell, domed stopper and base inset millefiore flowers in turquoise and yellow, 20thC, 7in high. *Hartleys, Ilkley. Aug 06. HP: £160. ABP: £188.*

Pair of cordial glasses, partly panelled bowls wheel cut with fruiting vines, faceted baluster stem, domed foot, 19thC, 6in high. *Hartleys, Ilkley. Feb 07. HP: £160. ABP: £188.*

Whitefriars textured tangerine glass banjo vase, No. 9681, designed by Geoffrey Baxter, cracked to reverse corner, 32cm. *Sworders, Stansted Mountfitchet. Sep 07. HP: £160. ABP: £188.*

Monart baluster vase, green swirls & aventurine inclusions (some damage to base), 27cm high. *Great Western Auctions, Glasgow. Dec 07. HP: £160. ABP: £188.*

Hammer: £160 - £150

Schneider twin handled glass vase, c1930, clear glass with orange/purple inclusions and bubbles, applied clear glass handles, etched mark to side, 15.5cm, & Murano style glass vase, grey ground with inclusions, leaf shape handle, 14cm high. (2) *Rosebery's, London. Jun 08. HP: £150. ABP: £176.*

Facet cut ball lacemakers glass lamp. *Tring Market Auctions, Herts. Jan 02. HP: £150. ABP: £176.*

19thC Bohemian ruby flash lidded glass tankard, engraved panels with German buildings, one panel inscribed 'Delphine', pewter mounts, 12.5cm high. *Sworders, Stansted Mountfitchet. Feb 04. HP: £150. ABP: £176.*

Victorian four branch green/ opaque glass table epergne, trumpet shaped vases with crimped spirals in relief to stems, petal type flared rims, 52cm high. *Hampton & Littlewood, Exeter. Jul 04. HP: £150. ABP: £176.*

19thC Bohemian amber over-laid glass goblet, engraved continuously with wildfowl & woodland, cut petal base, 6ins *Gorringes, Lewes. Jan 04. HP: £150. ABP: £176.*

Set of 4 Rene Lalique liqueur glasses. *W & H Peacock, Bedford. Dec 02. HP: £150. ABP: £176.*

Art glass footed bowl, possibly by Monart or WMF, mottled red/blue body with copper foil inclusions, 30cm dia. *Cheffins, Cambridge. Feb 05. HP: £150. ABP: £176.*

Whitefriars Kingfisher blue glass rectangular shaped vase, textured 'Bamboo' decoration designed by Geoffrey Baxter (1967-1973), 20cm high. *Clevedon Salerooms, Bristol. Jun 05. HP: £150. ABP: £176.*

Two late Victorian pig decanters, animals standing four square, one mounted with metal collar attached by a chain to the cork stopper in its mouth, 25.5cm wide. (D) *Cheffins, Cambridge. Apr 05. HP: £150. ABP: £176.*

Hammer: £150 - £140

20thC Lalique carafe, petal moulded rim, lobed stopper, base with stencilled mark R Lalique France, 8.5in high overall. Tring Market Auctions, Herts. Jul 04. HP: £150. ABP: £176.

Pair of German red cased cut glass decanters 11in high, c1900. Ewbank Auctioneers, Send, Surrey. Dec 05. HP: £150. ABP: £176.

Pair of blue glass lustre's, English 19thC, goblet form with clear cut drops, (one AF) 31cm high. Rosebery's, London. Feb 06. HP: £150. ABP: £176.

19thC Bohemian overlaid glass goblet, engraved with a stag-hunting scene, octagonal stem, cut base, 7in. Gorringes, Lewes. Apr 06. HP: £150. ABP: £176.

Lalique powder bowl. Cotswold Auction Company, Cheltenham. Dec 07. HP: £150. ABP: £176.

Scottish blue glass vase, tall ovoid fluted form, flared rim, spreading foot, 20thC, 32.5in high. Hartleys, Ilkley. Feb 08. HP: £150. ABP: £176.

Two Nailsea type flasks, 19thC, flattened form, white swirl decoration, 20cm long max, with one other similar smaller example. Rosebery's, London. Jun 03. HP: £140. ABP: £164.

Set of 10 cordial glasses, all with engraved garland to the bowl, facet cut stem and foot. (10) Sworders, Stansted Mountfitchet. Nov 04. HP: £140. ABP: £164.

Victorian silver mounted glass claret jug and stopper, maker Rupert Favell & Co, London 1886, 9in. Gorringes, Lewes. Jul 04. HP: £140. ABP: £164.

Late Victorian oak tantalus, silver plated handle/mounts, 3 cut glass spirit decanters, 12in. Gorringes, Lewes. Apr 03. HP: £140. ABP: £164.

Two early 20thC vaseline glass light shades, larger with foliate panels, 19cm dia, other 16cm dia. (2) Cheffins, Cambridge. Feb 05. HP: £140. ABP: £164.

Whitefriars experimental glass bowl designed by Geoffrey Baxter, c1969, kingfisher blue with green encircled spots, 29cm dia, with a Whitefriars random strapping vase designed by Geoffrey Baxter in indigo, 19cm high. Cheffins, Cambridge. Feb 05. HP: £140. ABP: £164.

> Prices quoted are actual hammer prices (HP) and the Approximate Buyer's Price (ABP) includes an average premium of 15% + VAT.

Art Nouveau green glass vase, c1900, decorated with raised abstract design, unmarked, minor damage, 33cm high. Sworders, Stansted Mountfitchet. Apr 05. HP: £140. ABP: £164.

Amber flash glass vase, Bohemian 19thC, tall neck, everted rim, body engraved with 4 putti drinking among fruiting vines, 30.5cm high. Rosebery's, London. Jun 05. HP: £140. ABP: £164.

Late Victorian Nailsea-type flask, in the form of a boot, 8in and 2 other Nailsea-type ovoid flasks. Gorringes, Lewes. Jan 03. HP: £140. ABP: £164.

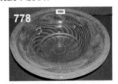

Monart glass dish. Orpington Salerooms, Kent. Nov 05. HP: £140. ABP: £164.

Pair Masonic master toasting glasses, square shaped foot, bowl decorated with Masonic symbols, 15cm high. Rosebery's, London. Dec 05. HP: £140. ABP: £164.

19thC Pekin glass snuff bottle, ruby red overlay cut from shoulders and to form roundels front and back against the snow glass ground the stopper, ice blue top, 9cm high. Cheffins, Cambridge. Feb 06. HP: £140. ABP: £164.

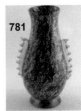

Venetian gilt frosted/mille-fiore cane included glass vase, applied twin stepped handles and circular foot, signed, 26cm. Locke & England, Leamington Spa. Mar 06. HP: £140. ABP: £164.

782

Novelty glass claret jug, as a bird, green applied details, plated mount & thumb piece, cracked, 25.5cm. Sworders, Stansted Mountfitchet. Apr 06. HP: £140. ABP: £164.

783

Pair Art Nouveau ruby glass vases overlaid with thistles, 24cm. Sworders, Stansted Mountfitchet. Apr 06. HP: £140. ABP: £164.

784

Jack Ink vase, sides applied with thick abstract trailing in green shading to blue, flared rim, 8in wide. Hartleys, Ilkley. Oct 06. HP: £140. ABP: £164.

785

Gallé cameo vase, sweet peas in low relief on green, purple and orange ground, signed, 3in wide. Hartleys, Ilkley. Dec 06. HP: £140. ABP: £164.

786

Monart mottled blue/aventurine vase. Great Western Auctions, Glasgow. May 07. HP: £140. ABP: £164.

787

Four items of vaseline glass. Orpington Salerooms, Kent. Jul 07. HP: £140. ABP: £164.

788

Whitefriars totem vase, green glass, 10.25in high. Hartleys, Ilkley. Jun 07. HP: £140. ABP: £164.

789

Monart glass vase, flared rim, green/blue swirl body with gold inclusions, 7.25in high, label to base. Hartleys, Ilkley. Jun 07. HP: £140. ABP: £164.

790

Pair of Bohemian white overlaid and ruby flash beakers painted with flowers/foliage, 14.5cm high, a lamp with similar decoration, 39cm high. (3) Rosebery's, London. Jul 07. HP: £140. ABP: £164.

791

Pair of Lalique frosted glass menu holders, arched form, moulded with a pair of birds, 2in wide, signed R. Lalique, France. Hartleys, Ilkley. Apr 08. HP: £140. ABP: £164.

792

Clyne Farquarson for John Walsh glass, 1930s, clear cut glass tapered vase, signed & No. '37', 25cm high. Richard Winterton, Lichfield. Jan 08. HP: £135. ABP: £158.

Hammer: £140 - £130

793

Late Victorian single bottle inkstand. Tring Market Auctions, Herts. Oct 04. HP: £135. ABP: £158.

794

Two pairs crystal decanters, hallmarked silver collars. Orpington Salerooms, Kent. May 06. HP: £135. ABP: £158.

795

Pair of Bohemian blue glass vases. Rye Auction Galleries, Sussex. Jan 08. HP: £135. ABP: £158.

796

Legras glass vase with overlay and painted landscape decoration, 6in. Gorringes, Lewes. Sep 00. HP: £130. ABP: £152.

797

WMF iridescent glass comport, pedestal base, 8.75in dia. Gorringes, Lewes. Jul 03. HP: £130. ABP: £152.

798

R. Lalique opalescent glass moulded Fleurons No.2 bowl, moulded with swirl ridges, 8in. (stencilled mark) Gorringes, Lewes. Jul 08. HP: £130. ABP: £152.

799

Green-overlaid glass decanter, globe-and-shaft form cut with bands of circles/stars, silver collar hallmarked London 1967, with stopper, 14.5in. Gorringes, Lewes. Jun 05. HP: £130. ABP: £152.

800

Lalique 'Chicorée' pattern bowl, No.3213, moulded with radiating leaves, engraved signature mark, 24cm dia. Cheffins, Cambridge. Apr 05. HP: £130. ABP: £152.

801

Green cut glass vase decorated with irises/waterlilies, signed Walsh. Great Western Auctions, Glasgow. Jun 05. HP: £130. ABP: £152.

802

12 various plain drinking glasses, tallest 15cm. Sworders, Stansted Mountfitchet. Jul 05. HP: £130. ABP: £152.

803

Late 19thC Bohemian ruby glass bud vase, decorated with fruiting vines, circular foot, 13.5in. Gorringes, Lewes. Apr 08. HP: £130. ABP: £152.

Hammer: £130 - £120

Lalique, France, early 20thC frosted glass vase, applied with two doves, pedestal foot, signed, 12.5cm. Locke & England, Leamington Spa. Jul 05. HP: £130. ABP: £152.

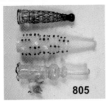

Three coloured glass cheroot holders, one mounted with a bird, longest 9.5cm. Sworders, Stansted Mountfitchet. Jul 05. HP: £130. ABP: £152.

Art glass vase. Great Western Auctions, Glasgow. Apr 06. HP: £130. ABP: £152.

Whitefriars tangerine concentric TV vase, designed by Geoffrey Baxter 9677, c1967. Kent Auction Galleries, Folkestone. Feb 07. HP: £130. ABP: £152.

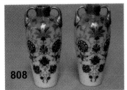

Pair Victorian opaque glass twin handled vases, applied gilt floral decoration, 7.5in. Denhams, Warnham, Sussex. Jun 06. HP: £130. ABP: £152.

Set of 6 boxed, etched, cut & flashed drinking glasses by Walsh. Great Western Auctions, Glasgow. Jan 07. HP: £130. ABP: £152.

Early 20thC silver mounted glass riding flask, original leather carrying case. Reeman Dansie, Colchester. Apr 06. HP: £130. ABP: £152.

Four items of Victorian vaseline glass, tallest 33cm. (4) Sworders, Stansted Mountfitchet. Feb 07. HP: £130. ABP: £152.

The numbering system acts as a reader reference as well as linking to the Analysis of each section.

Baccarat style Art Deco style hexagonal glass decanter, black geometric decoration, and matching set of 6 liqueur glasses. (7) Charterhouse Auctioneers, Sherborne. Apr 07. HP: £130. ABP: £152.

Monart glass vase, shape RA, mottled green glass body with aventurine/amethyst inclusions to rim, 17.5cm high. Lyon & Turnbull, Edinburgh. Apr 08. HP: £130. ABP: £152.

Set of 12 gilt hock glasses, floral decoration, double knopped stems, 5in. Gorringes, Lewes. Apr 08. HP: £130. ABP: £152.

Schneider acid etched glass bowl, c1930, amethyst colour bowl etched with diagonal trailing, 13cm high, stencil mark Schneider to edge of foot. Rosebery's, London. Mar 05. HP: £125. ABP: £147.

1930s Stuart's Art Deco cut crystal vase, base cut with a facet collar rising to a wheel cut repeat pattern of stylised leaves, acid mark to base, 11.5in high. Fieldings, West Hagley, Worcs. Jun 05. HP: £125. ABP: £147.

Oak three decanter tantalus with brass fittings and lock. Black Country Auctions, Dudley. Dec 05. HP: £125. ABP: £147.

Victorian glass decanter and stopper, graduated rings to neck, engraved fruiting vine, 10.5in. Gorringes, Lewes. Mar 04. HP: £120. ABP: £141.

Val St Lambert glass vase, amethyst body with irregular faceted design, 23cm high, engraved 'Val St Lambert' to underside. Rosebery's, London. Sep 04. HP: £120. ABP: £141.

19thC glass lustre candlestick, heavy slice cut body, shaped rim, cut glass drops, 13.25in high, (chipped) and one other lustre candlestick, 6.25in high. Canterbury Auction Galleries, Kent. Mar 05. HP: £120. ABP: £141.

Vetreria 'La Murrina' Murano glass bowl & matching table lamp, clear cased white body with blue and yellow Murrie design, bowl 21cm high, lamp 21.5cm high, maker's paper label. (2). Rosebery's, London. Sep 04. HP: £120. ABP: £141.

Edwardian claret jug of cut baluster form, plated mount open scroll handle, 9.5in high. Tring Market Auctions, Herts. Apr 05. HP: £120. ABP: £141.

Russian cut glass bowl, silver rim, swing handle, 12.5 cm. Rosebery's, London. Mar 06. HP: £120. ABP: £141.

824

Late 19thC Bohemian glass pickle jar and cover, ruby overlaid and engraved, 7in. Gorringes, Lewes. Mar 04. HP: £120. ABP: £141.

825

Cut glass decanter/stopper, hexagonal, cut with diamonds, silver collar by William Hutton & Sons Ltd., Sheffield 1907, with stopper, 13.75in. Gorringes, Lewes. Jun 05. HP: £120. ABP: £141.

826

Whitefriars textured tubular 'Willow' vase designed by Geoffrey Baxter, 30cm high. Cheffins, Cambridge. Apr 05. HP: £120. ABP: £141.

827

Art Deco sherry decanter & six sherry glasses. Orpington Salerooms, Kent. Jun 05. HP: £120. ABP: £141.

828

Two Val St Lambert glass vases, French 20thC, both cut with geometric designs, one overlay blue glass, one tinted yellow, one with stenciled 'S' mark to base, tallest 17cm. Rosebery's, London. Apr 05. HP: £120. ABP: £141.

829

Tiffany Favrile vase, moulded form, flared rim, in peacock iridescence, gilt metal/green fluted base moulded with stylized foliage, signed and inscribed 159, 12.25in high. Andrew Hartley, Ilkley, W Yorks. Feb 06. HP: £120. ABP: £141.

830

Victorian claret jug, heavy diamond/slice cutting, mount with cast bearded mask to spout, engraved with fruiting vines, cover with fruiting vine knop, fruiting vine handle, 11.25in high. Canterbury Auction Galleries, Kent. Feb 06. HP: £120. ABP: £141.

831

Suite of ten ruby flash wine glasses, star cut bowls, clear glass stems, with 17 champagne glasses, facet cut stems. Rosebery's, London. May 06. HP: £120. ABP: £141.

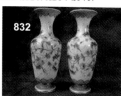

832

Pair of French milk glass vases, late 19thC, painted with pink rose branches and other flowers, 24.5cm high. Rosebery's, London. May 06. HP: £120. ABP: £141.

Hammer: £120 - £115

833

Suite of machine etched drinking glasses, c1900, with floral and arched motif: 2 decanters, 28cm high, 8 wine glasses, 2 sherry glasses, 17 tumblers. (29) Rosebery's, London. Jan 07. HP: £120. ABP: £141.

834

Modern Lalique frosted glass powder bowl and cover, lid moulded in relief, 'Dahlia' design, 5.5in dia, etched stencil mark to base 'R. Lalique, France'. Canterbury Auction Galleries, Kent. Feb 07. HP: £120. ABP: £141.

835

Glass inkwell, form of a jockey's cap, hinged lid/mount, 6in long, London 1914. Hartleys, Ilkley. Jun 07. HP: £120. ABP: £141.

836

Pair green glass wine jugs, flattened circular form, loop handle, beaded metal rim & cork stopper, 8.5in high, and a green glass wine decanter, 9.5in high. (3) Hartleys, Ilkley. Dec 07. HP: £120. ABP: £141.

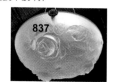

837

Pair of moulded glass ceiling bowls decorated with roses. Great Western Auctions, Glasgow. Feb 08. HP: £120. ABP: £141.

838

Whitefriars concentric TV cinnamon vase designed by Geoffrey Baxter, 1976, pattern No. 9677. Kent Auction Galleries, Folkestone. Mar 08. HP: £120. ABP: £141.

839

Venini green/red glass sand timer, hour glass form, 7.5in high. Hartleys, Ilkley. Jun 07. HP: £120. ABP: £141.

840

Orrefors 'Hallon' glass bowl, designed by Anne Nilsson, c1970, flared form, moulded with globular mounds, signed to underside, 20cm dia, with two Orrefors glass bowls of castellated form, both signed. (3) Rosebery's, London. Mar 08. HP: £120. ABP: £141.

841

Tapio Wirkkala for Iittala, organic form glass vase, vertical cut grooves, etched marks 'Tapio Wirkkala Iittala 57', 16cm high. Lyon & Turnbull, Edinburgh. Apr 08. HP: £120. ABP: £141.

842

Lalique style frosted glass ceiling light with moulded leaf design. Great Western Auctions, Glasgow. Dec 07. HP: £115. ABP: £135.

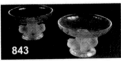

Pair of modern Lalique clear and frosted glass sweetmeat dishes, plain shallow bowls, stems moulded in bold relief with 4 love birds, 5.5in dia x 3.5in high, engraved 'Lalique, France' to bases. Canterbury Auction Galleries, Kent. Apr 06. HP: £115. ABP: £135.

Lalique 'Moineau' clear and frosted glass bowl, clear thick walled body moulded with 2 frosted sparrow birds, engraved mark 'Lalique France' to underside, post 1950, 30.5cm dia. Rosebery's, London. Jan 08. HP: £115. ABP: £135.

Whitefriars glass cinnamon woven basket vase by Geoffrey Baxter. Great Western Auctions, Glasgow. Feb 08. HP: £115. ABP: £135.

Miniature Gallé cased green cameo glass vase carved with water lillies and leaves, signed 'Gallé', 3.5in high. Tring Market Auctions, Herts. Mar 03. HP: £110. ABP: £129.

Baccarat frosted/clear glass ashtray modelled with sunbathing nude, 3.5in. Gorringes, Bexhill. Mar 02. HP: £110. ABP: £129.

Webb glass vase, cut with floral festoons, 11.75in. Gorringes, Lewes. Mar 05. HP: £110. ABP: £129.

Cut glass desk seal, tapering facetted handle and another with oval handle. Gorringes, Lewes. Mar 05. HP: £110. ABP: £129.

The illustrations are in descending price order. The price range is indicated at the top of each page.

Zawiercie ovoid crystal cut glass vase, with urn shaped cut glass vase. (2) Rosebery's, London. Jun 05. HP: £110. ABP: £129.

Pair of Mary Gregory style green glass ewers, clear glass handles decorated with cherubs, base marked 167, 8in. Denhams, Warnham, Sussex. Jul 05. HP: £110. ABP: £129.

Set of six harlequin wines, baluster bowl wheel cut with flowers, panelled stem and star cut foot, 7in high, mark for Royal Brierley. Hartleys, Ilkley. Dec 07. HP: £110. ABP: £129.

Nine pieces of Mary Gregory style green glass: pair of mugs with gilt rims, enamelled with boy and girl, 4cm high, two beakers, a mug, jug & three vases with similar decoration. (9) a/f. Rosebery's, London. Oct 06. HP: £110. ABP: £129.

Art deco drinks set: frosted glass cocktail shaker painted with a silver diaper pattern, chrome plated mounts, 9.75in high, and a set of six glasses to match. (7) Hartleys, Ilkley. Feb 07. HP: £110. ABP: £129.

Monart glass vase. Great Western Auctions, Glasgow. Mar 07. HP: £110. ABP: £129.

Victorian cut glass claret jug, white metal mounts, handle as branch of a vine, mounts to the body as a trailing vine, glass body with bold hatch cut decoration, 30cm high. Rosebery's, London. Jul 07. HP: £110. ABP: £129.

Large glass plate in the style of Klimt, etched Canoggio a Klimt. Great Western Auctions, Glasgow. Aug 07. HP: £110. ABP: £129.

Lalique frosted glass bowl, moulded in Cactus design, bands of flowerheads with black centres, etched mark Lalique France, 10in wide. Hartleys, Ilkley. Dec 07. HP: £110. ABP: £129.

Lalique bowl, clear glass supported by 5 moulded owls, frosted bellied base, 5in high, etched 'Lalique France'. Hartleys, Ilkley. Dec 07. HP: £110. ABP: £129.

Pair cut glass vases, bottle form, moulded/flared rim, bodies cut with panelled and diamond cut banding, 9.75in high, Birmingham 1944. Hartleys, Ilkley. Feb 08. HP: £110. ABP: £129.

Pair modern Lalique clear/ frosted moulded glass figural ashtrays, moulded with a fish swimming amongst air bubbles, cigarette holder at the tail, engraved 'Lalique France' to underside, 15.5cm dia. Rosebery's, London. Mar 08. HP: £110. ABP: £129.

WMF brass/blue glass tazza, applied white metal handles modelled as mythical birds. Great Western Auctions, Glasgow. Mar 08. HP: £110. ABP: £129.

PART I: Decorative & Functional Glass c1830-2000
Section V: £100-£50

'Today's nouveau riche prefer to show off the labels on their fine clarets and single malts.....the Regency opaline vase and the early nineteenth century Baccarat jug are good value.....beware of the 'Irish' cut glass sweetmeat.....if you are going to buy Kosta be more ambitious.....'

It is evident below a £100, that the quality is deteriorating and the big names, such as Lalique or Daum have been left behind, apart from the pressed glass and the reproductions. This is the twilight zone where it will be more difficult to find worthwhile glass with investment potential and very easy indeed to find lots enough to form an instant collection that will never show a profit or any investment potential, and that will also be very difficult to shift if you want to move on. Easy come is not easy go! Alternatively, the better pieces, by their nature are rarely around every corner. Let us track some of the lots in this Section and see if we can spot bargains and expose the poorer buys, and introduce the odd new subject on the way.

There is plenty of silver mounted glass commencing with an arts and crafts decanter at **866**, which, at £117 is cheap enough, because of course, decanters are out of fashion. Today's nouveau riche prefer to show off the labels on their fine clarets and single malts! The same goes for for the claret jug at **884** and a number of other similar lots. **929** is perhaps a better buy but in the main this selection is undistinguished. Quite a number by the way, are now plated. I do like the style of the Edwardian claret jug at **1006**, engraved and with a silver collar. At only £94 this is a good buy for a collector or for a dealer to sell on for at least £150. Better still are the three silver collared decanters at **1019**, two being a pair. These early machine cut decanters are an absolute snip at only £88 including premium and would grace any dining room. Note the good Hukin and Heath plated claret jug at **1062**. This is all about style and the name and is worth at least another £50. Now for drinking glasses. The nine at **873** are just about worth £117 but you would have to be selling on and you should make a profit. Don't get fooled by the 'Commemorative' goblet at **883**. This is more than enough to pay at £117. The Victorian goblets at **919** have also topped out at over £100, pity as they are nice, but they won't be lead crystal. Don't buy mixed lots such as at **944** and think very carefully about **950**. There is one Georgian goblet, second top right, worth about £50. As for the rest they will make good every day usable glasses. The price is right only on this basis. I am more impressed by the wine goblet at **984** which is in the facon de venise, and probably worth £200-£300! This is quality. At **1021** are a set of eight wines and four green 'flutes'. Yes, they are nineteenth century and they are probably Georgian. Note the wide foot on the clear glass. This is a real bargain buy and definitely worth

twice as much. Why is the commemorative at **1076** so cheap? Because it is a modern limited edition. At **1116** you can buy into the 1930s for a song but the goblet at **1134** is too much money at £60. These are plentiful.

Now for a survey over the Section. The Regency opaline vase at **879** is good value and so is the early nineteenth Baccarat jug at **890**. Check out the Moser at **900**, then go back to **206, 281, 332, 564** to pick up the story. Use the *Index* to find more examples. At **882**, the Bohemian overlay is much better than ordinary cranberry and the nineteenth century opaline inkwell at **920** is quality and could be displayed with the opaline vase at **879**. The Continental moonflask at **954** isn't. We should do better and certainly better than the repro Mary Gregory at **962**, money down the drain! The same goes for paying a £100 for the mixed coloured pressed glass at **970**. The Monart at **1052** should be given some serious consideration. It is certainly worth more if large. Why aren't we told the size? Beware of the 'Irish' cut glass sweetmeat at **1031**. If this were early and Irish it would have fetched hundreds. At **1016** you are better saving your money than spending a good £88 on a poor piece of pressed Lalique. I find it astonishing that people are prepared to pay more for modern Lalique than it costs new in a French high street, and if you are going to buy Kosta then be a little more ambitious than the three pieces at **1050**. I would have definitely gone for the 1930s French glass painted vase at **1086** and would have avoided the green glass bowl at **1067**, which at £76 was at least twice its value. Avoid things like the Gallé repro at **1101** and put your money into something like the cameo bowl at **1102** or the Stevens and Williams at **1105**. If you've got £60 plus to spend on pressed glass then go for the likes of the Sowerby Queens Ivory basket at **1113** rather than the pressed glass groups at **1129** and **1130**. Avoid the Mary Gregory style at **1144** but take a serious look at the art deco malachite lamp at **1145**. With the right shade this could have been the envy of all your friends. Who would want to pay £58 for the epergne with the missing branch at **1146**? Just in case anyone, having read the previous Sections, thinks I'm biased against Whitefriars, the £58 for the orange/apricot pair of vases at **1138** is reasonable and good value. I am not forgetting Strathearn. See **1106, 1143** and then follow the trail on to **1266** to get an idea of prices. Don't forget the Strathearn paperweights on pages 107 and 108. Finally the Kosta Boda *Atoll* vase by Anna Ehrner at **1150** is good value, if typical of the type. I think it is worth more than £58.

Set of 8 Murano pale amethyst glass dessert dishes, 4in dia. *Tring Market Auctions, Herts. Sep 02. HP: £100. ABP: £117.*

Unusual cut glass partners desk inkwell, 5in high. *Gorringes, Lewes. Oct 02. HP: £100. ABP: £117.*

Iridescent glass vase, green and opalescent, 13in high. *Gorringes, Bexhill. Nov 03. HP: £100. ABP: £117.*

Arts & Crafts Kuttrolf form glass decanter, top with a silver twin pouring lip set with a globular whirl pattern stopper, Birmingham 1894, 25cm high, with a mallet form glass decanter, 30cm high. *Thos Mawer & Son, Lincoln. Sep 04. HP: £100. ABP: £117.*

Three heavy conical rummers and a circular rummer, with unground pontils, 13/14cm high. *Thos Mawer & Son, Lincoln. Sep 04. HP: £100. ABP: £117.*

Collection of mainly 19thC ale glasses and three ribbed conical glasses with a note 'given to Martha Todd in her marriage to Henry Keightley June 28th 1851'. (16) *Thos Mawer & Son, Lincoln. Sep 04. HP: £100. ABP: £117.*

Victorian opaque pink glass table lustre, gilded/enamelled with floral garlands, clear lustre drops, 12.5in. *Gorringes, Lewes. Oct 04. HP: £100. ABP: £117.*

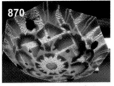

Loys Lucha octagonal Art Deco glass ceiling light bowl, geometric purple flashed decoration, signed, 14.5in. *Gorringes, Lewes. Oct 04. HP: £100. ABP: £117.*

Thirteen apothecaries glass bottles, each with a stopper & label, 10in high. *Sworders, Stansted Mountfitchet. Jul 01. HP: £100. ABP: £117.*

Pair of 19thC Pekin blood red glass bowls, exteriors shaped on a wheel, 16.5cm. (D) *Cheffins, Cambridge. Apr 05. HP: £100. ABP: £117.*

Nine various glasses in the 18thC style, to include a facet cut stem wine glass and a pair of spiral twist glasses with etched bowls. *Sworders, Stansted Mountfitchet. Nov 04. HP: £100. ABP: £117.*

Pair of cut glass bon bon dishes with covers, late 19thC, domed facet cut lids with finial, dishes with facet cut down turned edge upon a knopped stem, octagonal bases, 33cm high. (2) *Rosebery's, London. Jun 08. HP: £100. ABP: £117.*

> Categories or themes can be followed through the colour coded Index which contains over 4500 cross references.

Nine piece dessert service: 6 plates, 27cm, pair of footed dishes, 22cm and a comport 23cm dia, each piece cut with stylised diamonds and star banding. *Hampton & Littlewood, Exeter. Jul 04. HP: £100. ABP: £117.*

Pair of 'Bristol' blue glass decanters, mallet shape with 'bull's-eye' stoppers,11.5in, and an amethyst wine glass with knopped stem, 6.25in. *Gorringes, Lewes. Jul 04. HP: £100. ABP: £117.*

19thC Dutch engraved glass sugar box, octagonal shape with cover, 4in, and an oval cut glass bowl with engraved armorial 'Loyal au Mort', 6.25in. *Gorringes, Lewes. Jul 04. HP: £100. ABP: £117.*

Art Deco cut glass decanter, angular shape with abstract designs, ruby overlay, with stopper *Gorringes, Lewes. Jul 04. HP: £100. ABP: £117.*

Regency, opaline glass/gilt metal vase, classical shape. 32cm high. *Rosebery's, London. Dec 04. HP: £100. ABP: £117.*

Pair of late Victorian pink opaline glass vases, gilded bulbous bodies, 11in. *Gorringes, Lewes. Apr 02. HP: £100. ABP: £117.*

Three Jack-in-the-Pulpit vases, one striated green, one lavender, and one by Alum Bay Isle of White, rim white, body mottled brown/pink. (3) *Dee, Atkinson & Harrison, Driffield. Feb 05. HP: £100. ABP: £117.*

882

19thC Bohemian vase, ruby-overlaid, engraved with deer, 4.25in. Gorringes, Lewes. Mar 05. HP: £100. ABP: £117.

883

Commemorative glass goblet, c1878, probably Scottish commemorating the birth of 'James Farr, born March 3rd 1828' engraved with fruits/foliage, inverted baluster stem, wide foot, 25.5cm high, 14cm dia, ferns point to date in the 1870s. Sworders, Stansted Mountfitchet. Apr 05. HP: £100. ABP: £117.

884

Silver top & cut glass claret jug, jug with flared slab cut body with line/cross cutting, maker's mark JDWD (James Deakin & Son), Sheffield 1912. Kent Auction Galleries, Folkestone. Jul 05. HP: £100. ABP: £117.

885

Iridescent glass vase, late 19th/early 20thC, fluted waisted form, yellow mottled ground washed with blue, enamelled flower decoration, ornate gilded metal stand, 44cm. Rosebery's, London. Mar 06. HP: £100. ABP: £117.

886

Monart glass vase. Great Western Auctions, Glasgow. Aug 05. HP: £100. ABP: £117.

887

Whitefriars triangular bark vase in indigo, designed by Geoffrey Baxter, 18cm. Boldon Auction Galleries, Tyne & Wear. Sep 05. HP: £100. ABP: £117.

888

19thC Bohemian goblet, green glass decorated with gilt leaves, central porcelain oval plaque depicting two pretty girls, cracked, 32cm high. Boldon Auction Galleries, Tyne & Wear. Sep 05. HP: £100. ABP: £117.

889

Loetz-style iridescent green rectangular shaped ink well, stylized copper cover, 4.5 x 4.5in. Dee, Atkinson & Harrison, Driffield. Apr 06. HP: £100. ABP: £117.

890

Early 19thC Baccarat cut glass jug, frosted serpent handle, c1835, 9.25in. Gorringes, Lewes. Jul 08. HP: £100. ABP: £117.

Hammer: £100

891

Golden oak silver plated, mounted tantalus, 3 moulded glass decanters, 3 plated spirit labels. Kent Auction Galleries, Folkestone. Aug 06. HP: £100. ABP: £117.

892

Set of 6 early Victorian green wine glasses, knopped stems, 5in. Gorringes, Lewes. Mar 06. HP: £100. ABP: £117.

893

Orrefors engraved glass decanter, laurel wreath with a classical maiden seated at a shield holding olive branch, spurious date 1694, signed, 1983, 11in. Gorringes, Lewes. Jul 08. HP: £100. ABP: £117.

894

Victorian vaseline glass lamp shade, tapering panelled form, 5in high. Hartleys, Ilkley. Dec 06. HP: £100. ABP: £117.

895

19thC clear glass octagonal flask, silver plated cover, etched decoration of St. Laurence, cartouche of hand holding a burning heart and another holding a book, inscription reading 'Pietate et Doctrina Fulget', 19.5cm. a/f. Rosebery's, London. Jan 07. HP: £100. ABP: £117.

896

Pair of Victorian green glass lustres, prismatic drops, 26cm. Charterhouse Auctioneers, Sherborne. Sep 06. HP: £100. ABP: £117.

897

Pair of Georgian style ship's decanters, four ring necks and broad bases, 23cm high. Rosebery's, London. Jan 07. HP: £100. ABP: £117.

898

Pair ruby glass table lustres, large clear hanging drops, lustres with shaped rims, baluster stems, 27cm high, and a moulded glass figure of a cat, 12.5cm high. (3) a/f Rosebery's, London. Jan 07. HP: £100. ABP: £117.

899

Small Edwardian 1/4 bottle oak tantalus by Benjamens, 3 cut crystal decanters, 6in high. Golding Young & Co, Grantham. Nov 06. HP: £100. ABP: £117.

900

Moser glass jar and cover, overlaid silver decoration. Great Western Auctions, Glasgow. Jun 07. HP: £100. ABP: £117.

Set of eighteen green glasses, ovoid bowl, baluster faceted stem and spreading foot, late 19th/20thC, 5.25in high. Hartleys, Ilkley. Jun 07. HP: £100. ABP: £117.

Engraved white metal mounted cut glass claret jug, star & slab cut decoration. Kent Auction Galleries, Folkestone. Feb 08. HP: £100. ABP: £117.

Loetz style glass vase, shaped mushroom form, purple lustre body with blue inclusions, 6.75in high, and three similar lustre glass vases. (4) Hartleys, Ilkley. Feb 08. HP: £100. ABP: £117.

Whitefriars textured tubular glass vase, willow, designed by Geoffrey Baxter, 20.5cm high. Charterhouse Auctioneers, Sherborne. Apr 08. HP: £100. ABP: £117.

Three Victorian silver mounted cruet bottles, maker Edward Barnard & Sons, London 1870/71, 3 matching glass bottles. Gorringes, Lewes. Apr 08. HP: £100. ABP: £117.

Set of Rosenthal drinking glasses, 30 wine glasses, 24 tumblers and 17 shot glasses, all with cut spear design. Rosebery's, London. Jul 07. HP: £100. ABP: £117.

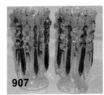

Pair glass lustres, cut glass dished tops, alternating clear, amethyst and amber drops, moulded glass candlestick, 9.25in high. Hartleys, Ilkley. Apr 08. HP: £100. ABP: £117.

Pair of reeded Vaseline glass table lamps 16in. Denhams, Warnham, Sussex. Mar 06. HP: £95. ABP: £111.

Blue glass and parcel gilt trumpet vase, frilled rim, 15.5in. Gorringes, Lewes. Jul 00. HP: £95. ABP: £111.

Pair of cut glass compotes/covers, turnover rims, knopped stems and cut bases, 12.75in, and a tall novelty wine glass, hollow stem, bowl engraved with grapes/vine leaves, 12in. Gorringes, Lewes. Jul 04. HP: £95. ABP: £111.

Victorian glass claret jug, tinted in green, silver plated mounts, 26cm high. Rosebery's, London. Mar 05. HP: £95. ABP: £111.

Pair of green vaseline glass Jack-in-the-Pulpit vases, circular foot, 6.25in high. Fellows & Sons, Hockley, Birmingham. Oct 03. HP: £95. ABP: £111.

Continental amethyst/frosted cameo glass vase, elongated form, landscape scene, 26cm high, and a Bohemian glass vase, fluted shaped clear glass, silvered foliate decoration, 22cm. Rosebery's, London. Sep 04. HP: £95. ABP: £111.

1930s iced water jug, slice & star cuttings, plated neck, bakelite finial, 12.5in high, lacking liner. Canterbury Auction Galleries, Kent. Apr 06. HP: £95. ABP: £111.

Seven items of crackle glassware, each painted with coral, one with a fish, pair of vases 12.5cm, 2 squat vases, a twin handled vase, another and a jug. (7) Sworders, Stansted Mountfitchet. Apr 06. HP: £95. ABP: £111.

Enamelled art glass Deco design vase, signed 'Quenlit P' attributed to Legras c1920-25. Great Western Auctions, Glasgow. Sep 07. HP: £95. ABP: £111.

Silver plated claret jug, flat lid with plain thumb piece, fluted neck, wheel cut foliage, early 20thC, 12in high. Hartleys, Ilkley. Feb 08. HP: £95. ABP: £111.

Victorian glass ewer, silver plated top, anthemion thumb piece, incised floral band, bellied/fluted body applied with green trails, 10.25in. Hartleys, Ilkley. Jun 07. HP: £95. ABP: £111.

919

Pair Victorian goblets, ovoid bowls, large cushion knops to stem, domed circular bases, 5.75in high. Tring Market Auctions, Herts. May 02. HP: £90. ABP: £105.

920

19thC opaline glass bodied inkwell, hinged domed cover, pineapple finial, hinged and banded, cast leaf raised circular base, 5in high. Tring Market Auctions, Herts. May 02. HP: £90. ABP: £105.

921

Early 20thC green iridescent glass vase, white metal dragonfly rim, 10in. Gorringes, Lewes. Jan 04. HP: £90. ABP: £105.

922

French opalescent glass dish, underside moulded in relief with head of a young girl, base marked 'Verre Artistique', 'Paris-544', 35.5cm. Hampton & Littlewood, Exeter. Apr 04. HP: £90. ABP: £105.

923

Seventeen various eye-baths, incl. Victorian examples. Gorringes, Bexhill. Jun 05. HP: £90. ABP: £105.

924

Art glass biscuit barrel streaked with a bronzed web design, 10in incl. handle, & a lime-green glass bowl, 6.25in dia. Gorringes, Lewes. Oct 04. HP: £90. ABP: £105.

925

Edwardian cut glass pedestal bowl, deeply cut with castellations to rim and diamonds to exterior, circular base, 14.25in. Gorringes, Lewes. Oct 04. HP: £90. ABP: £105.

926

'Nailsea' glass pipe, knopped and swelling stem, blue glass with trailed opaque white decoration, 42cm long. Bearne's, Exeter. Jun 05. HP: £90. ABP: £105.

927

Pair large cut glass candlesticks, early 20thC, hexagonal knopped stems, domed bases, 27cm high. Rosebery's, London. Sep 04. HP: £90. ABP: £105.

928

Whitefriars 'Concentric Rectangles' vase, designed by G. Baxter, tangerine glass, c1966, 6.75in. Gorringes, Lewes. Jan 05. HP: £90. ABP: £105.

Hammer: £90

929

Silver mounted cut glass claret jug, French 19thC, body cut with flutes, silver neck with alternate gadroon and husk decoration grape finial. 7.5in high. Rosebery's, London. Sep 04. HP: £90. ABP: £105.

930

Pair Art Nouveau style glass vases, raised green glass decoration to rim and stem, silver plate bases, stamped James Weir 91870 and a glass ovoid shaped posy vase with inlaid spiral decoration, engraved mark, Kosta, 7in Gorringes, Lewes. Jan 04. HP: £90. ABP: £105.

931

19thC table centre, heavy slice, diamond, hobnail and strawberry cuttings, upper vase pattern section with flared/shaped rim, engraved with a crest, knopped cylindrical base, 30in high. Canterbury Auction Galleries, Kent. Mar 05. HP: £90. ABP: £105.

932

Italian ruby glass charger, 41cm. Gorringes, Bexhill. Dec 04. HP: £90. ABP: £105.

933

Iridescent glass vase streaked with peacock feather devices, violet ground, 12.5in. Gorringes, Lewes. Oct 02. HP: £90. ABP: £105.

934

Lalique clear/frosted glass plate, base moulded in deep relief with 'Cerises' design of cherries in bold relief, 9.5in, moulded mark 'R. Lalique', surface of plate scratched. Canterbury Auction Galleries, Kent. Feb 07. HP: £90. ABP: £105.

935

Venetian pink/lemon glass latticinio decorated vase, boat shaped bowl, griffin stem, 9.5in. Gorringes, Bexhill. Mar 02. HP: £90. ABP: £105.

936

Opaque glass Art Deco table lamp, enamelled with leafy branches, shade with opposing cartouches of female figures bearing garlands, 11.5in high. Dee, Atkinson & Harrison, Driffield. Apr 06. HP: £90. ABP: £105.

Hammer: £90

Eight various glasses incl. Winston Churchill 1874-1965, Edward VIII 'Coronation' 1937, two double-ended measures, and Edward VII glass plaque. (9) Sworders, Stansted Mountfitchet. Jul 05. HP: £90. ABP: £105.

Three late Victorian Nailsea-type glass pipes, longest 18in. Gorringes, Lewes. Jan 03. HP: £90. ABP: £105.

19thC Nailsea style glass pipe, opaque white glass with pink combed decoration, length 19.5in. Fellows & Sons, Hockley, Birmingham. Oct 03. HP: £90. ABP: £105.

Art Nouveau style mottled orange and green glass vase. Gorringes, Bexhill. Oct 05. HP: £90. ABP: £105.

Three small Victorian glass witches balls. (3) Reeman Dansie, Colchester. Apr 06. HP: £90. ABP: £105.

Whitefriars indigo Double Diamond vase, bearing label to base, 15.5cm high. Gorringes, Bexhill. Dec 05. HP: £90. ABP: £105.

Pair of etched ruby glass lustres, decorated birds in flight and animals. Charterhouse Auctioneers, Sherborne. Feb 06. HP: £90. ABP: £105.

18-piece suite of etched drinking glasses, for sherry, port and wine, and 3 other glasses. Gorringes, Lewes. Apr 04. HP: £90. ABP: £105.

Victorian glass table lustre, prism drops, 12.5in. (restored) Gorringes, Lewes. Apr 00. HP: £90. ABP: £105.

19thC etched/faceted glass vase, shaped foot,chip to top and base, 10in. Denhams, Warnham, Sussex. Nov 05. HP: £90. ABP: £105.

Set of eight glass drug jars, English early 20thC, with Latin labels and with square shaped stoppers, 24cm/26cm high. Rosebery's, London. May 06. HP: £90. ABP: £105.

Pair late 19thC cut glass rummers, vine etched decoration. Reeman Dansie, Colchester. Apr 06. HP: £90. ABP: £105.

Cut glass decanter, bottle form, disc cut stopper, lobed neck, body cut with diamond/ fan banding, star cut spreading foot, 11.5in high, Sheffield 1924. Hartleys, Ilkley. Aug 06. HP: £90. ABP: £105.

Nine glass rummers, tallest 13.5cm. Sworders, Stansted Mountfitchet. Jul 05. HP: £90. ABP: £105.

Okra lustre glass vase, bottle form with frilled rim, white flowerhead inclusions on a purple and gold patchwork ground, 9.25in high, etched mark 'Okra 1991'. Hartleys, Ilkley. Dec 06. HP: £90. ABP: £105.

Large Scottish glass cylindrical pot. Great Western Auctions, Glasgow. Aug 06. HP: £90. ABP: £105.

Pair of Victorian ruby glass lustres, prismatic drops, 28cm. Charterhouse Auctioneers, Sherborne. Sep 06. HP: £90. ABP: £105.

Continental moon flask painted with spring flowers and nasturtiums. Great Western Auctions, Glasgow. Oct 06. HP: £90. ABP: £105.

19thC Glass candlestick, turned sconce with flared rim, knopped stem with bubble inclusions, domed foot, 8in high. Hartleys, Ilkley. Feb 07. HP: £90. ABP: £105.

W.M.F. Ikora bowl, foldover brown rim, white vein effect, mottled red base, 13in wide. Hartleys, Ilkley. Dec 07. HP: £90. ABP: £105.

957

Etling opalescent glass vase, decorated flowerheads, moulded Etling France, 23cm. Charterhouse Auctioneers, Sherborne. Apr 07. HP: £90. ABP: £105.

958

Chinese crystal snuff bottle, moonflask form, inside painted depicting land-scapes, green jadite stopper, 19thC, 2.75in high, and a similar item. (2) Hartleys, Ilkley. Apr 08. HP: £90. ABP: £105.

The numbering system acts as a reader reference as well as linking to the Analysis of each section.

959

Decanter stand: pierced circular holders, central stem, leaf moulded loop handle, 3 cut glass bottle shaped decanters, inscribed labels, scrolled feet. Hartleys, Ilkley. Jun 07. HP: £90. ABP: £105.

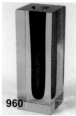

960

Stromberg B985 rectangular glass vase, etched signature to base, and No. N129J5/25, 19cm high. Charterhouse Auctioneers, Sherborne. Nov 07. HP: £90. ABP: £105.

961

Monart vase, oranges/green with aventurine inclusions. Great Western Auctions, Glasgow. Dec 07. HP: £90. ABP: £105.

962

Pair of Mary Gregory style green glass bottle decanters. Great Western Auctions, Glasgow. Nov 07. HP: £90. ABP: £105.

963

Green glass flask etched with hunting scene, another in enamels with a deer's head and oak leaf wreath and a similar glass, painted with a chamois. Great Western Auctions, Glasgow. Dec 07. HP: £90. ABP: £105.

964

Victorian faceted/waisted glass decanter, flared silver collar, William Hutton & Sons Ltd., London 1896, 28cm high. Locke & England, Leamington Spa. Mar 08. HP: £90. ABP: £105.

965

Whitefriars purple TV vase. Great Western Auctions, Glasgow. Aug 07. HP: £88. ABP: £103.

966

Ruby tinted/cut glass vase, waisted form, decorated with stylised banding, knop stem, stepped square base, 39cm high. Hampton & Littlewood, Exeter. Jul 04. HP: £88. ABP: £103.

967

St Louis baluster shaped glass vase, everted rim, 9.5cm high. Dreweatt Neate, Newbury. Apr 00. HP: £85. ABP: £99.

968

19thC German pewter mounted blue glass vase, gilt floral decoration, 10.5in. Gorringes, Lewes. Feb 01. HP: £85. ABP: £99.

969

Lalique Tourbillon glass ceiling light. Gorringes, Bexhill. Oct 05. HP: £85. ABP: £99.

970

Sowerby glass posy basket and vase with various coloured glassware. Gorringes, Bexhill. Oct 05. HP: £85. ABP: £99.

971

Pair of enamelled, marbled pink glass vases, Continental 19thC, slender neck, band of Arabesque decoration, body with gilt highlights, 28.5cm high. Rosebery's, London. Jun 05. HP: £85. ABP: £99.

972

Art glass vase, ovoid form, 3-colourway decoration, possibly Swedish, 6in. Gorringes, Lewes. Jan 03. HP: £85. ABP: £99.

973

19thC yellow glass oval tray, gilded border, Mary Gregory type decoration, 10.5in long. Tring Market Auctions, Herts. Jan 03. HP: £85. ABP: £99.

974

Pair Oriental green opaque glass vases painted with finches perched in blossom in a moonlit setting, 4.75in high. Tring Market Auctions, Herts. Mar 04. HP: £85. ABP: £99.

975

Cut glass claret jug, flared body wheel cut with garlands & flowerheads, plated mount foliate engraved, scroll handle, 11in high. Dee, Atkinson & Harrison, Driffield. Nov 07. HP: £85. ABP: £99.

Hammer: £85 - £80

3 19thC blue glass lidded chemist's jars, black labelling on gilt ground, with a reeded green glass jar & Bristol blue rolling pin, traces of decoration, 24.5cm & 45cm. Locke & England, Leamington Spa. Nov 05. HP: £85. ABP: £99.

Glass vase, flared top, decorated with fish lilies & reeds, wood base, marked T Goode and Co., London, 10.5in. high. Ewbank Auctioneers, Send, Surrey. Dec 05. HP: £85. ABP: £99.

Cut glass dish/cover and two oval cut glass bowls. (3) Rosebery's, London. Aug 06. HP: £85. ABP: £99.

Oak cased tantalus, plated mounts, three cut glass spirit decanters, 37cm long. Rosebery's, London. Aug 06. HP: £85. ABP: £99.

Glass vase painted in enamels with sealife. Great Western Auctions, Glasgow. Nov 06. HP: £85. ABP: £99.

19thC Bohemian ruby flash faceted glass etched with a harbour view, 5in. Gorringes, Lewes. Jun 00. HP: £80. ABP: £94.

Pair Bohemian amber flash glass tots with bird and floral panels, 4in. Gorringes, Lewes. Sep 00. HP: £80. ABP: £94.

Thomas Webb & Sons Queens Burmese ware satin glass vase, factory mark to base, 8.5cm high. Sworders, Stansted Mountfitchet. Dec 03. HP: £80. ABP: £94.

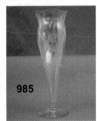

19thC conical ale glass, double knop stem, folded foot, 19cm high. Thos Mawer & Son, Lincoln. Sep 04. HP: £80. ABP: £94.

Glass vase engraved with ribbons and garlands, 14.5in. Gorringes, Lewes. Sep 04. HP: £80. ABP: £94.

Rosenthal tall glacier glass vase, poss. by Tapio Wirkala, c1960s, compressed form moulded to resemble ice, 27cm high, stencilled Rosenthal mark to underside. Rosebery's, London. Sep 04. HP: £80. ABP: £94.

Whitefriars Kingfisher blue glass Bark vase designed by Geoffrey Baxter (1967-1980), 16cm high. Clevedon Salerooms, Bristol. Jun 05. HP: £80. ABP: £94.

The illustrations are in descending price order. The price range is indicated at the top of each page.

Whitefriars Greek key pattern vase designed by Geoffrey Baxter, square section body, circular neck, tangerine, 20cm high Cheffins, Cambridge. Feb 05. HP: £80. ABP: £94.

Two Bohemian clear glass goblets: one engraved and flashed in pink, round panel depicting St John the Baptist, underside inscribed with initials AB, 13cm high, 3rd qtr 19thC, some scratching, the other similar. Dreweatt Neate, Donnington. Nov 02. HP: £80. ABP: £94.

Moser blue glass goblet, faceted bowl with classical scene in gilt, spreading foot, etched marks, 22cm high. Cheffins, Cambridge. Feb 05. HP: £80. ABP: £94.

Royal Brierley glass vase, bright iridescence, red ground, engraved mark, 4in. Gorringes, Lewes. Jul 03. HP: £80. ABP: £94.

Footed glass vase in manner of Archimede Seguso, internally decorated in alternating panels of maroon/white threads, 16cm high, with another similar glass vase. Rosebery's, London. Mar 05. HP: £80. ABP: £94.

Whitefriars Kingfisher blue glass tapered rectangular vase, textured decoration designed by Geoffrey Baxter (1969-1977), 18cm high. Clevedon Salerooms, Bristol. Jun 05. HP: £80. ABP: £94.

Legras cameo glass vase, c1900, two colour overlaid woodland decoration, 14.5cm. damaged, restuck. Sworders, Stansted Mountfitchet. Apr 05. HP: £80. ABP: £94.

995

Twelve glass pharmacy jars mainly clear and with glazed labels, 3 green, largest 26cm high. (12) Cheffins, Cambridge. Apr 05. HP: £80. ABP: £94.

996

Various Victorian/Edwardian green wine glasses with clear stems. (31) Sworders, Stansted Mountfitchet. Jul 05. HP: £80. ABP: £94.

997

Miniature Monart vase, 2.5in high. Great Western Auctions, Glasgow. Aug 05. HP: £80. ABP: £94.

998

Large cut glass decanter, Irish 19thC, hexagonal mallet form, circular lenses beneath a double ring neck, faceted stopper, neck chipped, 38cm. Rosebery's, London. Jan 06. HP: £80. ABP: £94.

999

Cut glass table lamp/shade. Great Western Auctions, Glasgow. Dec 05. HP: £80. ABP: £94.

1000

Whitefriars orange banjo vase. Great Western Auctions, Glasgow. Dec 05. HP: £80. ABP: £94.

1001

WMF 'Ikora' glass bowl, early 20thC, amber body washed with purple/green iridescence, pontil to underside, 30cm dia. Rosebery's, London. Mar 06. HP: £80. ABP: £94.

1002

Timo Sarpaneva, 'Orchid' vase, first designed c1957, this example believed to be a re-issued version c1987, tapered clear form, large air inclusion bubble/aperture, engraved 'Timo Sarpaneva' 3568 to underside, 16.5cm high. Rosebery's, London. Mar 06. HP: £80. ABP: £94.

1003

John Ditchfield glasform vase. Great Western Auctions, Glasgow. Mar 06. HP: £80. ABP: £94.

1004

Art Deco Continental square glass spirit decanter/stopper with silver collar, inscribed. Denhams, Warnham, Sussex. Apr 06. HP: £80. ABP: £94.

Hammer: £80 - £76

1005

Heavy mouth blown smokey blue glass footed vase, 14in high. Golding Young & Co, Grantham. Feb 06. HP: £80. ABP: £94.

1006

Edwardian cut glass jug, spreading base, engraved with pheasants and foliage, silver collar, Chester 1904, 23cm high. Charterhouse Auctioneers, Sherborne. Sep 06. HP: £80. ABP: £94.

1007

Persian amber glass bottle, possibly 11th/12thC, neck with applied spiralling decoration, body with scrolling forms, 17cm high,damaged. Rosebery's, London. Jan 07. HP: £80. ABP: £94.

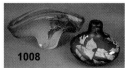

1008

Two contemporary art glass vases possibly French, by Le Loup, c1990, first of squat form, blue ground, abstract murrine design, second of compressed fan shape, frosted ground with pink and coloured murrine design, both signed to undersides, largest 34cm long. Rosebery's, London. Mar 08. HP: £80. ABP: £94.

1009

Continental green glass vase, six etched oval panels, one bearing the initials 'SR' and the date '1845', others with buildings with inscriptions below, 12cm high. Rosebery's, London. Jan 07. HP: £80. ABP: £94.

1010

Crescent pattern salad dish, moulded/frosted with design of 'Six Thistles', 8 x 6.5in, engraved mark 'Lalique, France'. Canterbury Auction Galleries, Kent. Feb 07. HP: £80. ABP: £94.

1011

Three Whitefriars textured glass vases: orange coffin vase, a ruby and a blue cylinder vase. (3) Richard Winterton, Lichfield. Jan 08. HP: £80. ABP: £94.

1012

Cut glass decanter, lobed tapering form, mushroom stopper, moulded flared rim, cut with diamond and fern banding, 10in high, Birmingham 1931. Hartleys, Ilkley. Feb 08. HP: £80. ABP: £94.

1013

Three bottle tantalus with plated mounts. Great Western Auctions, Glasgow. Dec 07. HP: £76. ABP: £89.

Hammer: £75

Set of four Lalique clear and frosted glass side plates, nude child centres, etched in script Lalique France, 6.25in. Gorringes, Lewes. Jun 00. HP: £75. ABP: £88.

Pair Bohemian ruby flashed and engraved glass beakers and 3 ruby engraved bowls, minor chips to bowls. Gorringes, Lewes. Sep 00. HP: £75. ABP: £88.

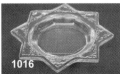

R.Lalique clear glass Fauvettes pattern ashtray, 7in. Gorringes, Lewes. Apr 02. HP: £75. ABP: £88.

Rummer glass engraved with shield and farming implements, entitled 'Speed the Plough', 6in high. Tring Market Auctions, Herts. Jan 03. HP: £75. ABP: £88.

Glass and silver plated claret jug, as a stylised duck, and a similar claret jug/stopper of bulbous form, 19cm & 36cm. Locke & England, Leamington Spa. Sep 04. HP: £75. ABP: £88.

66 *Glass Prices*

Matched pair of crystal wine decanters, flared rim, silver collar, facet cut necks and bulbous star cut bodies, Birmingham 1989, with a similar smaller decanter, Birmingham 1991. Locke & England, Leamington Spa. Sep 04. HP: £75. ABP: £88.

P.Koennig,iridescent purple glass inkwell, brass inkwell, 3 brass collared pen holes to sides. 9cm high x 10cm wide. Rosebery's, London. Dec 04. HP: £75. ABP: £88.

Categories or themes can be followed through the colour coded Index which contains over 4500 cross references.

Set of four 19thC green glass ale flutes, 5in, and a set of 8 clear wine glasses, engraved borders, 5in. Gorringes, Lewes. Apr 02. HP: £75. ABP: £88.

Pair modern Lalique moulded & frosted glass bulbous vases, fronts moulded in relief with 2 lovebirds, engraved mark 'Lalique, France' to base, 5in high, both birds wings chipped. Canterbury Auction Galleries, Kent. Apr 05. HP: £75. ABP: £88.

Pair 19thC pink/gilt table lustres, one AF to rim, some rubbing to gilding. Kent Auction Galleries, Folkestone. Apr 05. HP: £75. ABP: £88.

Vaseline glass epergne, frilled edge, circular bowl, scrolled silver plated stand, sd, 10.5in high. Fellows & Sons, Hockley, Birmingham. Oct 03. HP: £75. ABP: £88.

Victorian glass flask, etched glass decoration, stag in a forest, and another with engraved monogram, both with silver plated mounts. (2) Reeman Dansie, Colchester. Apr 06. HP: £75. ABP: £88.

Oak cased tantalus, three cut crystal spirit decanters, 34.5cm long. A/F. Rosebery's, London. May 06. HP: £75. ABP: £88.

Whitefriars turquoise vase, cylindrical form, moulded with bark effect, 8.25in high. Hartleys, Ilkley. Dec 06. HP: £75. ABP: £88.

Pair of tall glass vases, gilt panelling and painted with thistles. Great Western Auctions, Glasgow. Mar 07. HP: £75. ABP: £88.

Victorian blue glass Mary Gregory jug, loop handle, 6.5in high. Dee, Atkinson & Harrison, Driffield. Sep 07. HP: £75. ABP: £88.

Loetz glass vase, silver moulded rim, lustre body shading from red to gold/green, spreading base, 7.25in high. Hartleys, Ilkley. Dec 07. HP: £75. ABP: £88.

Irish cut glass sweetmeat dish, fan rim, square foot, associated lid. Great Western Auctions, Glasgow. Dec 07. HP: £75. ABP: £88.

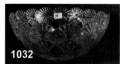

Cut glass circular fruit bowl, serrated rim, fan and panel cuttings, 12in dia x 5.5in high. Canterbury Auction Galleries, Kent. Feb 07. HP: £75. ABP: £88.

1033

Six Vasart orange glass dishes. Great Western Auctions, Glasgow. Dec 07. HP: £72. ABP: £84.

1034

Simon Moore. Amethyst glass comport, flared form, signed and dated '86, 10in wide. Andrew Hartley, Ilkley. Dec 99. HP: £70. ABP: £82.

1035

London Studio, 1987, green, blue/red glass bottle vase of flattened shouldered form, narrow neck and everted rim, indistinctly signed, 12in high. Andrew Hartley, Ilkley. Dec 99. HP: £70. ABP: £82.

1036

Edwardian silver mounted cut glass capstan inkwell, 3in. Gorringes, Lewes. Jul 00. HP: £70. ABP: £82.

1037

Opaque white glass vase by John Ditchfield, unsigned, 10.5in high. Andrew Hartley, Ilkley. Feb 03. HP: £70. ABP: £82.

1038

Iridescent glass vase, style of Loetz, waved everted rim, amber body with crackle iridescence in gold/purple, pontil to base, 19.5cm high. Rosebery's, London. Sep 04. HP: £70. ABP: £82.

1039

Pair of late 19thC ruby over-lay glass vases with lace-like decoration of butterflies and foliage, 7.5in high. Dee, Atkinson & Harrison, Driffield. Nov 04. HP: £70. ABP: £82.

1040

Pair of Victorian mauve blown posy glasses Gorringes, Bexhill. Dec 04. HP: £70. ABP: £82.

1041

Continental cut/etched glass vase, applied with white metal, amber foliate motifs, signed, Sirena?, 7in. Gorringes, Lewes. Oct 02. HP: £70. ABP: £82.

1042

1960s Whitefriars red waisted bowl 10.5in. Denhams, Warnham, West Sussex. Jan 05. HP: £70. ABP: £82.

Hammer: £72 - £70

1043

Whitefriars glass, textured bark vase, kingfisher blue, designed by Geoffrey Baxter, c1960, 23cm high. Rosebery's, London. Mar 05. HP: £70. ABP: £82.

1044

Art Deco amber coloured vase, each side with kneeling female figures, hands joined, 7.5in high. Dee, Atkinson & Harrison, Driffield. Feb 06. HP: £70. ABP: £82.

1045

Contemporary Murano glass vase by Archimede Seguso, c1980s, squat twisted form, deep blue, engraved Archimede Seguso Murano to underside, 12.5cm high. Rosebery's, London. Mar 06. HP: £70. ABP: £82.

1046

Amethyst ripple effect glass vase, 8in tall, with a royal blue similar example, 10in tall. Golding Young & Co, Grantham. Feb 06. HP: £70. ABP: £82.

1047

Pair of green decorated opaline glass table lamps, fitted for electricity, 25.5cm high. Rosebery's, London. May 06. HP: £70. ABP: £82.

1048

Ribbed/faceted Daum, Nancy glass vase, smoke glass tapered body, etched signature to base, 11cm high. Cheffins, Cambridge. Apr 05. HP: £70. ABP: £82.

1049

Trio of Continental milk-glass vases, scrolling handles and painted with flowers, tallest vase 13.5cm high, a/f. (3) Rosebery's, London. Aug 06. HP: £70. ABP: £82.

1050

Vicke Lindstrand for Kosta, 3 coloured glass art vases, two engraved to base 'Kosta LH' Nos. 1779 and 1845, tallest 16.5cm, smallest 8.5cm. (3) Sworders, Stansted Mountfitchet. Apr 06. HP: £70. ABP: £82.

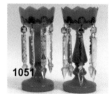

1051

Pair of Victorian blue glass lustres, gilt decoration and prismatic drops, 30cm. Charterhouse Auctioneers, Sherborne. Sep 06. HP: £70. ABP: £82.

1052

Monart glass vase in green & orange with aventurine. Great Western Auctions, Glasgow. Sep 07. HP: £70. ABP: £82.

Hammer: £70 - £65

Holmegaard Swedish bottle vase, flared rim, coloured red with a white interior, 17.25in high. Hartleys, Ilkley. Jun 07. HP: £70. ABP: £82.

Art glass vase, flared rim, crackled glass body shot through with red/white/yellow and black, spreading foot, 12.25in high. Hartleys, Ilkley. Jun 07. HP: £70. ABP: £82.

Whitefriars tangerine mobile vase designed by Geoffrey Baxter. Great Western Auctions, Glasgow. Feb 08. HP: £70. ABP: £82.

Pair of clear glass lustres. Black Country Auctions, Dudley. Sep 05. HP: £66. ABP: £77.

Pair of silver topped etched glass dressing table jars, Birmingham 1917. Great Western Auctions, Glasgow. Mar 08. HP: £66. ABP: £77.

Carin Von Drekle, irridescent glass bowl in form of a sea shell, splashed green/purple with yellow trailing on a pink shading to pale green ground, signed and dated 1983, 6in wide. Andrew Hartley, Ilkley. Dec 99. HP: £65. ABP: £76.

Karen Lawrence, purple irridescent glass vase, silver circles & swirling decoration, signed and dated 1986, 9in high, and a similar vase. Andrew Hartley, Ilkley. Dec 99. HP: £65. ABP: £76.

> Prices quoted are actual hammer prices (HP) and the Approximate Buyer's Price (ABP) includes an average premium of 15% + VAT.

Ruby overlaid cut glass vase, 31cm high. Lambert & Foster, Tenterden. Jun 03. HP: £65. ABP: £76.

Murano hexagonal optic crystal glass vase, clear glass with Sommerso interior of yellow and blue, 24cm dia. Rosebery's, London. Sep 04. HP: £65. ABP: £76.

19thC Hukin & Heath plate mounted cut glass claret jug, 8in. Gorringes, Lewes. Jul 04. HP: £65. ABP: £76.

George V silver mounted glass inkstand, 5in. Gorringes, Lewes. Jul 03. HP: £65. ABP: £76.

Art Deco green glass vase, base moulded 'Scailmont HH', 13.5in high. Sworders, Stansted Mountfitchet. Apr 01. HP: £65. ABP: £76.

Finnish glass vase in style of Gunnel Nyman, c1960, tear-drop form, green glass with minute air inclusions cased in clear, 24cm high, signature to underside. Rosebery's, London. Mar 05. HP: £65. ABP: £76.

Quantity Bimini glass buttons, various shapes, colours and sizes, some depicting animals etc, all have brass back plates with Bimini impressed mark and made in England. Rosebery's, London. Mar 05. HP: £65. ABP: £76.

Iridescent glass bowl/cover probably Austrian, green trailed body washed with blue, gilt metal cover with pierced foliate design, 8cm high. Rosebery's, London. Mar 05. HP: £65. ABP: £76.

Two Whitefriars square textured 'nail-head' vases designed by Geoffrey Baxter, ruby 20cm, willow 17cm. Boldon Auction Galleries, Tyne & Wear. Sep 05. HP: £65. ABP: £76.

Early 20thC gilt floral glass goblet, 7in. Gorringes, Bexhill. Mar 02. HP: £65. ABP: £76.

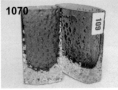

Two Whitefriars textured vases designed by Geoffrey Baxter, bowed form, pewter 11cm high, width 11.5cm and kingfisher blue, 11.5cm high. Boldon Auction Galleries, Tyne & Wear. Sep 05. HP: £65. ABP: £76.

Large Orrefors glass vase. Gorringes, Bexhill. Oct 05. HP: £65. ABP: £76.

1072

French 'Vannes' winged clear glass vase, 11.5in high, 21.5in span. Dee, Atkinson & Harrison, Driffield. Feb 06. HP: £65. ABP: £76.

1073

Late 19thC glass dome on wooden base, 50cm. Reeman Dansie, Colchester. Apr 06. HP: £65. ABP: £76.

1074

Two Victorian bell-shaped cloches, knop carrying handles, 13.5in high. (2) Dee, Atkinson & Harrison, Driffield. Jul 06. HP: £65. ABP: £76.

1075

Bohemian white cased green glass vase, 19thC, flared form, green glass overlaid in white and cut with a cross design, painted with pink roses/swags, 13cm high, with a Bohemian uranium glass vase of flared panelled form. (2) Rosebery's, London. Aug 06. HP: £65. ABP: £76.

1076

Limited edition rummer, commemorating the launch of the Queen Mary, September 26th 1934, wheel cut with an image of the vessel, waisted stem, circular foot, 7in high. Dee, Atkinson & Harrison, Driffield. Sep 07. HP: £65. ABP: £76.

1077

Pair of Victorian fly traps, typical dome shape, 3 stub feet, stoppers, 18cm high, and a pair of Edwardian decanters/stoppers, bulbous form, decorated with looped banding, 31cm high (8). Hampton & Littlewood, Exeter. Jul 04. HP: £64. ABP: £75.

1078

Sowerby purple malachite glass spill vase, double diamond shape, 13cm unmarked, Davidson's purple malachite ribbed vase, No. 236 unmarked, plus 2 others. Boldon Auction Galleries, Tyne & Wear. Sep 04. HP: £62. ABP: £72.

1079

Late Victorian opaline glass biscuit barrel, 25cm high. David Duggleby, Scarborough. Jun 01. HP: £60. ABP: £70.

1080

Powell Whitefriars pale green glass globular vase, with ribbed decoration, 7in. Gorringes, Lewes. Jul 08. HP: £60. ABP: £70.

Hammer: £65 - £60

1081

Carnival glass twin handled bowl, 'Lotus and Grape' blue. 7in. Potteries Specialist Auctions, Stoke on Trent. Mar 03. HP: £60. ABP: £70.

1082

Black glass rolling pin, engraved with Sunderland iron bridge and inscribed George and Elizabeth Little 1843. 34cm. Boldon Auction Galleries, Tyne & Wear. Oct 04. HP: £60. ABP: £70.

1083

Silver overlaid glass charger, pink glass body decorated with peacocks and foliage in silver, 30cm dia, marked 925. Rosebery's, London. Sep 04. HP: £60. ABP: £70.

1084

Gallé Cameo glass vase, pale pink ground overlaid in deep brown/green, decorated with leaves and ferns, 21cm high, cameo mark 'Gallé'. Rosebery's, London. Sep 04. HP: £60. ABP: £70.

1085

Sabino blue glass vase, decorated with moulded overlapping Rays around the body, gilded detailing, etched mark, 21.5cm high. Cheffins, Cambridge. Apr 05. HP: £60. ABP: £70.

1086

1930s French glass vase painted with a winter landscape, 3in. Gorringes, Lewes. Apr 02. HP: £60. ABP: £70.

1087

Pair of E100 Holophane light shades, moulded marks, patent numbers and date 1909, 22.5cm dia. (2) Cheffins, Cambridge. Feb 05. HP: £60. ABP: £70.

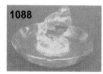

1088

Lalique yellow glass cendrier surmounted by a bird (chip to rim) engraved R.Lalique France in script, 3.75in dia. Gorringes, Bexhill. Mar 02. HP: £60. ABP: £70.

1089

Edwardian crystal bottle decanter poss. by Schindler, hallmarked silver collar with quatrefoil rim, body with a stylised cherry design in red/green glass, clear ground, hallmarked for 1904, 9in high. Fieldings, West Hagley, Worcs. Jun 05. HP: £60. ABP: £70.

1090

Pair of cut/etched crystal vases. Great Western Auctions, Glasgow. Aug 05. HP: £60. ABP: £70.

Hammer: £60

Whitefriars textured barkin vase, Kingfisher blue, designed by Geoffrey Baxter in 1966, issued 1967-1980, 9in high. Halls Fine Art, Shrewsbury. Jul 05. HP: £60. ABP: £70.

Two rectangular Art glass vases, one with random veining white/red on a blue ground, 10in high, other multi-coloured teardrops on a green ground, 7.5in high. (2) Dee, Atkinson & Harrison, Driffield. Sep 05. HP: £60. ABP: £70.

Set of three decanters and a tapered glass jar and cover. Gorringes, Bexhill. Oct 05. HP: £60. ABP: £70.

Cut glass decanter, inverted thistle form with ball stopper, lobed moulded rim cut with chequered banding, 12in high, London 1930, and a similar decanter. (2) Hartleys, Ilkley. Dec 06. HP: £60. ABP: £70.

Collection of glass bells, some with porcelain handles. Gorringes, Bexhill. Oct 05. HP: £60. ABP: £70.

Loetz-style glass vase, 11in. Gorringes, Lewes. Apr 04. HP: £60. ABP: £70.

Monart green glass dish with aventurine. Great Western Auctions, Glasgow. Mar 07. HP: £60. ABP: £70.

Moser amethyst glass vase, moulded with a horizontal band of figures, 8in, and a similar blue glass pedestal dish, 3in. Gorringes, Lewes. Apr 04. HP: £60. ABP: £70.

Strathearn green glass vase with aventurine. Great Western Auctions, Glasgow. Feb 06. HP: £60. ABP: £70.

Collection of 3 modern Gallé style glass vases, moulded with characteristic floral/leaf decoration, ochre ground, 24.5cm. Rosebery's, London. May 06. HP: £60. ABP: £70.

Cameo glass bowl early 20thC, frosted body carved with landscape scene overlaid in blue, cameo mark to body, 21.5cm dia. Rosebery's, London. May 06. HP: £60. ABP: £70.

The numbering system acts as a reader reference as well as linking to the Analysis of each section.

Moulded purple Tulip lamp, by Bagley & Co, Knottingley, c1936, 8.25in high. Dee, Atkinson & Harrison, Driffield. Jul 06. HP: £60. ABP: £70.

Bohemian overlaid glass beaker, 19thC, cut foliate scrolls, painted with a street scene, 12cm high with a ruby/white Bohemian overlaid glass vase with pink rose swags. (2) Rosebery's, London. Aug 06. HP: £60. ABP: £70.

Pair of Stevens & Williams vaseline glass vases, triangular form, flared rim, sides inset with brown banding, 4.25in high. Hartleys, Ilkley. Aug 06. HP: £60. ABP: £70.

Vasart pink glass vase. Great Western Auctions, Glasgow. Jun 06. HP: £60. ABP: £70.

Victorian glass pipe, ovoid bowl, triple knopped stem, blue/white streaked banding, 11.75in long. Hartleys, Ilkley. Feb 07. HP: £60. ABP: £70.

Silver hinged lid ink pot by 'HTB', approx 3in tall, cut glass pot, repousse patterned lid, gilt inner, h/m London 1910. A F Brock & Co Ltd, Stockport. May 07. HP: £60. ABP: £70.

Murano green glass bowl, 20thC, Renaissance style, centre enamelled with shield encompassing a mans head, exterior with a broad band of gilt scale pattern, scales enamelled with coloured dots, round foot, 20.5cm dia. Rosebery's, London. Jan 08. HP: £60. ABP: £70.

Blue cased Spa beaker, ruby flash Spa beaker and faceted Spa beaker for Bad Gastein, enamelled white flowers. (3) Dee, Atkinson & Harrison, Driffield. Apr 06. HP: £60. ABP: £70.

1110

S J, cut glass/silver mounted inkwell, hinged lid, pierced foliate collar, London 1904. Locke & England, Leamington Spa. Sep 06. HP: £60. ABP: £70.

1111 488

Four Latticino glass dishes. Great Westen Auctions, Glasgow. Feb 06. HP: £58. ABP: £68.

1112

Pair of opaque vaseline glass bowls, ribbon shaped rims. Black Country Auctions, Dudley. Sep 05. HP: £55. ABP: £64.

1113

Sowerby Queens Ivory Ware basket moulded with peacocks, makers mark, reg. diamond. Boldon Auction Galleries, Tyne & Wear. Sep 04. HP: £55. ABP: £64.

1114

Chinese pink speckled glass snuff bottle, jade stopper, 2.75ins Gorringes, Lewes. Jul 04. HP: £55. ABP: £64.

1115

Edwardian pressed glass inkwell, 6in. Gorringes, Lewes. Apr 04. HP: £55. ABP: £64.

1116

Set of six French, glass/silver overlaid cocktail glasses, c1930. each decorated with a chicken, also five, Stuart style, cut glass high ball tumblers, 20thC. (11) Rosebery's, London. Jun 05. HP: £55. ABP: £64.

1117

Pair of Victorian bohemian ruby overlay glass vases with a 19thC baluster form vase in brown glaze with floral decoration, af. Thimbleby & Shorland, Reading. Aug 05. HP: £55. ABP: £64.

1118

Murano L. Nason pink/white triform bowl, 12in dia, with a rainbow bowl, 10.75in dia. (2) Dee, Atkinson & Harrison, Driffield. Feb 06. HP: £55. ABP: £64.

1119

Mappin & Webb, pair of silver rimmed cut glass vases, of cylindrical tapering form, London 1927, 19.5cm. Locke & England, Leamington Spa. Nov 06. HP: £55. ABP: £64.

1120

Art Nouveau frosted green glass dish, lozenge form, pewter rim embossed with a dragonfly, 5in wide, and a Loetz style green iridescent glass shell, 5.5in wide. (2) Hartleys, Ilkley. Dec 06. HP: £55. ABP: £64.

Hammer: £60 - £52

1121

Cut glass and silver plated mounted claret jug, lion finial, Bacchus mask spout, slender loop handle, trellis cut body, 31cm. Locke & England, Leamington Spa. Sep 06. HP: £55. ABP: £64.

1122

Loetz glass vase, attributed to Michael Powolny, post 1914, orange ground with vertical black stripes beneath scalloped rim, 18.5cm high, with a glass/silvered metal tazza in same style, 19.5cm high. (2) Rosebery's, London. Oct 06. HP: £55. ABP: £64.

1123

Orrefors cased red/clear specimen flower vases, 12in & 9in high. Kent Auction Galleries, Folkestone. May 07. HP: £55. ABP: £64.

1124

Art Nouveau vase, lobed sides enamelled with green flowers, yellow textured ground, 6in. Hartleys, Ilkley. Oct 07. HP: £55. ABP: £64.

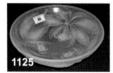

1125

French 1930s opalescent glass bowl, moulded with cherries, by G. Vallon. Great Western Auctions, Glasgow. Mar 07. HP: £55. ABP: £64.

1126

Palme Koenig threaded vase, clear body slip trailed with turquoise threads, 8in high. Hartleys, Ilkley. Dec 07. HP: £55. ABP: £64.

1127

19thC beaker, part mirrored & jewelled with enamelled trailing flora, 6.75in high. Dee, Atkinson & Harrison, Driffield. Nov 07. HP: £55. ABP: £64.

1128 117

Silver mounted thistle shaped decanter, Birmingham 1909. Great Western Auctions, Glasgow. Feb 08. HP: £55. ABP: £64.

1129

Five pieces purple malachite glass, various. Boldon Auction Galleries, Tyne & Wear. Sep 04. HP: £52. ABP: £61.

1130

Victorian pressed glass, seven items of black glass. Golding Young & Co, Grantham. Nov 06. HP: £52. ABP: £61.

Hammer: £50

Pale blue/amber glass flagon c1880, barley twist handle, facet cut stopper, 25cm high. (2). Hampton & Littlewood, Exeter. Jul 04. HP: £50. ABP: £58.

Art Nouveau glass vase, pinched body, flared top, 8.5in. Gorringes, Lewes. Jan 04. HP: £50. ABP: £58.

Pair of 19thC Mary Gregory green glass spill vases, decorated with a standing child, 34cm high. Locke & England, Leamington Spa. Jul 08. HP: £50. ABP: £58.

Victorian drinking glass with diamond-cut ovals and one panel engraved with spider's web and oak leaves, 7in. Gorringes, Lewes. Jun 03. HP: £50. ABP: £58.

Two plain glass rummers, one with chip, tallest 19cm. Sworders, Stansted Mountfitchet. Jul 05. HP: £50. ABP: £58.

Set of twelve green glass plates. Gorringes, Bexhill. Oct 05. HP: £50. ABP: £58.

Palme Konig iridescent green glass vase. Gorringes, Bexhill. Oct 05. HP: £50. ABP: £58.

Pair of square orange/apricot Whitefriars vases, alternate sides bark pattern and plain, each 7in high. Black Country Auctions, Dudley. Dec 05. HP: £50. ABP: £58.

Victorian Jack-in-the-Pulpit style vase, purple rim, body with applied crimping, five splay feet, 9.75in high, with a Victorian pale green trumpet shaped vase, shaped vaseline rim, 7.5in high. (2) Dee, Atkinson & Harrison, Driffield. Feb 06. HP: £50. ABP: £58.

Art Deco glass vase c1930s, flared form, upon pedestal grey glass engraved and cut with a stylised antelope, 20cm high. Rosebery's, London. Mar 06. HP: £50. ABP: £58.

Late Victorian ruby glass claret jug, spiral twist handle and star cut base, 19cm. Reeman Dansie, Colchester. Apr 06. HP: £50. ABP: £58.

Cameo glass vase, signed Gallé. (AF) Golding Young & Co, Grantham. Feb 06. HP: £50. ABP: £58.

Strathearn orange glass vase. Great Western Auctions, Glasgow. Aug 06. HP: £50. ABP: £58.

Two Mary Gregory style garnet glass vases, first of baluster form enamelled with a boy in a garden, 17.5cm high, second of tapering cylindrical form enamelled with a girl holding a flower, 17cm high. Rosebery's, London. Oct 06. HP: £50. ABP: £58.

Art Deco malachite glass lamp, panelled sides moulded with classical figures, reeded panels between, 10.5in high. Hartleys, Ilkley. Oct 06. HP: £50. ABP: £58.

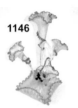

Late 19thC green vaseline glass epergne, applied crimped spiralling bands of decoration, 42.5cm high, lacking one branch/basket, a/f. Rosebery's, London. Oct 06. HP: £50. ABP: £58.

Viennese goblet, painted with a young girl on an opaque oval panel, gilded foliate borders, spreading foot, 5.75in high. Hartleys, Ilkley. Feb 07. HP: £50. ABP: £58.

Whitefriars Brown Bark vase, by Geoffrey Baxter, c1965, 7.25in high. Dee, Atkinson & Harrison, Driffield. Nov 07. HP: £50. ABP: £58.

Mary Gregory style amethyst glass rouge pot, lid decorated with a young child in coloured enamels, 5cm dia. Charterhouse Auctioneers, Sherborne. Apr 08. HP: £50. ABP: £58.

Kosta Boda 'Atoll' vase by Anna Ehrner. Great Western Auctions, Glasgow. Mar 08. HP: £50. ABP: £58.

PART I: Decorative & Functional Glass c1830-2000
Section VI: Under £50

**'This is not the price range where I would normally advocate buying.....
the decanters are not Georgian.....these are not rummers, being common
or garden pub glasses from the 1870s.....the Lalique *Nonnettes* is chipped
so must be left out.....you can find bargains at this level of the market.....'**

Worthwhile lots are even thinner below £50 and this is not the price range in which I would normally advocate buying. In fact this is the first Section that I have actually manipulated to exclude the hundreds of mixed lots that we should always avoid. In any event they would not provide the reader with any sense of values. Unless you are a trader at the lower end of the market, avoid them at all costs. Additionally the accepted wisdom is to always buy the very best you can afford and this means avoiding buying most of the time and saving your money until the better pieces come along, which won't be that often. Having said that are we able to point out worthwhile buys in this Section? I am certain they exist.

Damage to **1152**, the purple malachite and **1153**, the Gallé cameo excludes these otherwise acceptable lots. The set of six harlequin hocks at **1155** are an actual set because they were made with different coloured bowls. If they are lead crystal and heavy then they have gone cheaply. If not they are a poor buy. The decanters at **1160** are not Georgian and a poor buy, but at **1162,** the nineteenth century millefiore vase, without any ifs or buts, is one of the stars of the Section. The pair of c1979 Dublin ship's decanters with silver mounts are a better buy in today's anti-decanter market and could easily sell on for at least a £150. I like the Whitefriars vase at **1184** and only £49 but much more outstanding is the turquoise baluster jug at **1186** which looks to be nineteenth century but is not given any credit of age. If this is a period piece then it was a gift, as was the millefiore lamp base at **1187**. I would perhaps suggest that it would have been best to avoid most of the lots illustrated on pages 76 and 77 except the very nice silver mounted Edwardian hobnail cut glass sugar sifter at **1210**, with a 1903 Chester mark. The price is about right and if you are collecting and using table silver then it would have been a worthwhile buy. By the way the 'rummers' at **1221** are not rummers, being common or garden pub glass from the 1860s-1870s. Don't think of buying mixed lots like those at **1207**. At nearly £10 a piece and certainly hardly worth even that, what would be the point? The money could have bought one good piece or have gone towards buying something even better. The Orrefors at **1227**, the Joblings at **1228** and the **Kosta** at **1237** may well interest collectors on a tight budget. I would urge those interested in drinking glasses to look carefully at **1240**. Providing the engraving is of good quality, this is good value for money. Similarly the purple glass decagonal goblet at **1242** is a gift provided the gilding is intact. The

collection of 'Bristol blue' at **1246** works out at only £2 a piece but should we be interested? Alternatively the Stourbridge concentric millefiore door handle at **1257** is uncommon and a good collector's piece, worth every bit of £50. This was a good buy at £35. For the same money I hope there are no readers who would even consider getting stuck with the modern beer steins at **1265.** The blue glass hand-blown comport at **1271** is given no pedigree so may be modern. Even so, for decorative purposes, say as a table centre containing fruit it would be impressive, but how tall is it?

The pair of cordial glasses at **1289** are in fact wine glasses. As one Victorian airtwist should sell for about £30-£40 these are a bargain. At **1291** are 'ten green bottles' but hardly I suspect the ones that achieved fame in the song. In fact there are millions of these about and anyone who decides to collect such common or garden memorabilia will soon be able to fill every nook and cranny in the house. The problem will come when you try to get rid of them! Nor would I add the ten tots at **1302** to my collection. There is enough of this type of glass in the secondhand market to sink the Isle of Wight. On page 82 the Lalique *Nonnettes* is chipped so must be left out, but the Webb Crystal blue glass should be of good quality. I really admire the unusual style of the decanter at **1309** with the silver rims, except of course that this is a carafe and not a decanter and a seriously good bargain. However at **1312** the late Georgian toastmaster's glass looks suspiciously like a Victorian penny lick worth a fiver! There is one more item which should interest us, the literally gigantic red glass four-handled vase at **1222** which is getting on for twenty inches in height. I know nothing of its origin or quality but decorative glass of this size could make an important decorative statement in the home and may certainly be of commercial interest for a shop window display.

This analysis does show up the opportunities at this level, but such buying infringes the golden rule of always buying the very best we can afford. There seems to be a conflict of interests in these two arguments but I think not. The fact that you can still find bargains and worthwhile antiques and collectibles at this level of the market also suggests that our skills would be much better employed at a higher level of the market and that if we perhaps had not weakened our resources here we might more easily have put them to much better and more profitable use by sticking to the rule and only buying the very best we can afford.

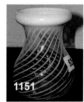

Vaseline glass hyacinth vase.
Great Western Auctions,
Glasgow. Jun 06. HP: £48.
ABP: £56.

Victorian pressed glass, pair
of obelisks (both with small
chips to angles), a pair of
shallow bowls, a lidded drum
pot and a small footed bowl
with registration & Sowerby
mark to inside of bowl, all in
purple malachite. (6)
Golding Young & Co,
Grantham. Nov 06. HP: £48.
ABP: £56.

Gallé green overlay cameo
vase, 2.75in. (top lip re-
ground) Gorringes, Bexhill.
Oct 02. HP: £45. ABP: £52.

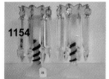

Pair of late Victorian opal
glass trumpet shape drop
lustre vases, entwined blue
snakes to stems, 27cm.
Boldon Auction Galleries,
Tyne & Wear. Sep 04. HP:
£45. ABP: £52.

Set of six harlequin hock
glasses. Gorringes, Bexhill.
Dec 04. HP: £45. ABP: £52.

Dimpled opaque white/amber
two handled art-glass vase,
amber circular foot, body
with blue wave effect, 14in
high. Dee, Atkinson &
Harrison, Driffield. Nov 04.
HP: £45. ABP: £52.

Pair of Victorian bell shaped
cut glass decanters, faceted
shoulder and neck, tapering
mushroom stopper, star cut
to base. (2) Dee, Atkinson &
Harrison, Driffield. Mar 04.
HP: £45. ABP: £52.

Bertil Valian (Kosta,
Sweden) an irridescent bottle
shaped glass vase, milky
white body, swirls of purple/
blue irridescence, engraved
marks to underside, 28cm
high. Rosebery's, London.
Jun 05. HP: £45. ABP: £52.

George VI cut glass decanter
with silver mount, Sheffield
1939, 10in high and two
silver napkin rings. Ewbank
Auctioneers, Send, Surrey.
Dec 05. HP: £45. ABP: £52.

Pair late Georgian decanters,
thumb cut to neck/shoulders,
star cut to base, faceted cone-
shaped stoppers. Dee, Atkinson & Harrison, Driffield.
Feb 06. HP: £45. ABP: £52.

Two Art Deco tazza's, etched
glass bowls, 4 fluted chrome
pillar supports, circular foot,
9in high. (2) Dee, Atkinson
& Harrison, Driffield. Feb
06. HP: £45. ABP: £52.

Late 19thC Millefiori vase,
blue, white and yellow, two
handles, 8in. Dee, Atkinson
& Harrison, Driffield. Feb
06. HP: £45. ABP: £52.

Lemonade set, unmarked.
Aladdins Cave Auction,
Danehill, Sussex. Mar 06.
HP: £45. ABP: £52.

Stevens & Williams green
and blue glass vase. Great
Western Auctions, Glasgow.
Sep 06. HP: £45. ABP: £52.

Strathearn glass vase. Great
Western Auctions, Glasgow.
Apr 06. HP: £45. ABP: £52.

Two Whitefriars clear glass
vases, 8in and 6.5in high and
lustrous purple & iridescent
blue/ green Art Glass vase,
7in high. (3) Dee, Atkinson
& Harrison, Driffield. Jul
06. HP: £45. ABP: £52.

Edwardian ruby/clear glass
decanter/stopper, etched with
fruiting vine, with set of four
conforming ribbed stemmed
glasses. Locke & England,
Leamington Spa. Nov 06.
HP: £45. ABP: £52.

Silver topped decanter/glass
set by Francis Howard
Silversmiths Ltd, cut glass
decanter, approx 85mm high,
silver collar, ball top stopper,
with two 'whiskey' glasses, in
presentation box. A F Brock
& Co Ltd, Stockport. Oct 06.
HP: £45. ABP: £52.

Pair of Irish cut glass/silver
mounted ships decanters,
Dublin, c1979, one stopper
re-ground, 24cm high.
Rosebery's, London. Jul 07.
HP: £45. ABP: £52.

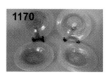

1170

Four Vasart glass dishes, c1930, amber ground with yellow/vermilion streaked effect, interspersed with air inclusions, original paper labels 'Vasart Perth Scotland', 19cm dia. Rosebery's, London. Apr 07. HP: £45. ABP: £52.

1171

Vaseline glass vase, waisted form, frilled rim, striped body, late 19thC, 6.25in high. Hartleys, Ilkley. Jun 07. HP: £45. ABP: £52.

1172

Late 19thC clear glass covered jar, orifice for a tap, faceted cover, steeple knop finial, 28.5in. Dee, Atkinson & Harrison, Driffield. Sep 07. HP: £45. ABP: £52.

1173

Wedgwood textured art glass vase designed by Ronald Stennet-Wilson. Great Western Auctions, Glasgow. Sep 07. HP: £45. ABP: £52.

1174

Pair of Art Nouveau glass vases, crackle finish, lustre glaze. Great Western Auctions, Glasgow. Feb 08. HP: £45. ABP: £52.

1175

Pallme Konig iridescent glass Art Nouveau vase. Great Western Auctions, Glasgow. Oct 07. HP: £45. ABP: £52.

1176

Ships decanter, cut glass, approx 8.5in, silver collar & silver port label, D337 h/m London 1972. A F Brock & Co Ltd, Stockport. Nov 07. HP: £45. ABP: £52.

> The illustrations are in descending price order. The price range is indicated at the top of each page.

1177

Clear glass vase by S. Hopea for Nuutajarvi Notsjo, with narrow aperture, signed to base, 20cm high. Rosebery's, London. Jan 08. HP: £45. ABP: £52.

1178

Antique & vintage glass marbles. (386) A F Brock & Co Ltd, Stockport. Feb 08. HP: £45. ABP: £52.

1179

Strathearn green/aventurine glass vase. Great Western Auctions, Glasgow. Nov 05. HP: £44. ABP: £51.

1180

Green glass spirit flagon, late 19thC, silver plated collar/cover, 18.5cm high. Hampton & Littlewood, Exeter. Jul 04. HP: £42. ABP: £49.

1181

Set of 7 Bristol green wine glasses, engraved decoration, vine leaves & bunches of grapes, ground pontil mark to base. Kent Auction Galleries, Folkestone. Feb 06. HP: £42. ABP: £49.

1182

George V silver mounted glass preserve jar and cover, Birmingham 1911, with a jam spoon. Golding Young & Co, Grantham. Feb 06. HP: £42. ABP: £49.

1183

Two 20thC large green glass vases. Golding Young & Co, Grantham. Feb 06. HP: £42. ABP: £49.

1184

Whitefriars deep green tinted vase, cylindrical undulating form, paper label, 21.5cm. Locke & England, Leamington Spa. Jul 06. HP: £42. ABP: £49.

1185

Strathearn green glass and aventurine vase. Great Western Auctions, Glasgow. Feb 07. HP: £42. ABP: £49.

1186

Turquoise blue glass jug, spiral moulded body, neck applied with clear glass prunts, flared foot, applied handle, 27cm. Woolley & Wallis, Salisbury. Sep 00. HP: £40. ABP: £47.

1187

20thC Italian millefiori glass lamp base, 8in. Gorringes, Lewes. Mar 01. HP: £40. ABP: £47.

1188

Three glass rolling pins, two blue glass with gilt/enamel decoration, rubbed and another. Sworders, Stansted Mountfitchet. Jul 01. HP: £40. ABP: £47.

Hammer: £40

Carnival glass Northwood vase, nobbled beads green, 10in. Potteries Specialist Auctions, Stoke on Trent. Mar 03. HP: £40. ABP: £47.

Pair of 19thC mallet form cut glass decanters, line/facet cut decoration, star cushion, triple ring neck, facet/star cut stopper, 26cm high. Thos Mawer & Son, Lincoln. Sep 04. HP: £40. ABP: £47.

Sowerby opaque glass vase of Chinese lantern hexagonal form in white/black mottled, 9cm, unmarked, No. 1170, plus 3 other small vases. Boldon Auction Galleries, Tyne & Wear. Sep 04. HP: £40. ABP: £47.

Iridescent amber glass Jack-in-the-Pulpit vase, silver plated scrolled triform stand, max 10in. Fellows & Sons, Hockley, Birmingham. Oct 03. HP: £40. ABP: £47.

Contemporary glass vase, by Simon Moores, c1988, flared/waved green body bordered & decorated with clear swirls, black glass pedestal, 23cm high, engraved 'Simon Moores' 88 to rim. Rosebery's, London. Sep 04. HP: £40. ABP: £47.

19thC glass decanter, painted with Ye Olde Curiositie Shoppe & related characters, with stopper, 11.5in. Gorringes, Lewes. Jul 04. HP: £40. ABP: £47.

> Categories or themes can be followed through the colour coded Index which contains over 4500 cross references.

Bohemian ruby flash tumbler engraved with a serpent and beehive, chipped, 4.5in. Gorringes, Bexhill. Mar 02. HP: £40. ABP: £47.

Bohemian ruby and amber flashed vase with floral and building panels, 6.75in. Gorringes, Bexhill. Mar 02. HP: £40. ABP: £47.

1930s Art Deco lemonade set: jug and 4 tumblers, decorated with wheel cut abstract floral motifs and flashes picked out in black enamel, clear ground. Fieldings, West Hagley, Worcs. Jun 05. HP: £40. ABP: £47.

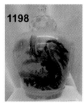

Internally painted glass jar, faceted glass cover, 5in high. Kent Auction Galleries, Folkestone. Jul 05. HP: £40. ABP: £47.

Pair of late 19thC pink overlay glass vases, frilled edges, clear white glass handles. Kent Auction Galleries, Folkestone. Jul 05. HP: £40. ABP: £47.

Whitefriars Powell & Sons large optic-moulded citrine vase, 31cm high. Gorringes, Bexhill. Jul 05. HP: £40. ABP: £47.

Three various glass vases, two green, one blue. Gorringes, Bexhill. Jul 05. HP: £40. ABP: £47.

Gilt-decorated opaque glass vase. Gorringes, Bexhill. Jul 05. HP: £40. ABP: £47.

Late Victorian amber glass bottle, applied handle, brass stopper, 7.5in and a Nailsea type amber/opaque white glass jug, 4.5in. Gorringes, Lewes. Jan 03. HP: £40. ABP: £47.

Loetz style glass vase. Great Western Auctions, Glasgow. Oct 05. HP: £40. ABP: £47.

Pair of Whitefriars solifleur bark vases, tangerine colour designed by Geoffrey Baxter, 14.5cm. Boldon Auction Galleries, Tyne & Wear. Sep 05. HP: £40. ABP: £47.

Victorian green Mary Gregory vase, crimped clear glass handles, 9.25in high. Dee, Atkinson & Harrison, Driffield. Feb 06. HP: £40. ABP: £47.

1207

Five pieces of Whitefriars and Whitefriars type glass, 3 of ruby colour and 2 amber. Boldon Auction Galleries, Tyne & Wear. Sep 05. HP: £40. ABP: £47.

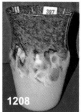

1208

Strathearn glass vase. Orpington Salerooms, Kent. Nov 05. HP: £40. ABP: £47.

1209

Two flash/enamel glass jars and covers, Bohemian 19thC, shouldered form. 16cm high. Rosebery's, London. Jan 06. HP: £40. ABP: £47.

1210

Edwardian hobnail-cut glass sugar sifter, silver-mounted, Chester 1903, makers mark GNRH. Gorringes, Bexhill. Feb 06. HP: £40. ABP: £47.

1211

Yellow tinted glass basket shaped vase, twisted handle and flowers in relief, 9in high. Ewbank Auctioneers, Send, Surrey. Dec 05. HP: £40. ABP: £47.

1212

Green Rhiimaki Lasi Oy vase, 6.5in high, with pair dimpled green Art Glass vases, vertically striated in yellow, 8.5in high. (3) Dee, Atkinson & Harrison, Driffield. Feb 06. HP: £40. ABP: £47.

1213

Two ruby red glass chemists display jars, spire stoppers. (2) Batemans, Stamford. Mar 06. HP: £40. ABP: £47.

1214

Victorian Vaseline glass vase, as an open petalled orchid, tapering looped stem, five pressed feet, 22.5cm. Locke & England, Leamington Spa. Mar 06. HP: £40. ABP: £47.

1215

Victorian blue Pearline jardiniere, square form, 4.5in high with similar small basket. (2) Dee, Atkinson & Harrison, Driffield. Apr 06. HP: £40. ABP: £47.

1216

Pale green glass 'Captains inkwell', conical form, 5in wide. Hartleys, Ilkley. Apr 08. HP: £40. ABP: £47.

Hammer: £40 - £38

1217

Two cut crystal mallet shape liqueur decanters. Golding Young & Co, Grantham. Feb 06. HP: £40. ABP: £47.

1218

Blue glass vase, silver overlay design of 'Fireflies' by Erte. Great Western Auctions, Glasgow. Oct 06. HP: £40. ABP: £47.

1219

Victorian pressed glass, two floral pedestal bowls, fluted vase and a shell spoon warmer, all purple malachite. (4) Golding Young & Co, Grantham. Nov 06. HP: £40. ABP: £47.

1220

Green/white marbled glass baluster vase, scribed Gray-Stan to base, 9in high. Golding Young & Co, Grantham. Nov 06. HP: £40. ABP: £47.

1221

Four 19thC rummer's. Dee, Atkinson & Harrison, Driffield. Sep 07. HP: £40. ABP: £47.

1222

Large red glass vase, tapering flared neck, 4 applied handles, 49cm. Rosebery's, London. Jan 08. HP: £40. ABP: £47.

1223

Swarovski crystal locomotive tender & carriage. Kent Auction Galleries, Folkestone. Jun 06. HP: £40. ABP: £47.

1224

EP 3 bottle decanter stand, 3 silver labels. Great Western Auctions, Glasgow. Mar 08. HP: £40. ABP: £47.

1225

19thC twin handled onion-shaped decanter and stopper, etched with panels of fruiting vine and motifs incl. a windmill, applied trailed borders, slight damage, 7.5in high. Fellows & Sons, Birmingham. Jul 03. HP: £38. ABP: £44.

1226

Large art glass vase. 11in tall. Black Country Auctions, Dudley. Sep 05. HP: £38. ABP: £44.

1227

Orrefors vase, engraved with a young girl being overflown by swans/cranes, clear glass, base signed Orrefors. P3845 H.C.L?, 8in tall. Golding Young & Co, Grantham. Feb 06. HP: £38. ABP: £44.

1228

Joblings opalique bowl with a shell design. Great Western Auctions, Glasgow. May 07. HP: £38. ABP: £44.

1229

Glass jug with lions head roundels, engraved 'Augeor dum Progtedior' (I increase as I proceed) above crescent moon. Great Western Auctions, Glasgow. Oct 07. HP: £38. ABP: £44.

1230

Unsigned Mdina glass vase. Great Western Auctions, Glasgow. Mar 08. HP: £38. ABP: £44.

1231

Victorian Nailsea type glass rolling pin decorated with hooped bands of opaque and raspberry, 29cm. Locke & England, Leamington Spa. Jul 07. HP: £36. ABP: £42.

1232

Two hand-blown studio art glass vases, frill tops, blue grounds, applied orange/yellow decoration. (2) Batemans, Stamford. Mar 06. HP: £36. ABP: £42.

1233

John Derbyshire matt jet glass ribbed vase moulded with swags and fruit, 14cm, anchor mark, Reg. diamond for 1876. Boldon Auction Galleries, Tyne & Wear. Sep 04. HP: £35. ABP: £41.

1234

Bohemian opaque white wine glass decorated with grape vines. Boldon Auction Galleries, Tyne & Wear. Sep 04. HP: £35. ABP: £41.

1235

Venetian bon bon dish, vertical strands of white latticino and blue/pink ribbon twists, 4.75in dia. Dee, Atkinson & Harrison, Driffield. Jul 04. HP: £35. ABP: £41.

1236

Mottled blue glass jug, green streaks, applied clear glass handle, 12.5in. Gorringes, Lewes. Apr 02. HP: £35. ABP: £41.

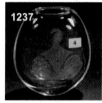

1237

20thC Swedish Kosta glass vase, flattened ovoid shape, engraved with a half length portrait of a woman, marked Kosta L6255, 8.25in high. Diamond Mills & Co, Felixstowe. Dec 04. HP: £35. ABP: £41.

1238

Edward Roman lustrous yellow splash vase, signed/dated 81, 6.75in high with an iridescent Inwald vase with trailed decoration, 5.25in high. (2) Dee, Atkinson & Harrison, Driffield. Sep 05. HP: £35. ABP: £41.

> Prices quoted are actual hammer prices (HP) and the Approximate Buyer's Price (ABP) includes an average premium of 15% + VAT.

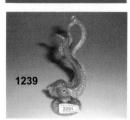

1239

Venetian glass flask, as a curling fish, pink/clear glass, gold dust inclusions, yellow/black eyes, 6in. Golding Young & Co, Grantham. Feb 06. HP: £35. ABP: £41.

1240

Bohemian engraved glass goblet, late 19thC, panelled form, flaring foot, engraved with goats in a landscape, 12cm high. Rosebery's, London. Aug 06. HP: £35. ABP: £41.

1241

Victorian pressed glass, top hat, slipper and pair of bugle vases, all purple malachite. (4) Golding Young & Co, Grantham. Nov 06. HP: £35. ABP: £41.

1242

Continental purple glass decagonal goblet, gilt decoration of a lady & gentleman taking tea, 16cm high. Rosebery's, London. Jan 07. HP: £35. ABP: £41.

1243

Strathearn glass vase in mottled blue. Great Western Auctions, Glasgow. Mar 07. HP: £35. ABP: £41.

1244

Two Victorian Vaseline baskets, oval form, two loop handles, crimped feet, 2.25in high. (2) Dee, Atkinson & Harrison, Driffield. Sep 07. HP: £35. ABP: £41.

1245

Late 19thC cut glass water jug, slice and diamond cut decoration, circular foot with star cut base, 24cm. Reeman Dansie, Colchester. Apr 06. HP: £34. ABP: £39.

Collection Bristol blue wine glasses, beakers and finger bowl. (19) Reeman Dansie, Colchester. Apr 06. HP: £34. ABP: £39.

Davidson's primrose pearline glass basket of ribbed form, Rd. 130643 for 1889, 16cm wide. Boldon Auction Galleries, Tyne & Wear. Sep 04. HP: £32. ABP: £37.

Joblings green tinged glass fir cone pattern plate 31cm, 2 green tinged 1930s vases, triangular with flowers 20cm & 2-handled circular, 23cm. Boldon Auction Galleries, Tyne & Wear. Sep 04. HP: £32. ABP: £37.

Early 20thC vase, possibly Monart, cushion foot, ovoid body with roll rim, detailed with an internal swirled and mottled pale pink ground, 7.75in high. Fieldings, West Hagley, Worcs. Jun 05. HP: £32. ABP: £37.

Silver/cut glass sugar dredger, Sheffield 1938. Kent Auction Galleries, Folkestone. Jul 05. HP: £32. ABP: £37.

Oy Kumela Finnish glass vase, signed to base by Kaj Blomquist. Orpington Salerooms, Kent. Mar 06. HP: £32. ABP: £37.

Frosted amethyst flared vase. Golding Young & Co, Grantham. Feb 06. HP: £32. ABP: £37.

Six 20thC cut crystal large flared glasses, ringed stems, cut base marked WALSH, one chipped. Golding Young & Co, Grantham. Feb 06. HP: £32. ABP: £37.

Banded glass hankerchief type vase, 14in tall. Golding Young & Co, Grantham. Feb 06. HP: £32. ABP: £37.

Monart glass dish. Great Western Auctions, Glasgow. Jan 07. HP: £32. ABP: £37.

Murano glass bowl with bubble decoration. Great Western Auctions, Glasgow. Jun 07. HP: £32. ABP: £37.

Hammer: £34 - £30

Stourbridge concentric mille-fiori door handle, canes in shades of pale pink, blue and dark pink, gilt metal mount, 1.75in. Gorringes, Lewes. Mar 03. HP: £30. ABP: £35.

Small 20thC Venetian glass vase, spherical form, high collar, roll rim, body cased with spiral white cane work, pale pink ground, 3.5in high. Fieldings, West Hagley, Worcs. Jun 05. HP: £30. ABP: £35.

Bohemian blue overlaid glass decanter. Kent Auction Galleries, Folkestone. Jul 05. HP: £30. ABP: £35.

Art Glass bowl, with broad fold over rim, striated in red, white and blue, 8.5in dia x 2.25in high. Dee, Atkinson & Harrison, Driffield. Jul 08. HP: £30. ABP: £35.

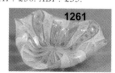

Murano Vetro Filigrana dish, pink and white, triangular form, 5in dia. Dee, Atkinson & Harrison, Driffield. Apr 06. HP: £30. ABP: £35.

Cut glass bottle decanter, body engraved with grape & vine decoration. Gorringes, Bexhill. Oct 05. HP: £30. ABP: £35.

Pair of green glass bottle decanters, EP stands. Great Western Auctions, Glasgow. May 08. HP: £30. ABP: £35.

Victorian liquer glass decanter/stopper, bird and floral etched body, 7.5in. Gorringes, Lewes. Jul 00. HP: £30. ABP: £35.

Pair of German amber glass beer steins painted with armorials and pewter domed lids, 24cm high. Rosebery's, London. Jan 06. HP: £30. ABP: £35.

Gold/red flecked Strathearn bowl, 7in dia, with a similar waisted vase, 7.5in high. (2) Dee, Atkinson & Harrison, Driffield. Feb 06. HP: £30. ABP: £35.

Victorian clear glass vase, pink frill rim, applied blue flowerheads, shaped briar handle, 7.25in high, with a blue glass basket, crimped rim, clear glass barley twist handle, 11.25in high. (2) Dee, Atkinson & Harrison, Driffield. Feb 06. HP: £30. ABP: £35.

Victorian pressed glass, double dish bowl, a smaller version, small 'bucket' planter and a 3 lobed bowl, all purple malachite. (4) Golding Young & Co, Grantham. Nov 06. HP; £30. ABP: £35.

Victorian pink overlay egg shaped vase, encrusted with fruit and flora, rustic amber front feet, 6.5in high, with a pair of clear glass grape encrusted vases, 7in high. (3) Dee, Atkinson & Harrison, Driffield. Feb 06. HP: £30. ABP: £35.

Style of Gallé, cameo glass vase, amber ground overlaid in mauve/brown, etched with lakeside landscape, cameo mark, 23cm high. Rosebery's, London. Mar 06. HP: £30. ABP: £35.

Blue glass hand-blown comport. Batemans, Stamford. Mar 06. HP: £30. ABP: £35.

Set of 5 late 19thC Venetian gold speckled amber glass side plates, 21cm. Reeman Dansie, Colchester. Apr 06. HP: £30. ABP: £35.

The numbering system acts as a reader reference as well as linking to the Analysis of each section.

Pair of Mary Gregory style cylindrical green glass vases, enamelled with a boy and a girl in a garden, 15.5cm high, & 2 other vases with similar decoration. (4) a/f. Rosebery's, London. Oct 06. HP: £30. ABP: £35.

Cut glass bowl, moulded body diamond cut within moulded swathed bands, 9.5in wide, London? Hartleys, Ilkley. Jun 07. HP: £30. ABP: £35.

Two Bohemian faceted mugs engraved with deer in forest setting, 11.5cm and 9cm high. (2) Rosebery's, London. Apr 07. HP: £30. ABP: £35.

Victorian pressed glass, a pedestal dish, bowl, mug and goblet, all purple malachite. (4) Golding Young & Co, Grantham. Nov 06. HP: £30. ABP: £35.

Webb Corbett frosted glass lamp, tapering shade, cut with stylised butterflies, 12.5in high. Hartleys, Ilkley. Oct 07. HP: £30. ABP: £35.

Three pieces of Sowerby moulded turquoise glass, a basket 1876, 3in high, grape hod 1876, 4in high & basket weave plate, pierced border, 8in dia. (3) Dee, Atkinson & Harrison, Driffield. Nov 07. HP: £30. ABP: £35.

Five flint glass plates, Roberts Pretoria, Baden Powell Mafeking, Give Us This Day our Daily Bread, 1902 Coronation with coat of arms, Empire Countries and another 1902 Coronation. Boldon Auction Galleries, Tyne & Wear. Sep 04. HP: £28. ABP: £32.

A c1970s Art glass bowl of flared form with lime/forest green inclusions, 30.5cm. Locke & England, Leamington Spa. Jul 06. HP: £28. ABP: £32.

Mottled green overlay glass vase of bulbous form, slender neck 13.5in high with a lustrous green art glass vase, all-over white piping 13.25in high. (2) Dee, Atkinson & Harrison, Driffield. Nov 04. HP: £28. ABP: £32.

Green glass vase, enriched with applied beaded foliate tendrils & lion mask prunts, 16cm. Rosebery's, London. Jan 06. HP: £28. ABP: £32.

White opaline carafe, and matching tumbler, gilded jewelling. (2) Dee, Atkinson & Harrison, Driffield. Sep 07. HP: £28. ABP: £32.

Silver topped and butterfly wing decorated jar, Birmingham 1925. Great Western Auctions, Glasgow. Mar 08. HP: £28. ABP: £32.

6in high flattened tear drop shaped vase, Isle of Wight Glass, paper label, cranberry with metallic finish. Kent Auction Galleries, Folkestone. Jul 05. HP: £27. ABP: £31.

1286

Three Chemist bottles: one Bristol blue, one amber & one clear glass. Boldon Auction Galleries, Tyne & Wear. Sep 04. HP: £26. ABP: £30.

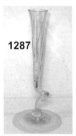

1287

Vaseline glass bud vase, twisted stem. 11in high. Black Country Auctions, Dudley. Sep 05. HP: £26. ABP: £30.

1288

Two opaline flared glass vases, one decorated with red/blue flower sprigs, other with garlands of flowers, late 19th/early 20thC, 12.5cm. Woolley & Wallis, Salisbury. Sep 00. HP: £25. ABP: £29.

1289

Pair of 19thC conical cordial glasses, air twist stems, unground pontils, 18cm high. Thos Mawer & Son, Lincoln. Sep 04. HP: £25. ABP: £29.

1290

Pair of 19thC opaque glass bottle vases. Gorringes, Bexhill. Dec 04. HP: £25. ABP: £29.

1291

Collection of clear glass bottles, 19thC and later. Gorringes, Bexhill. Jun 05. HP: £25. ABP: £29.

1292

Two turquoise opaque glass vases probably Edward Moore, anthemion pattern 18.5cm and garland pattern, 16.5cm, and 2 other turquoise glass vases. Boldon Auction Galleries, Tyne & Wear. Sep 04. HP: £25. ABP: £29.

1293

Amber art glass vase, triangular form with slender neck striated in white, 19in high with a cream coloured art glass vase entwined amber tubing 19in high. (2) Dee, Atkinson & Harrison, Driffield. Nov 04. HP: £25. ABP: £29.

1294

Davidsons blue pearline glass dish, melon slice form, shell decoration, 15cm, Rd. 212684. Boldon Auction Galleries, Tyne & Wear. Sep 05. HP: £25. ABP: £29.

1295

Blue glass table lamp, metal mounts, plus one blue hand-painted vase. Kent Auction Galleries, Folkestone. Apr 05. HP: £25. ABP: £29.

Hammer: £26 - £25

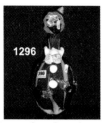

1296

Murano glass clown decanter, red/white striped body, multi-coloured bow tie, white frill. Kent Auction Galleries, Folkestone. Jul 05. HP: £25. ABP: £29.

1297

Glass jars with silver lids, different shapes/sizes, from gent's vanity set, lids monogrammed 'TW', stamped 'FS Ltd', h/m London 1925 & 1929 and Birmingham 1928 and 1929. (6) A F Brock & Co Ltd, Stockport. Nov 05. HP: £25. ABP: £29.

1298

Four items of coloured art glass, leaf shaped dish, ashtray, cylindrical vase and a lustre jar/stopper. Ewbank Auctioneers, Send, Surrey. Dec 05. HP: £25. ABP: £29.

1299

Signed Albert Lazoyer vase, enamelled with stylized orange fruit, 9in high, lattice gilded cylindrical vase, 5.75in high and a cased Caithness vase, multi coloured flecks on a striated amber ground, 6.5in high. (3) Dee, Atkinson & Harrison, Driffield. Feb 06. HP: £25. ABP: £29.

1300

Heavy cut crystal jug and bowl. Golding Young & Co, Grantham. Feb 06. HP: £25. ABP: £29.

1301

Continental glass vase, Bohemian style, tapering panelled sides enamelled with bands of leopard spots, unmarked, 20thC, 9.25in high. Hartleys, Ilkley. Dec 06. HP: £25. ABP: £29.

1302

Set of 10 tot glasses, etched with an African wild animal. Great Western Auctions, Glasgow. Jan 07. HP: £25. ABP: £29.

1303

Victorian pressed glass: pair of bud vases in plain pink, 4 footed vases and a handled basket, all candy twist pink and white glass. Golding Young & Co, Grantham. Nov 06. HP: £25. ABP: £29.

1304

Green/white marbled glass footed vase, flared rim, scribed Gray-Stan to base, 6in tall. Golding Young & Co, Grantham. Nov 06. HP: £25. ABP: £29.

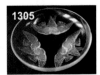

Lalique 'Nonnettes' bowl, moulded mark, chipped. Great Western Auctions, Glasgow. May 07. HP: £25. ABP: £29.

Heavy 1950s amber glass vase, wide white internal spiral decoration, 21.5cm. Boldon Auction Galleries, Tyne & Wear. Sep 05. HP: £24. ABP: £28.

Two pieces of Webb Crystal blue glass. Black Country Auctions, Dudley. Sep 05. HP: £24. ABP: £28.

Pair of gesso and enamel decorated glass vases. Great Western Auctions, Glasgow. Aug 07. HP: £22. ABP: £25.

Victorian claret glass decanter, silver top/neck, Birmingham assay. Golding Young & Co, Grantham. Nov 06. HP: £22. ABP: £25.

1960s Riihimaki of Finland red glass vase, base cased in clear, 20cm. Boldon Auction Galleries, Tyne & Wear. Sep 05. HP: £22. ABP: £25.

Cut glass bowl on stand. Great Western Auctions, Glasgow. Jan 07. HP: £22. ABP: £25.

Late Georgian toastmaster glass of plain form, 9.5cm. Boldon Auction Galleries, Tyne & Wear. Sep 04. HP: £22. ABP: £25.

Green carnival glass bowl, moulded sunflower design, triple branch feet, 10cm high. Richard Winterton, Lichfield. Jan 08. HP: £22. ABP: £25.

Art Deco glass standish. Gorringes, Bexhill On Sea. Dec 04. HP: £20. ABP: £23.

Loetz style iridescent glass bowl, green trail design, 15.5cm dia. Gorringes, Bexhill. Jul 05. HP: £20. ABP: £23.

Pair of clear glass decanters/ stoppers, cut trellis pattern bodies, gilt decoration, 23cm. Thos Mawer & Son, Lincoln. Mar 04. HP: £20. ABP: £23.

Art Deco pink glass bowl, moulded decoration of child & lamb. Gorringes, Bexhill. Jul 05. HP: £20. ABP: £23.

> The illustrations are in descending price order. The price range is indicated at the top of each page.

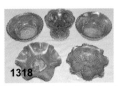

Orange carnival glass: bowls (2), fruit bowl, grapes/leaves design, tripod feet, pedestal bowl, and bowl with wavy edges, horse's head motif to centre. (5) A F Brock & Co Ltd, Stockport. Aug 05. HP: £20. ABP: £23.

Art Deco glass vase, painted with coaching scenes and figures. Gorringes, Bexhill. Oct 05. HP: £20. ABP: £23.

Bohemian glass handled bowl, painted panels, gilding. Black Country Auctions, Dudley. Dec 05. HP: £20. ABP: £23.

Victorian green glass cream jug and matching sugar bowl, enamelled with lily of the valley. (2) Dee, Atkinson & Harrison, Driffield. Apr 06. HP: £20. ABP: £23.

Hexagonal orange/apricot Whitefriars vase, 7in high. Black Country Auctions, Dudley. Dec 05. HP: £20. ABP: £23.

Georgian style glass, enamel twist stem, 28cm high, a/f. Rosebery's, London. Oct 06. HP: £20. ABP: £23.

Decorative smokey glass covered punch bowl, enamelled with swags of holly, 12in high. Dee, Atkinson & Harrison, Driffield. Apr 06. HP: £20. ABP: £23.

Pair lustrous green crimped carnival glass bowls, 7in dia. (2) Dee, Atkinson & Harrison, Driffield. Apr 06. HP: £20. ABP: £23.

PART II:
Cranberry Glass

'Despite the downturn in the market collectors are still being ruled by their hearts rather than their heads.....remember the golden rule about pairs.....the drinks set is rather a 'pink' elephant.....you may collect cranberry for a lifetime and never find a silver mounted match striker....'

The great period of manufacture in the UK was from c1870 to c1930. Cranberry was also made in France, Belgium, Bavaria, Bohemia and the USA. Its manufacture across the Atlantic took place mainly in New England, where in fact cranberries are grown, and it is perhaps here that the name was first coined. In the European mainland it is called gold ruby. Cranberry glass is made by adding a gold chlorine which has been dissolved in nitric and hydrochloric acids. It was certainly made in Roman times. We have the famous Lycurgus cup from the fourth century. However its origins appear to have been lost and were only rediscovered in the seventeenth century by either Johann Kanckel in Bohemia or perhaps Antonio Neri in Florence. All of the nineteenth century manufacturers produced cranberry but there was also a cottage industry carried on in backyard 'factories'.

Despite the downturn in the market in the early years of the twenty-first century prices show that collectors are still being ruled by their hearts rather than their heads. I cannot say that there has ever been an upper market but there is a middle market and a burgeoning lower market, which has taken a pounding in recent years. However such is its popularity, that when it appears at auction there always appears to be plenty of bidders, despite the fact that the market has been flooded for years with reproductions, which are now also for sale in high street stores. The trade could, as in many other areas of the market, try to prevent the sale of reproductions and new goods in their outlets and this would certainly go some way towards restoring confidence in the industry. Having said that it's never easy. I have valued several cranberry collections in recent years and even the owners in some cases hadn't spotted the reproductions.

Let us examine the market in more detail. Here I offer 124 illustrated lots from recent sales. There are several examples of cameo cranberry in **Part I** at **77** and **95** and it is also worth a glance at the section on perfume bottles. The price of the best cranberry is clearly around the £1,000-£1,500 range but the highest price paid would appear to be £1,900 hammer for a pair of lustres in 2006. Remember one of the golden rules. Pairs are very sought after. But so are singles when they are cranberry epergnes and I have ensured there are enough examples in these pages to give the reader a sense of values, which are in the range £350 to £750.

The drinks set at **1330** holds a high position but only because there are 15 items in the set, fine in a museum I

would have thought, but rather a 'pink' elephant for the collector, unless you live in a mansion. Cranberry claret jugs are popular and there are some good examples at **1348**, **1360** and **1368**. I doubt if they have ever performed their function, but they are a good display item. In fact most cranberry is tableware but I doubt if it ever gets used. The same goes for the over fussy tray sets at **1350** and **1351**, more pink elephants that can take up a lot of space, yet perform poorly on display. They are also prone to damage which knocks the bottom out of their value. Notice the cranberry collection at **1358** has damages and no date attribution. At about £35 a piece I would suggest this is money down the drain and it will take some getting back if bought by the trade in 2007. Despite the space filling potential of wine glasses they remain popular, but if you have to buy them go for the actual sets which look to have quality and could be used like hock glasses. Avoid groups like **1374**, **1401**, **1404** and **1405**. For example the eight mismatched, bottom-of-the-market glasses at **1404** cost the buyer almost £13 each and they are only worth half of that. To me, glass should function for its intended purpose and if this is to display as an ornament, fine, but useful wares that are as cheap and as plain as these are better hidden! Worse than that though, they never get used! Far better to buy something like the trumpet vases at **1363** or in particular the fine amphora shaped jug at **1372,** which is highly decorative with its white coiled ornament in the ancient style. I've noticed another at **1431** and five years later it fetched only £64, an incredible bargain. Why should people pay a premium for cheap wine glasses and a pittance for fine quality, married to good design?

At **1377** is a dealers lot, bought cheaply enough at about £10 a piece. There is profit here. Collectors should avoid such lots and aim to buy much better examples. Note that auctions tend to put their heads on the block and credit cranberry to a period. Most here seems to be genuine whereas in the retail sector it is not. Always ask for an invoice when buying and ensure the outlet attaches an approximate date to your purchases, otherwise walk away.

One of the more unusual items in this selection is the silver mounted match striker at **1399**, a real collectors piece and the price at £100 hammer is not unreasonable. This is dateable and uncommon enough that you may collect cranberry for a lifetime and never find another. Similarly gimbal flasks are uncommon and the example at **1443** is a bargain providing that it is antique.

Hammer: £1,600 - £340

Russian silver mounted ruby glass decanter, St Petersburg late 19thC, chased owl's head hinged lid, central band above star cut glass bowl, maker's mark poss. Hiskias Pondinen & Issac Warelius, 25cm, and similar ruby glass decanter, St Petersburg late 19thC, chased cockerel's head, same maker's mark, 26.5cm high. (2) Rosebery's, London. Jun 08. HP: £1,600. ABP: £1,882.

Pair of mid 19thC Bohemian cranberry glass lustres overlaid with white, crinoline tops oval vignettes of white enamel painted with flowers, faceted lustres & drop. Kent Auction Galleries, Folkestone. Mar 07. HP: £1,200. ABP: £1,411.

Thomas Webb cranberry/ white cameo glass vase carved with convolvulus, 5.25in. Gorringes, Lewes. Apr 01. HP: £1,100. ABP: £1,293.

Late 19thC Webb's cameo glass biscuit barrel, body cased in white over deep cranberry, cut back with a pattern of flowering apple blossom boughs, white metal domed cover & swing handles, 6in high, 6in across. Fieldings, West Hagley, Worcs. Jun 05. HP: £920. ABP: £1,082.

Late 19thC cranberry and iridescent glass drinks set: pair of decanters, 12 stemmed glasses and a circular tray, gilt rims. (15) Wintertons Ltd, Lichfield. Mar 01. HP: £900. ABP: £1,058.

Cranberry glass/gilt-metal cylindrical sleeve vase, 38cm high. Gorringes, Bexhill. Sep 04. HP: £900. ABP: £1,058.

Victorian cranberry glass epergne, frilled bowl with central upright funnel, two smaller funnels and 2 green glass wrythen moulded canes, canes supporting two cone-shaped baskets, clear glass trailed decoration, 22in high. Fellows & Sons, Birmingham. Jul 03. HP: £550. ABP: £646.

Pair 19thC cranberry glass lustre vases, shaped cut rims, tapered centre columns and circular bases, cut prismatic drops, 11.25in high. Canterbury Auction Galleries, Kent. Dec 05. HP: £500. ABP: £588.

Victorian pink and milk glass epergne, central trumpet vase flanked by two further vases and two hanging baskets, square base bowl, 23in high. Andrew Hartley, Ilkley. Aug 05. HP: £480. ABP: £564.

Victorian cranberry glass epergne, central trumpet, two outer trumpets & two twisted canes supporting hanging baskets, frilled edge bowl base, 21.5in high. Diamond Mills & Co, Felixstowe. Mar 06. HP: £425. ABP: £499.

Victorian cranberry glass four division epergne, flared wavy rimmed trumpets, wavy rimmed circular base, 52cm high. Wintertons Ltd, Lichfield. Mar 00. HP: £400. ABP: £470.

Pair of late 19thC gilded cranberry glass liquer decanters/stoppers and ten matching glasses. Gorringes, Lewes. Apr 00. HP: £380. ABP: £446.

Victorian cranberry glass epergne, central large trumpet with trailed clear glass decoration, 2 similar smaller trumpets and two wrythen moulded clear glass canes, each cane supporting a cranberry hanging basket, (one a.f), shaped square base with frilled rim, (s.d.), 21.5in high. Fellows & Sons, Hockley, Birmingham. Oct 03. HP: £380. ABP: £446.

Pair of Edwardian cranberry glass lustre vases, prismatic lustre drops, 8in high. Andrew Hartley, Ilkley. Aug 00. HP: £360. ABP: £423.

Categories or themes can be followed through the colour coded Index which contains over 4500 cross references.

Pair of Victorian cranberry and white flashed glass table lustres. Gorringes, Bexhill. Dec 04. HP: £360. ABP: £423.

Elkington & Co., late 19thC oval sweet dish, cranberry glass in a cast silver wire carrier with a ribbon tied mount, Birmingham 1898, 8in wide, Amersham Auction Rooms, Bucks. Jun 01. HP: £340. ABP: £399.

1342

Cranberry glass epergne, clear spiral bands, central trumpet, 3 others, 3 hanging vases hung from clear spiral moulded branches, 52cm, two of hanging baskets with cracks. Bearne's, Exeter. Jun 05. HP: £340. ABP: £399.

1343

Victorian cranberry glass epergne, 7 trumpet shaped fitments, clear trailed glass decoration, 18.75in high, one trumpet chipped. Canterbury Auction Galleries, Kent. Jun 07. HP: £320. ABP: £376.

1344

Cranberry glass epergne, central trumpet & 4 smaller trumpets, ribbed outline, wavy rim, scrolled EPNS stand, 4 ball feet, 13in high. Fellows & Sons, Hockley, Birmingham. Oct 03. HP: £310. ABP: £364.

1345

Cranberry/clear glass epergne, central trumpet clear twist decoration, 3 candy twist canes supporting cranberry baskets, 21in. Golding Young & Co, Grantham. Nov 06. HP: £310. ABP: £364.

1346

Set of 3 Victorian cranberry glass bells, each with pale green handle, 11.5in & 12in. high. Gorringes, Lewes. Oct 04. HP: £300. ABP: £352.

1347

Victorian cranberry glass epergne, circular crimped rim to base, centre fitted with a tall trumpet shaped centre vase, clear trailed decoration, and six smaller conforming trumpet shaped vases, 23in high. Canterbury Auction Galleries, Kent. Dec 05. HP: £300. ABP: £352.

1348

19thC ruby coloured claret jug with heraldic mount. Richard Winterton, Burton on Trent, Staffs. Feb 03. HP: £300. ABP: £352.

1349

Cranberry glass epergne, central trumpet vase, clear glass waved rim and applied spiral flanked by 3 smaller vases & 3 baskets, saucer base with waved rim, 20.5in high. Hartleys, Ilkley. Jun 07. HP: £300. ABP: £352.

Hammer: £340 - £240

1350

Cranberry glass sherry set: decanter and six stemmed glasses, painted with figures in Mary Gregory style, 9in decanter. Hartleys, Ilkley. Oct 06. HP: £300. ABP: £352.

1351

Mary Gregory type cranberry glass jug, c1900, a tray and three goblets, jug 35cm, chips. (5) Sworders, Stansted Mountfitchet. Feb 07. HP: £300. ABP: £352.

1352

Pair of cranberry glass lustres. John Taylors, Louth. Apr 01. HP: £290. ABP: £341.

1353

Pair of late 19thC Bohemian ruby overlaid glass vases engraved with stags/woodland, knopped hollow stems, 8.25in and similar German mug with pewter mounted cover, 5in. Gorringes, Lewes. Oct 02. HP: £290. ABP: £341.

1354

Victorian lime-green/cranberry glass epergne, trumpet vase, 3 smaller vases & 3 pendant baskets, all with trailed ornament, 17.5in. Gorringes, Lewes. Jul 06. HP: £280. ABP: £329.

1355

Victorian cranberry glass epergne, central frilled trumpet with clear glass trailing, flanked by scrolled branches hanging with baskets, and two similar trumpets, dished base, 19.5in high. Hartleys, Ilkley. Aug 06. HP: £280. ABP: £329.

1356

19thC Bohemian cranberry/white overlaid glass vase, slender flared neck, pedestal foot, facet cut and gilt arabesque decoration, 11.5in high. Fellows & Sons, Birmingham. Jul 03. HP: £260. ABP: £305.

1357

Enamelled cranberry glass vase, Continental c1900, near cylindrical form with shaped tapered rim, enriched with enamel chrysanthemum flowers, stems and foliage in gilt, 39cm high. Rosebery's, London. Jun 05. HP: £260. ABP: £305.

1358

Collection of Cranberry glass, to incl. a pair of dishes with crimped clear glass borders, 17cm wide, vases and other dishes, a/f. Rosebery's, London. Jan 07. HP: £240. ABP: £282.

Hammer: £240 - £150

19thC Bohemian ormolu mounted ruby glass casket, 4in. Gorringes, Lewes. Apr 02. HP: £240. ABP: £282.

Victorian ruby glass claret jug, globular form, plated mount. Gorringes, Lewes. Jun 03. HP: £240. ABP: £282.

Two Victorian cranberry glass fruit comports with gilt decoration. John Taylors, Louth. Dec 01. HP: £210. ABP: £247.

Cranberry glass and opaque flashed bell, and an overlaid glass vase. Gorringes, Bexhill. Sep 04. HP: £200. ABP: £235.

Pair of Victorian cranberry glass trumpet shaped vases, crimped and folded rims, clear trailed decoration and clear footrims, 10.5in high. Canterbury Auction Galleries, Kent. Oct 05. HP: £200. ABP: £235.

Victorian cranberry glass claret jug, Mary Gregory, enamelled with children and birds. Gorringes, Bexhill. Mar 02. HP: £200. ABP: £235.

Set of 14 wine glasses, cut, ruby-overlaid bowls, clear hexagonal stems, 7.25in. Gorringes, Lewes. Jul 06. HP: £200. ABP: £235.

Prices quoted are actual hammer prices (HP) and the Approximate Buyer's Price (ABP) includes an average premium of 15% + VAT.

Two Masonic cranberry rummers, symbol engraved bowls, clear feet, one with star cut square foot, 10.5cm, other with circular foot, 14cm. (2) Cheffins, Cambridge. Apr 05. HP: £200. ABP: £235.

Pair of Victorian cranberry glass claret jugs, panelled baluster form with pointed clear glass finials, fluted handles, spreading foot, 11in high. Hartleys, Ilkley. Feb 08. HP: £180. ABP: £211.

Late 19thC cranberry claret jug, clear glass barley sugar handle, star cut to base, plated mount engraved swags & tassles, ivory knop handle, 10.5in. Dee, Atkinson & Harrison, Driffield. Jul 04. HP: £170. ABP: £199.

Victorian cranberry/white cased glass epergne, decorated with gilt scrolls, castellated rim, cut glass drops. Rosebery's, London. Mar 05. HP: £160. ABP: £188.

19thC Bohemian red flashed glass liqueur decanter, six liqueur glasses, circular tray, decanter with slice cut body, 6.5in high and stopper, liqueur glasses, slice cut bowls, clear stems & footrims, 3.25in high, circular tray with star cut base, 12in dia. Canterbury Auction Galleries, Kent. Oct 05. HP: £160. ABP: £188.

Late Victorian cranberry glass epergne, tapered form with clear glass crimped rim, two conforming baskets, plain clear footrim, 10.75in high. Canterbury Auction Galleries, Kent. Oct 05. HP: £160. ABP: £188.

Cranberry glass jug, amphora shaped body, clear handle and foot, neck applied with fine opaque white coil, late 19thC, 22.5cm. Woolley & Wallis, Salisbury. Sep 00. HP: £150. ABP: £176.

Late Victorian cranberry glass epergne, 17.5in high, one branch in need of repair. Tring Market Auctions, Herts. Nov 02. HP: £150. ABP: £176.

21 pieces of Victorian cranberry glassware. Sworders, Stansted Mountfitchet. Mar 03. HP: £150. ABP: £176.

Pair cranberry glass candlesticks, gilt borders, one with minute rim chip, 8.5in high. Tring Market Auctions, Herts. Mar 03. HP: £150. ABP: £176.

Victorian cranberry glass claret jug, Mary Gregory enamelled with girl carrying a basket. Gorringes, Bexhill. Mar 02. HP: £150. ABP: £176.

1377

Collection of Victorian cranberry glass, incl. a pair of claret jugs, pipe, jar/cover, with a ruby flash jar/cover and a green coloured wine glass in Venetian style. Rosebery's, London. Mar 06. HP: £150. ABP: £176.

1378

Late 19thC Stourbridge cranberry glass epergne possibly by Richardson's, frill edge bowl, tall central flute, two side flutes, barley twist canes set, cranberry hanging baskets, applied crimped clear crystal spirals, S/D. Fieldings, Stourbridge. Nov 05. HP: £140. ABP: £164.

1379

Pair of Victorian cranberry glass bulbous jugs, partly moulded bodies with crimped rims, plain clear loop handles, 8.5in high. Canterbury Auction Galleries, Kent. Oct 05. HP: £140. ABP: £164.

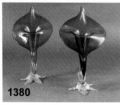

1380

Pair of late Victorian cranberry glass posy vases, leaf pattern tops, clear glass twisted stems, star pattern bases, 9.5in high. Canterbury Auction Galleries, Kent. Oct 05. HP: £140. ABP: £164.

1381

Pair of Mary Gregory cranberry glass carafes, 9.25in high. (2) Dee, Atkinson & Harrison, Driffield. Sep 07. HP: £140. ABP: £164.

1382

Two similar Victorian glass fruit comports, circular top with slice cut cranberry glass rim, 7.25in wide. Andrew Hartley, Ilkley. Aug 00. HP: £140. ABP: £164.

1383

Pair of oval lobed cranberry baskets, plated rims/swing handles, baskets highlighted with gilding, rubbed, 7.25in wide. Tring Market Auctions, Herts. Jan 04. HP: £130. ABP: £152.

1384

Collection Victorian & later cranberry/ruby glassware, incl. top hat with plated brim, powder bowls, loop handled jugs, single stem vases, leaf shaped dish, decanters etc. (18) Locke & England, Leamington Spa. Mar 06. HP: £130. ABP: £152.

1385

Victorian cranberry glass jug, patterned body, clear glass reeded handle, a cranberry glass powder bowl/cover and matching 2-handled cranberry glass vase and another vase, 7.5in. Gorringes, Lewes. Mar 04. HP: £120. ABP: £141.

Hammer: £150 - £100

1386

Victorian cranberry tinted water jug, double ringed neck, 10in high. Canterbury Auction Galleries, Kent. Aug 02. HP: £110. ABP: £129.

1387

Victorian Cranberry glass wine jug, body with wheel-cut decoration, clear glass rope-twist handle, 7in high, Victorian cranberry glass goblet, clear glass knop stem, circular foot, an Edwardian Cranberry glass waisted vase, 10in high. (3) Dee, Atkinson & Harrison, Driffield. Nov 05. HP: £110. ABP: £129.

1388

Pair late Victorian cranberry glass vases, crimped/folded rims, each with two clear glass handles, plain clear glass footrims, 11.75in high. Canterbury Auction Galleries, Kent. Oct 05. HP: £110. ABP: £129.

1389

Victorian cranberry glass bell, vaseline rim, clear glass handle tipped with blue, 34cm high, with a smaller cranberry glass bell, clear handle, 25cm high. (af) Frank Marshall & Co, Knutsford. Jan 06. HP: £110. ABP: £129.

1390

Cranberry and vaseline glass jack-in-the-pulpit vase Gorringes, Bexhill. Sep 04. HP: £110. ABP: £129.

1391

Pair of late 19th/early 20thC glass tazzas, etched Greek key motifs, cranberry border, 24cm wide. (2) Locke & England, Leamington Spa. Jan 08. HP: £110. ABP: £129.

1392

Cranberry glass circular box/ cover, dimpled surface, applied clear glass finial, slight damage, 4.75in dia & a similarly decorated tapered jar/cover, a small bulbous footed vase, & 2 other pieces of glassware. (some pieces s.d). (5) Fellows & Sons, Hockley, Birmingham. Oct 03. HP: £105. ABP: £123.

1393

Late Victorian cranberry glass bulbous water carafe and tumbler for same, 8in high, two red flashed cylindrical scent bottles, slice cut bodies, clear cut stoppers, 5.5in and 6.5in high, similar cylindrical jar/cover, 2 cranberry glass 'Pony' tumblers, & 3 other pieces of cranberry glassware. Canterbury Auction Galleries, Kent. Oct 05. HP: £100. ABP: £117.

Two Victorian cranberry glass beakers, Mary Gregory enamelled with children, and a cranberry tot. Gorringes, Lewes. Mar 02. HP: £100. ABP: £117.

Victorian glass epergne, cranberry coloured trumpet vase and 3 clear glass leaves on mirror base, 18in. (incomplete) Gorringes, Lewes. Apr 02. HP: £100. ABP: £117.

Pair of cranberry glass waisted cylindrical vases, decorated with a gilt metal ribbon holding a miniature shovel and rake, 5.5in high. Fellows & Sons, Hockley, Birmingham. Oct 03. HP: £100. ABP: £117.

Small Victorian cranberry tinted vase, surface with moulded narrow banding, applied green glass crimped wavy rim and border to body, in a silver plated scrolled frame with carrying handle, overall height 8in. Fellows & Sons, Hockley, Birmingham. Oct 03. HP: £100. ABP: £117.

Quantity of cranberry ware and Bohemian glass. Gorringes, Bexhill. Oct 05. HP: £100. ABP: £117.

Late Victorian cranberry glass match tidy, ribbed globular form, silver mounted rim, 2.25in. Gorringes, Lewes. Jun 03. HP: £100. ABP: £117.

Victorian deep cranberry glass bulbous jug, partly panelled body, reeded clear glass loop handle, 8in high, and another late Victorian cranberry glass jug, tapered form, clear crimped glass handle, 5.25in high. Canterbury Auction Galleries, Kent. Oct 05. HP: £95. ABP: £111.

Eight Victorian wine glasses, cranberry tinted glass bowls, clear stems and footrims, 5in high, and six late Victorian plain cranberry glass 'Pony' tumblers, 4.25in high. Canterbury Auction Galleries, Kent. Oct 05. HP: £95. ABP: £111.

Large bulbous cranberry glass jug, reeded handle, 8in tall. Golding Young & Co, Grantham. Feb 06. HP: £90. ABP: £105.

Two 'Nailsea' pipes, multiple knopped stems formed from cranberry glass with combed obaque white decoration, longest 46cm long, glue repair. Bearne's, Exeter. Jun 05. HP: £90. ABP: £105.

Eight Victorian cranberry wine glasses, mismatched. Golding Young & Co, Grantham. Nov 06. HP: £90. ABP: £105.

Set of seven cranberry glass wines, ovoid bowl on clear stem and foot, and a similar set of six green glass wines, 19thC. (13) Hartleys, Ilkley. Dec 06. HP: £85. ABP: £99.

Victorian 'Mary Gregory' type cranberry glass decanter, typical enamelled decoration in white, clear handle/stopper. 24.5cm. Boldon Auction Galleries, Tyne & Wear. Sep 05. HP: £80. ABP: £94.

Two late Victorian cranberry glass posy vases, squat bulbous form, clear crimped and moulded glass girdles, 3in high, and a similar powder bowl/cover, moulded /crimped girdle, clear knop to lid, 5.75 x 4.25in high. Canterbury Auction Galleries, Kent. Oct 05. HP: £80. ABP: £94.

19thC cranberry glass jug, clear glass loop handle, 7.5in high. Dee, Atkinson & Harrison, Driffield. Apr 06. HP: £80. ABP: £94.

Cranberry glass jug, another similar and 3 other cranberry glass items. Gorringes, Bexhill. Jun 05. HP: £80. ABP: £94.

19thC Bohemian floral decorated cranberry glass vase, white metal foot, 9in high. Golding Young & Co, Grantham. Feb 06. HP: £80. ABP: £94.

Cranberry glass celery vase, frilled rim, etched with foliage, clear glass lobed foot, 7in high, & a cranberry glass jug, clear loop handle, white enamel flowers, 7.5in high. (2) Hartleys, Ilkley. Dec 06. HP: £80. ABP: £94.

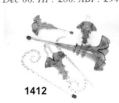

Central trumpet, side trumpet, two cups and arms from a cranberry glass epergne, central trumpet 42cm high, a/f. Rosebery's, London. Jan 07. HP: £80. ABP: £94.

1413

Victorian cranberry glass vase, applied with a white opaque oval panel painted with the portrait of a lady, foliate gilded ground, gilded feet, 7.5in high. Hartleys, Ilkley. Dec 07. HP: £80. ABP: £94.

1414

Cranberry glass: six wine glasse, plain stem, circular foot, with a wine jug, clear glass handle/stopper. (6) Dee, Atkinson & Harrison, Driffield. Feb 05. HP: £75. ABP: £88.

> The numbering system acts as a reader reference as well as linking to the Analysis of each section.

1415

Late 19thC cranberry glass jug, clear glass handle, 7in high. Dee, Atkinson & Harrison, Driffield. Apr 06. HP: £75. ABP: £88.

1416

Victorian cranberry wine decanter, waisted baluster form, long neck, clear glass stopper and strap handle, 11.25in high. Dee, Atkinson & Harrison, Driffield. Jul 08. HP: £70. ABP: £82.

1417

Pair of cranberry glass circular sugar bowls, clear crimped rims, plain stem and footrim, 4.75in dia x 4in high, and two small cylindrical handled dishes, clear crimped rims. Canterbury Auction Galleries, Kent. Oct 05. HP: £70. ABP: £82.

1418

Small cranberry glass straight sided jug, 4in, grape vine framed bowl, cranberry glass liner, 4in dia and a squared fluted edge cranberry glass bowl, clear glass shell feet, 3in. Golding Young & Co, Grantham. Feb 06. HP: £70. ABP: £82.

1419

Cranberry glass biscuit barrel, white metal mounts. Great Western Auctions, Glasgow. Sep 06. HP: £70. ABP: £82.

1420

Cranberry glass spirit flagon, late 19thC, metal collar inscribed 'Barnes and Mortlake Regatta', cork/metal stopper, 20cm high. Hampton & Littlewood, Exeter. Jul 04. HP: £66. ABP: £77.

1421

Four Cranberry glass wines on clear glass stems and feet. Lambert & Foster, Tenterden. Sep 02. HP: £65. ABP: £76.

Hammer: £80 - £60

1422

Cranberry glass decanter, clear glass stopper and loop handle, (s.d), 10in high. Fellows & Sons, Hockley, Birmingham. Oct 03. HP: £65. ABP: £76.

1423

Pair cranberry glass bottles with all over gilt decoration. Great Western Auctions, Glasgow. Jun 07. HP: £65. ABP: £76.

1424

Victorian cranberry glass sugar bowl, wavy rim and crimped feet, 6in. Gorringes, Lewes. Sep 00. HP: £60. ABP: £70.

1425

Three late Victorian cranberry glass vases, crimped rims, clear stems/footrims, 11.75in, 12in and 12.75in high. Canterbury Auction Galleries, Kent. Dec 05. HP: £60. ABP: £70.

1426

Four small cranberry glass items. Golding Young & Co, Grantham. Feb 06. HP: £60. ABP: £70.

1427

Late Victorian cranberry glass bulbous basket, clear glass crimped and patterned rim, conforming footrim and reeded clear glass twisted handle, 8.75in high, and a similar bowl, crimped and patterned rim, 6in dia x 3.25in high. Canterbury Auction Galleries, Kent. Oct 05. HP: £60. ABP: £70.

1428

Cranberry glass decanter & 10 glasses. Great Western Auctions, Glasgow. Jul 08. HP: £60. ABP: £70.

1429

Late Victorian cranberry glass circular bowl, clear crimped /moulded rim, 5.75in dia, a similar bulbous vase with six pointed star pattern rim, 5in high, and a similar bulbous jug, crimped rim, 4.5in high. Canterbury Auction Galleries, Kent. Oct 05. HP: £60. ABP: £70.

1430

Late 19thC cranberry glass jug, clear glass handle, 5.25in high, with faceted Edwardian cranberry glass carafe with tumbler. (3) Dee, Atkinson & Harrison, Driffield. Feb 06. HP: £60. ABP: £70.

Hammer: £55 - £22

Late 19thC Stourbridge cranberry glass ewer, clear circular foot set with a tall graduated shouldered body, high collar, heart shaped rim, decorated with a threaded white collar and applied clear crystal loop handle, 8in high. Fieldings, West Hagley, Worcs. Jun 05. HP: £55. ABP: £64.

Two cranberry glass leaf pattern chamber candlesticks, clear loop handle, crimped and moulded footrim, a late Victorian cranberry glass circular bowl/cover, crimped and moulded footrim, clear knop to cover, 5.75in high, and another dimpled cranberry glass jar/cover with clear bulbous knop, 7.5in high. Canterbury Auction Galleries, Kent. Dec 05. HP: £55. ABP: £64.

Wavy edge cranberry glass bowl, multi ribbed border, 13cm dia., and a cranberry glass jam pot and cover with clear glass knop, 10cm dia. Thos Mawer & Son, Lincoln. Apr 02. HP: £50. ABP: £58.

Cranberry glass bell. Gorringes, Bexhill. Dec 04. HP: £50. ABP: £58.

Pair cranberry glass tapered bud vases, trailed decoration, (both s.d), 8in high. Fellows & Sons, Hockley, Birmingham. Oct 03. HP: £50. ABP: £58.

Cranberry glass tapered water jug, wavy rim, applied clear glass loop handle, (s.d), 6.5in high and with five various cranberry beakers, and two wine glasses. (some with slight damage). (8) Fellows & Sons, Hockley, Birmingham. Oct 03. HP: £50. ABP: £58.

19thC cranberry/clear white glass handled water jug, approx 9in. Kent Auction Galleries, Folkestone. Feb 06. HP: £47. ABP: £55.

Cranberry claret jug, clear faceted stopper, strap handle, ground pontil mark to base. Kent Auction Galleries, Folkestone. Jul 05. HP: £45. ABP: £52.

Cranberry glass dimpled decanter, reeded clear handle, 26cm and another smaller similar, 17.5cm. Boldon Auction Galleries, Tyne & Wear. Sep 05. HP: £45. ABP: £52.

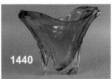

Val Saint Lambert cranberry coloured vase, flared form, etched mark to base, 8.5in high. Dee, Atkinson & Harrison, Driffield. Sep 07. HP: £45. ABP: £52.

> The illustrations are in descending price order. The price range is indicated at the top of each page.

19thC cranberry jug, 8in and pair of 19thC cranberry jugs with stoppers, 10in. Ewbank Auctioneers, Send, Surrey. Dec 05. HP: £42. ABP: £49.

Nine cranberry glass wine glasses. Black Country Auctions, Dudley. Dec 05. HP: £40. ABP: £47.

Cranberry glass moulded gimble flask. Black Country Auctions, Dudley. Sep 05. HP: £40. ABP: £47.

Cranberry glass centre piece, cranberry bowl, metal stand and centre fitting, cranberry trumpet vase, 19in. Golding Young & Co, Grantham. Nov 06. HP: £30. ABP: £35.

Victorian cranberry glass handbell, knopped clear glass handle. 29cm. Boldon Auction Galleries, Tyne & Wear. Sep 05. HP: £25. ABP: £29.

Bohemian ruby glass vase, circular amber panels of etched decoration of world cities, octagonal cut stem, shaped base, 16cm, damaged. Rosebery's, London. Oct 06. HP: £25. ABP: £29.

Silver plated stand, flashed cranberry glass jam dish, floral decoration. Golding Young & Co, Grantham. Nov 06. HP: £25. ABP: £29.

Large 20thC cranberry glass basket, compressed frill rim set with clear crystal twisted handle, 11in high. Fieldings, West Hagley, Worcs. Jun 05. HP: £22. ABP: £25.

PART III:
Perfume & Scent Bottles

'Lalique's L'Air du Temps could only raise £22 hammer.....English cameos dominate the early pages.....the Hukin & Heath silver mounted glass scent jug has everything.....pieces of glass which stretched my limit years ago have increased in value.....double ended scents were designed...'

Whilst the twentieth century, and indeed the collector of twentieth century has a love affair with pre-packaged scents, this is clearly not the case at auction where the earlier century is still in vogue. However the co-operation in the early days between the perfumeries and companies like Lalique and Baccarat was revolutionary in the sense that the pre-packaged industry was to prevail in the twentieth century. As a result most of the sales in these pages are of antique bottles manufactured before c1900, with a smattering of commercial scents. Pre-packed scents can fetch a lot of money. A Lalique *Bouchon Mures* sold at Bonhams in 1990 for £38,000 and at a more mundane level *Girlandes de Perles* and *Cactus Pattern Globular* have sold at auction in recent times for £240 hammer. More realistically most commercial bottles have too low a value to sell at auction. Check out **1595** where a collection of late twentieth century miniatures including the Lalique *Dans La Nuit* and *L'Air du Temps* could only raise £22 hammer, although earlier bottles would fetch more.

At the top end of the market at **1449** a Daum scent, despite a chip to the rim, a reduced stopper and a crack fetched over £7,000, whilst at **1450,** a Webb Cranberry and opaque white scent bottle, as a swan's head, with a silver gilt cap (Mordan, 1884) fetched over £3,000. The earliest scent on display here is the French eighteenth century example at **1452** and £1,352 including premium in the summer of 2008. English cameos dominate the first page at **1451, 1453, 1454, 1455** and **1461**, in the price range £2,700-£500. At **1457** we have our first pre-packaged or commercial example being Lalique's *Le Jade* for Roger et Gallet at £846 including premium. I was surprised to see a Monart entry at **1458** and £764. I have checked the web and not found another, so I am unable to comment further. Check the caskets of scents at **1459** and **1460,** the latter of particular interest as the casket is glass and at £550 hammer I think this a good buy with its ormolu mounts and gilding, plus enamel painting. It has everything! Appealing as a display item is the Hukin and Heath silver mounted glass scent jug at **1468**. I believe that if it were to reappear in the market today, some seven years later, it should show a good profit. Investing in the best is the best that collectors can achieve. Those pieces of glass which stretched my limit years ago are the pieces today that have increased in value, whilst the more common or garden items have usually lost ground. At **1469** is our second commercial bottle, designed for Worth, *Je Reviens*. This made a very

creditable £400, although I prefer the gold mounted opaline scent at **1472,** despite the monogram. Cranberry enthusiasts will find examples in these pages, although it is difficult to distinguish from ruby as at **1463.** I would expect that the decision to call this ruby was a commercial one as the term *Cranberry* does connotate to cheaper and more popular glass. See also the casket and bottles at **1473**. The Venetian millefiore example at **1471** is the only example I could find. I cannot see that it can serve any other than a decorative purpose and at 10 inches in height I am not certain that it was ever intended to hold contents. At **1476** the dealers' lot averaged about £30 each and at **1483** almost £50 each. There must be profit but it is difficult to see if these lots contain any exceptional bottles. It's not be surprising that the pair of bottles at **1477** fetched £390. The silver work is special. Similarly the pierced silver mounts on the pair of bottles at **1479** guaranteed the £300 price tag.

At **1482** we have our first double ended scent bottle and there are further examples at **1486, 1495, 1497, 1501, 1507, 1508, 1512** etc; about fifteen lots in all. Expect to pay about a £100 or there abouts, but silver, silver gilt or gold mount, or special effects, such as the cut overlay at **1486**, added to precious metals, will push prices further. Although there are plenty at auction collectors are advised to go for the best and also to seek the unusual in terms of style and colour. Double ended scents were designed to house a scent and smelling salts.

At **1484** is a Lalique apple and note the price at about £250. This could cost more at retail but if you have the usual dealer guarantee this is not a problem. Lalique's *Dahlia* design appears at **1485** as a bottle and a powder bowl. Note the price and note these were not in good condition. Note the Lalique *The Duncan* bottle at **1488** and the nice S. Mordan bottle at **1490,** London 1876, which fetched a very reasonable £235 only in November 2007. Scent bottles were carried on chatelaines in earlier times and we have an example at **1499** and at **1529**, a horn shaped flask which would have been carried discreetly on the person for emergency use.

At **1545** is a modern Lalique bottle for Nina Ricci, Paris, which fetched a £100 in 2001. What would it fetch today? I am not sure that it will do well. As we go below about £50 there are more commercial lots. Take **1566** which includes Nina Ricci's *L'Air du Temps* which we have already noted at **1595**. I have read that examples fetch a £100 but there is no evidence of this at auction, unless the reference is to original 1940s bottles.

Hammer: £6,200 - £430

Daum scent bottle/stopper, c1907, clear glass body as a pumpkin, incised mark 'Daum Nancy', overall 13cm high, chip to bottle rim, stopper reduced/crack. Sotheby's, Billingshurst. Mar 00. HP: £6,200. ABP: £7,292.

Webb, Stourbridge, cranberry & opaque glass scent bottle, as a swan's head, silver gilt cap with marks for Mordan & Co, London, dated 1884, 14.5cm. Locke & England, Leamington Spa. Feb 06. HP: £2,700. ABP: £3,175.

Webb cameo carved glass atomiser, silver mounts by Middleton Chapman, London 1887, body decorated with flowering branches, blue ground, concentric bands, central sprung button, 19cm high. Sworders, Stansted Mountfitchet. Nov 07. HP: £2,300. ABP: £2,705.

French gilt mount cut crystal scent bottle, Paris 1756-1762, faceted glass body, engraved mount, scrolled stopper, Paris charge mark, maker's mark I V H, 12cm long. Rosebery's, London. Jun 08. HP: £1,150. ABP: £1,352.

English cameo glass scent bottle overlaid in red glass, possibly by Webb & Sons Ltd., 9.5cm high. Sworders, Stansted Mountfitchet. Oct 02. HP: £1,100. ABP: £1,293.

Victorian Webb cameo glass scent bottle, 4.25in. Louis Taylor, Stoke on Trent. Sep 03. HP: £920. ABP: £1,082.

Categories or themes can be followed through the colour coded Index which contains over 4500 cross references.

Victorian cameo glass scent bottle, poss. by Webb & Sons, body decorated with flowers, silver-gilt top, fitted case, retailed by Samuel Dixon, 23 Cornhill Street. Gorringes, Bexhill. Dec 05. HP: £850. ABP: £999.

French blue cut glass/ormolu mounted perfume casket, opening to reveal four lidded bottles, 19.5cm. Sworders, Stansted Mountfitchet. Feb 07. HP: £800. ABP: £941.

Lalique green glass/white metal mounted scent bottle 'Le Jade' for Roger et Gallet moulded with a displaying exotic bird amongst dense foliage, first issued 1926, 8.5cm high,. Bearne's, Exeter. Nov 07. HP: £720. ABP: £846.

Monart perfume bottle in amethyst bubble glass, flared shape millefiori 'paper-weight' stopper, paper label, Monart Glass, Moncreiff, Scotland VII and HE246A, 5in tall. Golding Young & Co, Grantham. Feb 06. HP: £650. ABP: £764.

Victorian calamander/brass bound square dressing table box, Bramah lock, enclosing four square cut glass bottles with plated/monogrammed mounts, 6 x 6 x 4.75in, leather carrying case stamped 'Austins, Dublin' on handle and a label Dreweatt Neate, Donnington. Nov 04. HP: £560. ABP: £658.

19thC opaque glass/ormolu mounted scent casket, canted corners, opaque glass painted and gilded with flowers, six glass bottles with engraved gilt metal hinged cover, ormolu frame, ring handles, ball feet, 7in. Gorringes, Lewes. Dec 06. HP: £550. ABP: £646.

Webb style cameo glass scent flask, foliate decoration, silver dome screw top lid, London, maker's marks part erased SM, 10cm. Rosebery's, London. Mar 08. HP: £520. ABP: £611.

19thC silver mounted glass combination scent bottle/vinaigrette, S. Mordan, London 1881, fluted body, pierced foliate grille, 5in. Gorringes, Lewes. Apr 07. HP: £500. ABP: £588.

Victorian silver gilt mounted ruby glass combined scent bottle/vinaigrette, makers S Mordan & Co, 1874, 3.75in. Gorringes, Lewes. Apr 00. HP: £480. ABP: £564.

Lalique Fleurettes clear glass scent flask/stopper, stained blue floral edges, 7.5in, early moulded mark. Gorringes, Bexhill. Mar 02. HP: £440. ABP: £517.

Late 19thC Cameo glass scent bottle possibly Thomas Webb's, cased in ruby over ivory, cut back wild goose-berries and leaves, central monogrammed cartouche, initials R.T. 4.25in long. Fieldings, Stourbridge. Apr 05. HP: £430. ABP: £505.

Early 20thC French Gallé red overlaid glass scent flask, floral decoration, gilt metal atomiser mount, signed, 18cm. Reeman Dansie, Colchester. Apr 06. HP: £400. ABP: £470.

Pair of silver topped/overlaid cut glass scent bottles, Moroccan leather case, Birmingham 1899. Great Western Auctions, Glasgow. May 05. HP: £390. ABP: £458.

Edwardian silver mounted cut glass scent jug, 7in, maker's Hukin & Heath, Birmingham 1906. Gorringes, Lewes. Feb 01. HP: £380. ABP: £446.

1940s Lalique blue stained glass display perfume bottle/ stopper, designed for Worths, decorated with stars in 'Je Reviens' pattern, engraved Lalique, France to base, 10.5in high. Diamond Mills & Co, Felixstowe. Mar 06. HP: £340. ABP: £399.

Two 19thC Bohemian scent bottles, overlaid with cut decoration, 7.25in, stoppers damaged. Gorringes, Lewes. Apr 07. HP: £340. ABP: £399.

Millefiore perfume bottle, Venetian, c1900, globular stopper, 10in. Gorringes, Lewes. Jun 07. HP: £340. ABP: £399.

Victorian 18ct gold mounted opaline glass scent bottle, enamelled monogram, 3in. Gorringes, Lewes. Mar 03. HP: £330. ABP: £388.

Pair Victorian scent bottles, gilt metal tops, painted landscape panels, clear squared bottles in a cranberry glass casket, gilded metal loop handles, gadrooned rim and pierced scroll feet, 4.75in wide. Hartleys, Ilkley. Oct 06. HP: £330. ABP: £388.

Two Gallé cameo glass atomisers, c1900, frosted yellow body overlaid with red and carved with prunus, frosted amber body overlaid with brown and carved with clematis, both with gilt metal mounts, and cameo marks 'Gallé' tallest 12cm high. (2) Rosebery's, London. Sep 04. HP: £320. ABP: £376.

Hammer: £400 - £210

Pair Edwardian silver mounted cut glass globular scent bottles, 6in. Gorringes, Bexhill. Mar 02. HP: £320. ABP: £376.

Purple cased glass scent bottle, tapering body cut with bands of ovals, hinged white metal lid, 5in long, a similar double ended scent, gilt metal lids, and 9 other coloured/cut glass scent bottles. (11) Hartleys, Ilkley. Oct 07. HP: £290. ABP: £341.

Pair silver mounted cut glass scent bottles, Birmingham 1900, cut with star bursts & small diamonds, pierced flowering foliage, tear drop form cover, one with silver mounted foot, 16cm high. Rosebery's, London. Mar 06. HP: £280. ABP: £329.

Victorian glass scent bottle, silver mount, Mordan, London 1884, 15cm high. Richard Winterton, Burton on Trent. Apr 03. HP: £275. ABP: £323.

Pair of Victorian globular cut glass scent bottles with stoppers and pierced silver mounts, Birmingham 1898. Denhams, Warnham, Sussex. Jan 06. HP: £260. ABP: £305.

19thC Millefiori paperweight scent bottle, white, red & blue floret cushion, engraved shoulder with mono 'EK', facet cut blown stopper, poss. Whitefriars, 6.25in, slightly af. Tring Market Auctions, Herts. May 02. HP: £240. ABP: £282.

Pair of Victorian silver mounted cut glass scent bottles, Birmingham 1894. Gorringes, Lewes. Apr 03. HP: £220. ABP: £258.

Victorian cranberry glass double ended scent bottle, metal mounts with embossed floral decoration, 4.7in long, with another similar blue glass example. Fellows & Sons, Hockley, Birmingham. Oct 03. HP: £220. ABP: £258.

Collection of five Bohemian scent bottles, 19thC, various sizes & shapes. (5) Rosebery's, London. Mar 06. HP: £210. ABP: £247.

Lalique scent bottle, form of an apple, frosted glass, cover formed as two leaves, 5.25in. Gorringes, Lewes. Oct 06. HP: £210. ABP: £247.

Hammer: £210 - £150

Lalique moulded, frosted and brown opalescent scent bottle and matching powder bowl, 'Dahlia' design, scent bottle moulded with 2 flowerheads, 7.25in high, stopper badly chipped, powder bowl 5.25in x 3.25in high, base badly chipped in one place, etched stencil mark to bases 'R. Lalique, France'. Canterbury Auction Galleries, Kent. Feb 07. HP: £210. ABP: £247.

Victorian silver-gilt mounted cut clear/blue glass overlay double-ended scent bottle, London 1861, 14.75cm long overall. Dreweatt Neate, Donnington. Nov 04. HP: £200. ABP: £235.

Silver lidded ruby glass scent flask, a ruby overlaid glass caster and green glass scent bottle. Gorringes, Lewes. Oct 02. HP: £200. ABP: £235.

Modern Lalique clear/frosted glass scent bottle, recessed centre panels moulded in relief with 'The Duncan' design of two dancing female figures, frosted glass stopper, 8in high, engraved mark 'Lalique, France' to base. Canterbury Auction Galleries, Kent. Feb 07. HP: £200. ABP: £235.

Edwardian cranberry glass perfume decanter, various indistinct marks, 5.5in high. Amersham Auction Rooms, Bucks. Mar 04. HP: £200. ABP: £235.

Victorian silver-gilt mounted glass perfume bottle/vinai-grette, by Sampson Mordon, London 1876, scrolling foliate designs, canted corners, 9.6cm. Sworders, Stansted Mountfitchet. Nov 07. HP: £200. ABP: £235.

Prices quoted are actual hammer prices (HP) and the Approximate Buyer's Price (ABP) includes an average premium of 15% + VAT.

Glass flattened oval scent flask, blue tinted and opaque spiral twist canes, 12cm long, two similar flattened round flasks decorated with red tinted and opaque twist canes, and two other glass scent flasks. Dreweatt Neate, Newbury. Apr 00. HP: £190. ABP: £223.

Late Victorian silver/cut glass scent bottle, Maker John Grinsell, 1896. Gorringes, Lewes. Mar 03. HP: £190. ABP: £223.

Victorian silver mounted ruby overlaid glass scent flask, silvered interior and scroll engraved sprung lid. Gorringes, Lewes. Mar 03. HP: £190. ABP: £223.

Victorian cut glass scent bottle, silver top, Maker William Comyns, 1893, 6.25in. Gorringes, Lewes. Jun 03. HP: £180. ABP: £211.

Victorian cranberry glass double ended scent bottle, base metal mounts, 5in long, with clear cut glass example, 4.75in long. Fellows & Sons, Hockley, Birmingham. Oct 03. HP: £180. ABP: £211.

Early 20thC cut glass scent bottle, silver collar, tortoise-shell lid, inset silver garland, London 1917, 16cm high. Charterhouse Auctioneers, Sherborne. Feb 07. HP: £180. ABP: £211.

Victorian green glass double ended scent bottle, base metal mounts embossed with foliate decoration, 4in long and a similar blue glass example. Fellows & Sons, Hockley, Birmingham. Oct 03. HP: £170. ABP: £199.

Bohemian scent bottle/stopper, late 19thC, ruby glass with overlaid and cut decoration, gilt metal base,12cm. (2) Sworders, Stansted Mountfitchet. Feb 05. HP: £170. ABP: £199.

Continental pink glass scent bottle, gilt metal flowerhead decoration on matching chatelaine hook. Gorringes, Lewes. Dec 00. HP: £160. ABP: £188.

Glass scent bottle, overlaid with white metal, a cut glass and white metal example as a horn and a blue glass scent bottle. Gorringes, Bexhill. Jul 05. HP: £160. ABP: £188.

19thC Bristol blue double ended scent bottle gilt metal caps to both ends. Kent Auction Galleries, Folkestone. Jun 06. HP: £160. ABP: £188.

Pair of cut glass dressing table bottles, silver/tortoise-shell hinged lids, Birmingham 1919, 13.5cm high. (4) Sworders, Stansted Mountfitchet. Feb 07. HP: £150. ABP: £176.

1503

Pair of silver mounted cut glass scent bottles and an overlaid bottle. Gorringes, Lewes. Apr 03. HP: £150. ABP: £176.

1504

Mid-19thC ruby overlaid glass and gilt floral scroll decorated scent bottle, spearhead stopper, 22cm. Reeman Dansie, Colchester. Apr 06. HP: £150. ABP: £176.

1505

Lalique frosted glass scent bottle moulded in relief, decorated in black with Cactus design, 3in high, conforming stopper, etched stencilled mark 'Lalique, France' to base, tips of raised surface rubbed and slightly chipped. Canterbury Auction Galleries, Kent. Jun 07. HP: £150. ABP: £176.

1506

19thC Continental clear glass scent bottle, blown and cut, silver mounts, stopper, 4.25in wide. Tring Market Auctions, Herts. Sep 02. HP: £140. ABP: £164.

1507

Victorian double ended green glass and silver capped scent bottle, faceted body, foliate decorated caps, unmarked, 4.75in. Gorringes, Lewes. Jan 04. HP: £140. ABP: £164.

1508

19thC cut glass double scent flask with niello decorated lids. Gorringes, Lewes. Apr 02. HP: £140. ABP: £164.

1509

Victorian silver gilt mounted white opaque glass perfume bottle/vinaigrette, Sampson Mordan, London, 1863, grille missing, 9.5cm. Sworders, Stansted Mountfitchet. Apr 05. HP: £140. ABP: £164.

1510

Two Victorian scent bottles, one with ruby coloured glass body, other with green glass body each with a white metal hinged cap revealing a stopper, each 7cm high. (2) Cheffins, Cambridge. Apr 05. HP: £140. ABP: £164.

1511

Georgian cut glass and gold mounted fan-shaped scent flask and a Victorian silver ditto. (2) Reeman Dansie, Colchester. Apr 06. HP: £140. ABP: £164.

1512

Late Victorian gold mounted and facetted clear glass double-ended scent bottle, engraved with a monogram 'FPJE', stamped '18', 14cm overall. Dreweatt Neate, Donnington. Nov 04. HP: £130. ABP: £152.

Hammer: £150 - £120

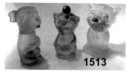

1513

Three frosted glass Bonzo perfume bottles with painted features, originally contained Potter & Moore, Mitchum lavender perfume, 7cm high. Ambrose, Loughton. Mar 02. HP: £130. ABP: £152.

1514

Victorian silver mounted ruby glass scent bottle. Gorringes, Lewes. Jun 03. HP: £130. ABP: £152.

1515

Late Victorian silver topped cut glass scent bottle, London 1900. Great Western Auctions, Glasgow. May 05. HP: £130. ABP: £152.

1516

Three late Victorian silver mounted toilet jars, tortoiseshell plique decoration. Gorringes, Bexhill. Mar 02. HP: £130. ABP: £152.

1517

Cut glass scent bottle, central sulphide portrait & a blue glass wine bottle. Great Western Auctions, Glasgow. Aug 07. HP: £130. ABP: £152.

1518

Victorian opaque glass scent bottle, opalescent glass overlaid with foliate pierced silver mount, 2.75in, unmarked. Hartleys, Ilkley. Dec 07. HP: £130. ABP: £152.

1519

Bohemian glass scent bottle, hinged silver colour metal top, clear stopper, cranberry overlaid body, engraved to centre piece with monogram, 9.5cm. Sworders, Stansted Mountfitchet. Apr 05. HP: £120. ABP: £141.

1520

Three Victorian, coloured glass/gilt metal double ended scent bottles, 2 cranberry & one green, (1 af) also a milk glass scent bottle, gilt metal cover. (4) Rosebery's, London. Jan 06. HP: £120. ABP: £141.

1521

Pair of late Victorian scent bottles, clear glass, hobnail cuttings, silver screw-on covers embossed/chased with floral/leaf scroll ornament, London 1892, 4.25in. Canterbury Auction Galleries, Kent. Dec 05. HP: £120. ABP: £141.

1522

Bohemian ruby glass scent bottle/stopper, faceted shape, decorated with floral sprigs, 6in. Gorringes, Lewes. Jul 03. HP: £120. ABP: £141.

Hammer: £115 - £90

1523

Yellow cut glass scent bottle, disc form, oblong stopper, body cut/frosted with flowers and foliage, 20thC, 4.75in high. Andrew Hartley, Ilkley. Jun 02. HP: £115. ABP: £135.

1524

Victorian cameo glass scent bottle, panelled bottle form, painted stopper, flared rim, cut with ruby glass panels with gilding between, 7.25in high. Hartleys, Ilkley. Dec 06. HP: £115. ABP: £135.

1525

Victorian cranberry glass scent bottle, tapered outline, faceted decoration, clear glass spherical stopper, (damage), 3.25in, with similar lozenge shaped cranberry glass scent flask/stopper. (2) Fellows & Sons, Birmingham. Jul 03. HP: £110. ABP: £129.

1526

Chinese red lacquer scent bottle carved with figures, 6.5cm high, and a Chinese turquoise glass scent botle, (2). Rosebery's, London. Aug 06. HP: £110. ABP: £129.

1527

Cut glass globular shaped scent bottle, embossed silver lid. Denhams, Warnham, Sussex. Aug 07. HP: £110. ABP: £129.

1528

Shuco style scent bottle in the form of a bespectacled monkey, brown plush fur and glass eyes, 12cm high. Charterhouse Auctioneers, Sherborne. Feb 06. HP: £110. ABP: £129.

1529

Victorian silver mounted cut glass horn shaped scent flask. Gorringes, Lewes. Sep 00. HP: £100. ABP: £117.

1530

Silver mounted cut glass scent bottle, Birmingham 1906, spherical form, scroll moulded lobed silver shoulder, hinged cap, 4.25in high. Rosebery's, London. Sep 04. HP: £100. ABP: £117.

1531

Millefiori glass scent bottle and stopper. Great Western Auctions, Glasgow. May 08. HP: £100. ABP: £117.

1532

Lalique scent bottle with flying dove stopper, 3.5in. Gorringes, Lewes. Jun 03. HP: £100. ABP: £117.

1533

Victorian cranberry glass scent bottle, base metal mount with embossed floral decoration, 3.5in. Fellows & Sons, Hockley, Birmingham. Oct 03. HP: £100. ABP: £117.

1534

Late Victorian scent bottle, spiral reeded clear glass body, silver spiral reeded folding cover, 5in high, Birmingham 1888. Canterbury Auction Galleries, Kent. Dec 05. HP: £100. ABP: £117.

1535

Ruby tinted facetted double ended scent flask, interior of one end with engraved grille, 3.5in. Ewbank Auctioneers, Send, Surrey. Dec 05. HP: £100. ABP: £117.

1536

Collection of four Art Deco glass scent sprays. (4) Dee, Atkinson & Harrison, Driffield. Apr 06. HP: £100. ABP: £117.

1537

Two silver mounted scent cut glass scent bottles, one ovoid form, silver collar, a spherical bottle, silver cap, with a third bottle. Rosebery's, London. Dec 04. HP: £95. ABP: £111.

1538

Late Victorian silver mounted scent bottle, heavy slice and diamond clear glass tear shaped body, cover embossed with floral/scroll ornament, 3in, by I.W.L. (?), Birmingham 1898, an Edward VII silver screw topped scent bottle, diamond cut spiral fluted body, 2.75in, Birmingham 1906. (2) Canterbury Auction Galleries, Kent. Dec 05. HP: £95. ABP: £111.

> The numbering system acts as a reader reference as well as linking to the Analysis of each section.

1539

Glass scent bottle/stopper, gilt metal mount, early 20thC, 13cm. Woolley & Wallis, Salisbury. Sep 00. HP: £90. ABP: £105.

1540

Pair of Edwardian silver topped cut glass globular scent bottles, 6in. Gorringes, Lewes. Apr 04. HP: £90. ABP: £105.

1541

Green glass scent bottle, disc form, arched faceted stopper, painted black sides, 7in high, and a grey glass scent bottle, 20thC. Andrew Hartley, Ilkley. Jun 02. HP: £90. ABP: £105.

Victorian green glass scent bottle, gilded ball stopper, applied with porcelain roundel painted with a girl's profile, 3.25in high. Hartleys, Ilkley. Aug 06. HP: £90. ABP: £105.

Art Deco enamel and glass vapouriser, baluster form, white metal top covered in yellow enamel, engine turned ground, star-cut base, 6.25in high. Hartleys, Ilkley. Feb 07. HP: £90. ABP: £105.

Ruby flash toilet bottle, engraved with scroll panels, flashed in ruby within a cloud scroll ground, 19cm high. Rosebery's, London. Sep 04. HP: £90. ABP: £105.

Modern Lalique scent bottle for Nina Ricci, Paris, white metal lid, 6in high. Sworders, Stansted Mountfitchet. Jul 01. HP: £85. ABP: £99.

Edwardian silver mounted and cut glass scent globe. (Birmingham 1902) Reeman Dansie, Colchester. Apr 06. HP: £85. ABP: £99.

Edwardian conical shaped cut glass scent bottle, silver neck, maker's mark CM, Birmingham 1906, 5.5cm high. Fellows & Sons, Hockley, Birmingham. Sep 03. HP: £85. ABP: £99.

Amanda Nicholson, cranberry and clear overlay glass scent bottle, clear stopper, body sand blasted with geometric design, 5.25in high, and a similar bottle, both signed. Andrew Hartley, Ilkley. Dec 99. HP: £80. ABP: £94.

Ruby tinted facetted double ended cylindrical scent flask, 4in. Ewbank Auctioneers, Send, Surrey. Dec 05. HP: £80. ABP: £94.

White opaque glass scent bottle, bell shape, gilded ball stopper, body gilded all over with stars, poss. Continental, 6in high and two others. Andrew Hartley, Ilkley. Jun 02. HP: £80. ABP: £94.

Ruby tinted facetted tapering double ended cylindrical scent flask, plain mounts, 3.75in. Ewbank Auctioneers, Send, Surrey. Dec 05. HP: £80. ABP: £94.

Hammer: £90 - £65

Late 19thC rectangular scent bottle, amethyst cut glass body, foliate embossed hinged white metal cover. 2.75in. Fieldings, West Hagley, Worcs. Jun 05. HP: £80. ABP: £94.

Ruby tinted facetted double ended cylindrical scent flask, unusual central hinge, 5.5in. Ewbank Auctioneers, Send. Dec 05. HP: £80. ABP: £94.

Art Nouveau glass vapouriser, circular green body applied bands of red petals, gilded metal top, 3.75in high, lobed green glass vapouriser with gilded vines, and two similar glass vapourisers. (4) Hartleys, Ilkley. Oct 07. HP: £80. ABP: £94.

Late 19thC scent bottle, faceted tapering blue glass body, white metal collar and foliate embossed cap, 3.75in. Fieldings, West Hagley, Worcs. Jun 05. HP: £75. ABP: £88.

Victorian silver mounted ruby glass scent flask, and a cut glass scent flask. Gorringes, Lewes. Jan 03. HP: £75. ABP: £88.

Pink Art Deco glass cologne bottle, faceted rectangular base, facet cut body with a panel of three naked women dancing, faceted diamond shape stopper approx 12in high. Kent Auction Galleries, Folkestone. Jun 06. HP: £75. ABP: £88.

Victorian red glass double ended scent phial, embossed silver lids, 4in. Denhams, Warnham. Aug 03. HP: £70. ABP: £82.

Pair green glass scent bottles, gilded with foliage, hexagonal stoppers, 4.5in. (one chipped) Gorringes, Lewes. Oct 02. HP: £65. ABP: £76.

Art Deco smoked cut/moulded glass scent flask, spearhead stopper, 17cm high. Reeman Dansie, Colchester. Apr 06. HP: £65. ABP: £76.

Victorian ruby glass/white metal mounted, double ended scent bottle, 9.5cm. Locke & England, Leamington Spa. Jul 07. HP: £65. ABP: £76.

Victorian ruby glass double scent flask, & similar smaller flask. Gorringes, Lewes. Sep 00. HP: £60. ABP: £70.

Flashed pale blue glass scent bottle, cut/etched decoration of swallows in flight amongst leafy undergrowth, silver collar/cover, Birmingham hallmarks 1951/1952, original glass stopper, 7in overall. Fellows & Sons, Birmingham. Jul 03. HP: £60. ABP: £70.

Early 19thC Dutch silver mounted cut glass scent bottle, another silver mounted double ended example, 3 others with plated mounts. (5) Sworders, Stansted Mountfitchet. Apr 05. HP: £60. ABP: £70.

Ruby tinted facetted double ended cylindrical scent flask, 4in. Ewbank Auctioneers, Send, Surrey. Dec 05. HP: £60. ABP: £70.

Later 20thC Lalique scent bottle for Nina Ricci perfume L'Air du Temps, wrythen fluted form, frosted glass stopper with two doves, acid mark to base, 3.5in high, with a similar example, single dove stopper, 2 other modern scents. (4) Fieldings, West Hagley, Worcs. Jun 05. HP: £58. ABP: £68.

Victorian cut glass perfume bottle, wavy pattern, tiny chips, silver bezel to neck & relief foliate patterned screw top, with cork, maker's mark indistinct, h/m London 1889. A F Brock & Co Ltd, Stockport. Nov 05. HP: £55. ABP: £64.

Rene Lalique scent bottle, black enamelled poppy finial, 16cm. Gorringes, Bexhill. Feb 06. HP: £55. ABP: £64.

Ruby tinted facetted scent bottle with gilt decoration, 4.5in. Ewbank Auctioneers, Send, Surrey. Dec 05. HP: £55. ABP: £64.

Victorian cut glass scent bottle, globular form, faceted ball stopper, moulded collar on fancy strawberry cut bottle, 5.25in high, London 1900. Hartleys, Ilkley. Dec 06. HP: £55. ABP: £64.

Silver top cut glass scent bottle, Mappin & Webb, spray attachment. Boldon Auction Galleries, Tyne & Wear. Sep 05. HP: £52. ABP: £61.

Victorian Bristol blue glass scent flask with painted floral decoration, 14cm. Reeman Dansie, Colchester. Apr 06. HP: £50. ABP: £58.

Karlin Rushbrooke profile bottle, green internal colouring, clear white glass stopper & stylized hair, Monpellier Contemporary Arts Stratford-upon-Avon, signature to base, opaque green/yellow cologne bottle, cologne applicating rod, 2 metal cased moulded glass cologne bottles with amethyst quartz & lappice finials to stoppers. (4) Kent Auction Galleries, Folkestone. Nov 07. HP: £50. ABP: £58.

The illustrations are in descending price order. The price range is indicated at the top of each page.

Art Deco perfume spray, 80mm high, cut rainbow glass bottle, brass pump fittings, 'working' order, by Marcel Franck, France. A F Brock & Co Ltd, Stockport. Nov 07. HP: £50. ABP: £58.

Enamel painted toilet bottle. Great Western Auctions, Glasgow. Aug 05. HP: £48. ABP: £56.

Frosted glass Bonzo dog scent bottle, seated on hind legs, painted details to head, moulded marks, Rd. No. 710 557, (s.d), 3in high. Fellows & Sons, Hockley, Birmingham. Oct 03. HP: £48. ABP: £56.

Collection of cut/moulded glass scent bottles/atomisers, Continental early 20thC and later, varying designs, to include two footed examples, tallest 18cm. Rosebery's, London. Jan 06. HP: £46. ABP: £54.

Bohemian flashed glass scent bottle. (stopper a.f) Gorringes, Bexhill. Jul 05. HP: £45. ABP: £52.

Art Deco clear/black glass atomizer of facet cut C scroll form, conforming coloured cotton tasselled bulb. Locke & England, Leamington Spa. Jul 06. HP: £45. ABP: £52.

19thC cranberry cut glass cologne bottle, hob nail cut diamond decoration, 2in high x 3in dia. Kent Auction Galleries, Folkestone. Dec 06. HP: £45. ABP: £52.

1581

Pair of cut-glass, silver and tortoiseshell-mounted scent bottles. Gorringes, Bexhill. Dec 04. HP: £40. ABP: £47.

1582

Victorian hobnail-cut glass scent bottle, and another. Gorringes, Bexhill. Dec 04. HP: £40. ABP: £47.

1583

Victorian ruby cased glass scent bottle/stopper, narrow rectangular outline, facet cut decoration, (s.d), 4in high, with Nailsea type lozenge-shaped scent flask/stopper, pale green glass combed with black, orange, gold trails, 2.75in long. (2) Fellows & Sons, Birmingham. Jul 03. HP: £40. ABP: £47.

1584

Ruby tinted facetted double ended cylindrical scent flask, plain mounts, 5in. Ewbank Auctioneers, Send, Surrey. Dec 05. HP: £40. ABP: £47.

1585

Edward VII cut glass scent bottle, flared circular form, silver collar, embossed with scrolls, faceted stopper, 8.25in high. Golding Young & Co, Grantham. Nov 06. HP: £40. ABP: £47.

1586

Silver topped scent bottle, 4in, square edged cut glass with stopper, ornately embossed patterned lid, h/m London 1903. A F Brock & Co Ltd, Stockport. Aug 07. HP: £40. ABP: £47.

1587

Late Victorian uranium yellow cut glass scent bottle, rounded rectangular flask, deep fan cut pattern, central cartouche with monogram, ball stopper, 4in. Fieldings, West Hagley. Jun 05. HP: £38. ABP: £44.

1588

Set four silver topped toilet bottles, one other and a cut glass/silver mounted scent bottle. (6) Reeman Dansie, Colchester. Apr 06. HP: £38. ABP: £44.

1589

Silver/tortoiseshell topped scent bottle, Birmingham 1922. Great Western Auctions, Glasgow. Mar 08. HP: £38. ABP: £44.

1590

Ruby flash hexagonal glass scent bottle and stopper, 4.5in. Gorringes, Lewes. Sep 00. HP: £35. ABP: £41.

Hammer: £40 - £20

1591

Edwardian cut glass scent bottle, silver collar. Black Country Auctions, Dudley. Dec 05. HP: £30. ABP: £35.

1592

Victorian Bohemian ruby cut glass scent flask/stopper, 22cm. Reeman Dansie, Colchester. Apr 06. HP: £30. ABP: £35.

1593

George IV silver mounted scent atomiser, slice/leaf cut glass body, 5.75in. Golding Young & Co, Grantham. Nov 06. HP: £28. ABP: £32.

1594

Blue opaline/gilt perfume bottle, steeple stopper, 9.25in. Dee, Atkinson & Harrison, Driffield. Sep 07. HP: £28. ABP: £32.

1595

Small collection later 20thC miniature commercial scent bottles by Lalique incl: Dans La Nuit & L'Air du Temps. (4) Fieldings, West Hagley. Jun 05. HP: £22. ABP: £25.

1596

Cut glass scent bottle, 6in high. Black Country Auctions, Dudley. Sep 05. HP: £22. ABP: £25.

1597

Cut glass atomizers and further cologne bottles incl. boxed Ma Griffe contained in wicker basket. Kent Auction Galleries, Folkestone. Dec 06. HP: £22. ABP: £25.

1598

2 silver topped scent bottles & another lacking stopper. Black Country Auctions, Dudley. Dec 05. HP: £20. ABP: £23.

1599

19thC Bohemian overlaid and gilt decorated ruby glass scent bottle/stopper, body with panels of flowers, 10cm high. Locke & England, Leamington Spa. Sep 06. HP: £20. ABP: £23.

1600

St. Louis style cut glass scent bottle, body with line/octagons, large oval stopper cut with a girl seated beside a peacock in a tree, 18cm high. Rosebery's, London. Apr 07. HP: £20. ABP: £23.

PART IV:
Paperweights & Dumps

'an extremely rare Pantin paperweight sold for £22,000.....pate de verre is a French technique of making a glass paste.....a George Bacchus concentric fetched £2,000.....below £500 hammer Paul Ysart appears..... dumps have risen in value.....and a good Kilner could set you back £100...'

Paperweights are one of the most aesthetic and artistic forms of glasswork whose development began in the 1840s. From ancient times, one of the earliest techniques was lampworking. Rods and tubes of clear/coloured glass was melted in the flame of an oil lamp, air being fed to the flame through a pipe. The millefiori technique was practiced in ancient Rome and re-appeared in Venice between the fourteenth and sixteenth centuries. The merging of these ancient skills saw the production of paperweights in Italy and France and this development was taken up quickly in England by firms such as Bacchus in Stourbridge. The main protagonists in this new field were the French firms of Baccarat, Clichy and St. Louis. Patterns such as concentric circles were created with thin slices from canes and enveloped in clear flint glass by fusion. Clichy went out of business in the 1880s, but Baccarat and St. Louis revived the craft in the 1960s. Modern paperweights are now most notably made in England, Scotland, Bohemia, Italy and the USA. Well known English manufacturers were William Gillender, before he emigrated to the USA, Bacchus, where he learned his trade, Arculus, Richardson and Walsh-Walsh. There appears to be some strange dispute as to whether Whitefriars (Powell) made paperweights in the nineteenth century and English firms tend to get lumped together under the generic term *Stourbridge*. In Scotland the twentieth century output emanated from Paul Ysart, Vasart and Strathearn, Perthshire Paperweights, Selkirk and Caithness. Chinese, and some Indian paperweights have appeared in numbers in the UK but so poor are the quality of most, that they are quite unmistakeable and sell for next to nothing. Dumps in the main are usually attributed to J. Kilner & Son of Wakefield and many are marked but some are not.

The top end of the market is overwhelmingly French, but they do not have it all of their own way. In July 2007 an extremely rare Pantin (French) paperweight, with lizards among aconites on a rocky base, sold for £22,000 hammer at Gildings in Market Harborough. Pantin is rare and evidence of their manufacture exists only in documents. A few months earlier in April 2007 a New England weight sold at Fieldings in Stourbridge for £5,700 hammer, and in 2003 a Pietro Bigaglia (Venice) scrambled weight, dated 1847, sold at Sothebys for £4,200. Mount Washington paperweights have also hit this price and a rare silhouette weight, possibly of Queen Victoria, and possibly by the Islington Glassworks, sold at Sothebys in 2003 for £3,360. Here French paper-

weights dominate from £12,000 downwards but it is not always possible to ascribe a manufacturer, such as the French millefiore at **1602** and an unascribed weight at **1604**. The Almeric Walter pate-de-verre at **1605** is a different animal, being a late nineteenth century French technique of making a glass paste from crushed glass, which is then mould-shaped into figures, slow fired, then hand finished with a spatula.

At **1616** is probably our first English entry being a George Bacchus concentric at £2,000 hammer, and at **1608** is a signed and dated Baccarat, with silhouette canes of animals. The B1847 mark is contained within the pattern and appears at the end of a cane. A St. Louis paperweight might typically be dated SL1848. Clichy weights are different in variety and colouring. They excelled in their flowers and many coloured grounds. The Clichy rose, in different colours, was a particularly recognisable feature of their millefiore. Only Clichy made swirl paperweights in the style of **1621** and nothing is more typical of Clichy than the millefiore at **1622**. Only when we come below about £500 hammer does Paul Ysart (Perth) appear, at **1628** and again at **1632**. The top end of glass dumps appears at **1629** and the use of the term *end of day* is a misnomer and should not be applied to these carefully manufactured objects. For many years dumps were literally 'down in the dumps' and as the poor relation to paperweights, prices were depressed for many years. This has now changed. Twenty years ago you could buy them for £20 or £30 but then you couldn't sell them on. Now a dump is going to set you back a £100, whereas a few years ago dumps could be had for £50-70. At **1630** is a Caithness, one of a limited edition of 100 which produced a buyer's price of nearly £500. As in all categories of collecting you have to know the market. French weights continue to dominate the low hundreds but Paul Ysart appear again at **1647** and **1655** with more later. A surprise is the £300 paid for the green glass paperweight at **1650** and there is a further sulphide example at **1689**, probably Kilner. Dumps do not always appear light bottle green. At **1714**, **1720**, **1728** they look decidedly turquoise. At **1664** is a rare Apsley Pellat and at **1666** an Arculus magnum. Paperweights are difficult to identify and the speculative attribution to Clichy at **1716** got a muted response from buyers. I will leave the reader to study the remaining pages. The best introductions to paperweights is *Miller's Paperweights of the 19th & 20th Centuries*, by Anne Metcalf, London, 2000 at only £5.99.

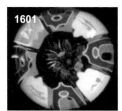

1601

St Louis paperweight, central spray mixed flowers lapped with panels of blue and white opaque glass, white opaque glass engraved with figures, star cut to base, 3.5in dia. Canterbury Auction Galleries, Kent. May 01. HP: £12,000. ABP: £14,115.

1602

Mid-19thC French millefiore paperweight, numerous coloured floral canes against a grass-green ground, 3in. Gorringes, Lewes. Jun 06. HP: £11,000. ABP: £12,938.

1603

Clichy 'cornucopia' weight five white, purple and red blooms formed from single canes, seven leaves within a pale lilac cornucopia, 7cm dia, minor surface wear. Bearne's, Exeter. Jun 05. HP: £2,600. ABP: £3,058.

1604

Large glass paperweight with central white flower and four blue flowers, 3.75in and another with faceted sides and multi-canes, 2.75in. Gorringes, Lewes. Jun 00. HP: £2,300. ABP: £2,705.

1605

Almeric Walter pate-de-verre snail paperweight, from a model by Henri Berge, yellow, green and tan, moulded signatures A Walter and H Berge, 3in. long. Gorringes, Lewes. Oct 04. HP: £2,100. ABP: £2,470.

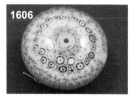

1606

Victorian paperweight by George Bacchus of Birmingham, concentric arrangement of floral and star canes in pastel colours, 3.5in. Gorringes, Lewes. Jun 06. HP: £2,000. ABP: £2,352.

Categories or themes can be followed through the colour coded Index which contains over 4500 cross references.

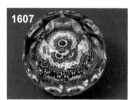

1607

Mid-19thC St Louis 'mushroom' paperweight, concentric coloured canes, exterior cut with circular panels, 3in. Gorringes, Lewes. Mar 06. HP: £1,500. ABP: £1,764.

1608

Mid-19thC Baccarat paperweight, 1847, inset with silhouette canes of cockerel, horse, elephant and others, upset muslin ground, signed and dated B 1847, 3in. Gorringes, Lewes. Mar 06. HP: £1,500. ABP: £1,764.

Hammer: £12,000 - £720

1609

Baccarat animal cane paperweight, animal silhouettes & scattered millefiori against an upset muslin ground, 2.5in. Gorringes, Lewes. Feb 06. HP: £1,400. ABP: £1,646.

1610

Paperweight, prob. St Louis, camomile flower, swirling latticino, 3in dia. Sworders, Stansted Mountfitchet. Oct 01. HP: £1,250. ABP: £1,470.

1611

Art Deco, prob. French, glass paperweight, depicting femme chariot racer, no markings, 12cm high, 18cm long. Rosebery's, London. Mar 04. HP: £1,050. ABP: £1,235.

1612

Mid-19thC Baccarat clematis paperweight, rare colours of ruby, white and green, star-cut underside, 2.5in. Gorringes, Lewes. Jun 06. HP: £1,000. ABP: £1,176.

1613

Mid 19thC Clichy scramble paperweight, colourful canes, central Clichy rose, 8cm dia. Cheffins, Cambridge. Dec 00. HP: £900. ABP: £1,058.

1614

Clichy paperweight, scattered fleurettes, apple green ground, 7.5cm. Charterhouse Auctioneers, Sherborne. Sep 06. HP: £880. ABP: £1,035.

1615

Mid 19thC Baccarat glass paperweight, inset with four 4-legged animal silhouettes, signed, dated b1848, 2.25in. Gorringes, Lewes. Jan 03. HP: £850. ABP: £999.

1616

Millefiori glass paperweight, disc-shaped, central floral design above blue/white air-twist, 8cm wide. Gorringes, Bexhill. Dec 05. HP: £800. ABP: £941.

1617

St Louis floral paperweight, pink dahlia against a white spiral latticinio ground, 2.5in. Gorringes, Lewes. Feb 06. HP: £800. ABP: £941.

1618

St Louis fruit paperweight, mid 19thC, set pears/cherries, 8cm dia, a Baccarat purple pansy weight and a Baccarat faceted double clematis weight, 4cm dia max. (3) Rosebery's, London. Jun 04. HP: £720. ABP: £846.

Hammer: £700 - £360

Large Baccarat paperweight, with a blue and white flower, star cut base, 3in. Gorringes, Lewes. Nov 05. HP: £700. ABP: £823.

Baccarat glass strawberry paperweight, 3in. Gorringes, Lewes. Nov 05. HP: £700. ABP: £823.

19thC French glass paperweight, turquoise and white swirl decoration with central flowers in the style of Clichy, 3in. Gorringes, Lewes. Oct 01. HP: £650. ABP: £764.

Mid-19thC Clichy millefiore paperweight, numerous coloured canes within green basket, 2.75in. Gorringes, Lewes. Mar 06. HP: £650. ABP: £764.

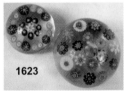

Two Clichy paperweights, c1845, each set with two concentric rows of millefiori canes, 6cm and 4.5cm. Sworders, Stansted Mountfitchet. Mar 04. HP: £600. ABP: £705.

Mid-19thC St Louis paperweight, pear, cherries and leaves on white basket, 2.75in. Gorringes, Lewes. Mar 06. HP: £600. ABP: £705.

Two Baccarat patterned millefiori paperweights, mid 19thC, each with interlaced trefoil cane garlands and scattered canes, and a French millefiori paperweight with 7 cane circles. (3) Rosebery's, London. Jun 04. HP: £580. ABP: £682.

Mid-19thC St Louis scrambled paperweight, coloured canes against upset muslin spirals, 3in. Gorringes, Lewes. Apr 07. HP: £550. ABP: £646.

Mid-19thC French glass paperweight, poss. Baccarat, inset with a clematis design in green, yellow/amethyst, star cut base, 2.5in. Gorringes, Lewes. Jan 03. HP: £500. ABP: £588.

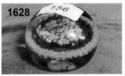

Paul Ysart Perth glass paperweight, millefiori centre and outer border, one stem signed 'PY', 7cm. Reeman Dansie, Colchester. Apr 06. HP: £460. ABP: £541.

Three green 'End of Day' glass dumps inset with cone shaped bubbles, 5.25in high, 6in high and 6.5in high. £115, £160 and £170. Tring Market Auctions, Herts. Sep 02. HP: £445. ABP: £523.

Caithness Ltd Edn Royal commemorative paperweight, to celebrate Princess Anne & Mark Philips marriage, No. 9/100, boxed, 3in. Gorringes, Lewes. Oct 05. HP: £420. ABP: £494.

Baccarat miniature millefiore paperweight, animal fleurettes, 4cm dia. Charterhouse Auctioneers, Sherborne. Sep 06. HP: £420. ABP: £494.

Paul Ysart aventurine butter-fly paperweight, surrounded by Millefiori canes, amethyst tinted surround, Monart glass label to base and PY cane. Great Western Auctions, Glasgow. Sep 06. HP: £410. ABP: £482.

Small crown paperweight, perhaps St Louis, 5cm. Woolley & Wallis, Salisbury. Sep 00. HP: £400. ABP: £470.

Two Victorian dumps/paper-weights, one green glass with fountain design, large clear glass round dump, ornamental bubbles surrounding larger bubble that contains liquid inside, & a millefiori design paperweight. (3) A F Brock & Co Ltd, Stockport. Feb 07. HP: £390. ABP: £458.

19thC French glass multi cane paperweight, 3in. Gorringes, Lewes. Jun 05. HP: £380. ABP: £446.

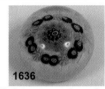

Clichy paperweight, with concentric rings of canes on a muslin ground, 5.5cm. Charterhouse Auctioneers, Sherborne. Sep 06. HP: £380. ABP: £446.

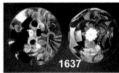

19thC Baccarat purple pansy weight, star/facet cut base, 8cm dia, and a Baccarat faceted double clematis weight. Rosebery's, London. Mar 05. HP: £370. ABP: £435.

Clichy style paperweight, 3 flower canes against a leaf ground and a similar weight with smaller flowers, 2.25in. Gorringes, Bexhill. Mar 02. HP: £360. ABP: £423.

1639

Daum clear/green opalescent dagger pattern paperweight, moulded tapered blade and horse-head pattern handle, 12in overall, engraved 'Daum', slight ding mark to rear of horse's head. Canterbury Auction Galleries, Kent. Feb 06. HP: £360. ABP: £423.

1640

Baccarat flower paperweight, mid 19thC, pink budding clematis plant, star cut base, 5.2cm dia. Rosebery's, London. Mar 05. HP: £340. ABP: £399.

1641

St Louis fruit paperweight, mid 19thC, set with pears & cherries in a ground of spiralling white latticino threads, 8cm wide. Rosebery's, London. Mar 05. HP: £340. ABP: £399.

1642

20thC Baccarat paperweight, central deer silhouette and alternate green and yellow concentric rows of canes within a twist of blue canes, 3in dia. Gorringes, Lewes. Jul 04. HP: £320. ABP: £376.

1643

Baccarat dog rose paperweight, 19thC, 7cm dia. Rosebery's, London. Mar 05. HP: £320. ABP: £376.

1644

Clear glass paperweight, probably New England Glass Company, 2 pale blue berries amongst 4 leaves & branches, 7cm dia, minor wear. Bearne's, Exeter. Jun 05. HP: £320. ABP: £376.

1645

Three Victorian green glass dumps of graduated form, each with flower inclusions, 6 .5in to 4.5in high. Andrew Hartley, Ilkley. Apr 06. HP: £320. ABP: £376.

Prices quoted are actual hammer prices (HP) and the Approximate Buyer's Price (ABP) includes an average premium of 15% + VAT.

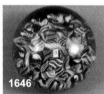
1646

Mid-19thC St. Louis scrambled paperweight, 1847, numerous coloured canes and tubes, dated cane central, 2.5in. Gorringes, Lewes. Apr 07. HP: £300. ABP: £352.

1647

Mid 20thC Paul Ysart paperweight, thirteen polychrome canes on a green ground, original presentation box, 3in dia. Gorringes, Lewes. Jul 04. HP: £280. ABP: £329.

Hammer: £360 - £220

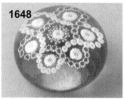
1648

Domed glass paperweight, bands of blue and white millefiori surrounded by a red roundel, 9.5cm high. Gorringes, Bexhill. Dec 05. HP: £280. ABP: £329.

1649

Glass millefiori paperweight, centre dated 1848. Boulton & Cooper, Malton. Jul 04. HP: £270. ABP: £317.

1650

19thC green glass paperweight with inset potted plant, 3in high. Gorringes, Bexhill. Mar 02. HP: £260. ABP: £305.

1651

19thC Clichy millefiori glass paperweight, inset coloured floral canes, 1.75in. Gorringes, Lewes. Jul 03. HP: £240. ABP: £282.

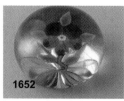
1652

Baccarat domed glass paperweight, millefiori design of a pansy, star-cut base, 6.5cm dia. Gorringes, Bexhill. Dec 05. HP: £240. ABP: £282.

1653

Clichy paperweight, with concentric rings of canes, 5cm. Charterhouse Auctioneers, Sherborne. Sep 06. HP: £240. ABP: £282.

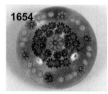
1654

Clichy paperweight, with concentric rings of canes, 6cm. Charterhouse Auctioneers, Sherborne. Sep 06. HP: £240. ABP: £282.

1655

Paul Ysart paperweight, flower and bud on red ground, latticino spokes, py sticker to base, 6cm. Charterhouse Auctioneers, Sherborne. Sep 06. HP: £240. ABP: £282.

1656

Mid-19thC Baccarat paperweight, a scattering of multi-coloured 'upset muslin', 3in. Gorringes, Lewes. Oct 04. HP: £230. ABP: £270.

1657

Clichy paperweight, red and white canes of intersecting garland design enclosing a central cluster, 3in dia, small bruise to base. Gorringes, Bexhill. Sep 02. HP: £220. ABP: £258.

Hammer: £220 - £150

1658

Victorian bottle-green glass 'dump' paperweight, inset with numerous air-tears, 4.5in and three other paper-weights. Gorringes, Lewes. Jul 03. HP: £220. ABP: £258.

1659

Set of 3 green glass dumps, slender tapering form with flower pot inclusions, 4.5in - 5.5in high. Hartleys, Ilkley. Oct 07. HP: £220. ABP: £258.

1660

Three Whitefriars millefiore glass paperweights. Potteries Specialist Auctions, Stoke on Trent. Mar 03. HP: £210. ABP: £247.

1661

Paul Ysart paperweight, with central pink flower on a speckled green ground, H cane and paper label to underside. (boxed) Great Western Auctions, Glasgow. Nov 05. HP: £210. ABP: £247.

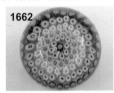

1662

Baccarat millefiore paper-weight, concentric rows of floral canes and a central cane with 2 B's, 3in. Gorringes, Lewes. Oct 02. HP: £180. ABP: £211.

1663

Millefiori in a basket paper-weight, probably experi-mental, possibly produced by Caithness or Murano, presentation box. Cheffins, Cambridge. Feb 05. HP: £180. ABP: £211.

1664

Early 19thC cut glass Apsley Pellat paperweight, decor-ated with a classical figure, 9cm. Sworders, Stansted Mountfitchet. Feb 04. HP: £180. ABP: £211.

1665

Three millifiori glass paper-weights, one of facetted design. Dreweatt Neate, Donnington. Nov 02. HP: £180. ABP: £211.

1666

Arculus magnum concentric milliefiori paperweight, clear body with 6 concentric rings of pink, yellow, blue/purple star shaped canes, 9.5cm dia. Bearne's, Exeter. Jun 05. HP: £180. ABP: £211.

1667

Seven various glass paper-weights, including a Home Guard example, a millefiori example, etc. Gorringes, Bexhill. Oct 05. HP: £180. ABP: £211.

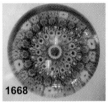

1668

19thC millefiori concentric paperweight, 3.25in dia. Dee, Atkinson & Harrison, Driffield. Dec 00. HP: £170. ABP: £199.

1669

Two bottle-green glass dump door-stops, each with internal three-tiered flower, (latter chipped) 7.5in & 5in. Gorringes, Lewes. Mar 03. HP: £170. ABP: £199.

1670

Star-shaped millefiori paper-weight and 11 other various paperweights, glass dumps etc. Gorringes, Bexhill. Feb 06. HP: £170. ABP: £199.

1671

Paul Ysart Harland period flower paperweight. (boxed) Great Western Auctions, Glasgow. May 07. HP: £170. ABP: £199.

1672

Two Victorian green bubble glass dump weights, tallest 13cm. Sworders, Stansted Mountfitchet. Sep 03. HP: £160. ABP: £188.

1673

Baccarat yellow ground paperweight, Ltd Edn No 289, dated 1978, central inclusion of a stage within a ground filled with square panels of flowerheads, 8cm wide, boxed. Rosebery's, London. Mar 06. HP: £160. ABP: £188.

1674

Pair of green glass dumps, tapering form, each with sulphide inclusion modelled as a cockerel, other modelled as thistle heads, 4in high, and a similar paperweight, with First World War Sulphide medal. (3) Hartleys, Ilkley. Oct 07. HP: £160. ABP: £188.

1675

Pair of Victorian glass dumps. Stroud Auctions, Stroud. Jul 05. HP: £155. ABP: £182.

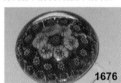

1676

Domed glass milllefiore paperweight, 7cm dia. Gorringes, Bexhill. Dec 04. HP: £150. ABP: £176.

1677

Six various glass paper-weights, incl. two with inset floral millefiore, 3.25in and 2.5in. Gorringes, Lewes. Jan 05. HP: £150. ABP: £176.

1678

Lalique, post-war frosted and clear glass paperweight, modelled as a horse, 10cm high, incised marks Lalique France, with clear/frosted cendrier modelled as a maiden, (a/f) (2). Rosebery's, London. Sep 04. HP: £150. ABP: £176.

1679

Millefiori paperweight, early 20thC, two Caithness paperweights, a Selkirk example and one other paperweight. Gorringes, Bexhill. Feb 06. HP: £150. ABP: £176.

1680

Glass millefiore paperweight, 3.25in.dia, another, domed and faceted,3.25in. high, and a concentric millefiore stopper. Gorringes, Lewes. Apr 03. HP: £140. ABP: £164.

1681

St. Louis miniature millefiore paperweight, 4.5cm. Charterhouse Auctioneers, Sherborne. Sep 06. HP: £140. ABP: £164.

1682

Small Victorian millefiori paperweight. Gorringes, Bexhill. Dec 04. HP: £140. ABP: £164.

1683

Victorian green glass dump, arched form with bubble inclusions, 4.75in high, and a similar dump with flower-head inclusion, 3.5in high. (2) Hartleys, Ilkley. Feb 07. HP: £140. ABP: £164.

1684

Large green glass dump door stop, 14cm high. Sworders, Stansted Mountfitchet. Jun 03. HP: £130. ABP: £152.

The numbering system acts as a reader reference as well as linking to the Analysis of each section.

1685

Pair of green glass dumps, tapering form with bubble inclusions, 4.25in high. Hartleys, Ilkley. Oct 07. HP: £130. ABP: £152.

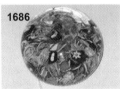

1686

Domed glass millefiore paperweight, 7cm dia. Gorringes, Bexhill. Dec 04. HP: £120. ABP: £141.

1687

Two concentric millefiore paperweights, 2.75in and two other paperweights. Gorringes, Lewes. Apr 03. HP: £120. ABP: £141.

Hammer: £150 - £100

1688

Two glass paperweights: a Perthshire weight with a butterfly insert, 7cm wide, and a millifiori glass paperweight, 8cm wide. Dreweatt Neate, Donnington. Nov 02. HP: £120. ABP: £141.

1689

Green glass 'dump' paper weight probably Kilner with a sulphide portrait in profile, 11cm high. Bearne's, Exeter. Jun 05. HP: £120. ABP: £141.

1690

Victorian green glass dump, ovoid form with flower pot inclusion, 6in high, and another with bubble inclusions, 5.75in high. (2) Hartleys, Ilkley. Apr 08. HP: £120. ABP: £141.

1691

Late 19thC sulphide paperweight, head and shoulders portrait of Prince Albert, 3.75in dia. Dee, Atkinson & Harrison, Driffield. Jul 04. HP: £110. ABP: £129.

1692

Victorian green glass dump, flower enclosed, 6in high. Golding Young & Co, Grantham. Feb 06. HP: £110. ABP: £129.

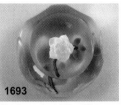

1693

Caithness Ltd Edn 'White Rose' paperweight, by William Manson, No. 28 of 150, original presentation box. Cheffins, Cambridge. Feb 05. HP: £100. ABP: £117.

1694

Millefiori paperweight. Black Country Auctions, Dudley. Dec 05. HP: £100. ABP: £117.

1695

Selkirk paperweight by Peter Holmes, designed with a frog character and snail, green terrain, initialled, 3in, boxed. Gorringes, Lewes. Apr 06. HP: £100. ABP: £117.

1696

Victorian green glass dump, flower enclosed, 5in high. Golding Young & Co, Grantham. Feb 06. HP: £100. ABP: £117.

1697

Miniature paperweight, flower head canes, 4cm dia, and another with scramble design, and another similar. (3) Charterhouse Auctioneers, Sherborne. Sep 06. HP: £100. ABP: £117.

Hammer: £100 - £70

Paul Ysart Harland period fountain paperweight, yellow and orange, sticker to base. Great Western Auctions, Glasgow. May 07. HP: £100. ABP: £117.

Paul Ysart Harland period millefiori paperweight. Great Western Auctions, Glasgow. May 07. HP: £100. ABP: £117.

Pair of Victorian green glass dumps, flower pot inclusions, 4.5in high. Hartleys, Ilkley. Jun 07. HP: £100. ABP: £117.

19thC green glass dump, internal sulphide head and shoulders portrait of Lord Roberts, 5.25in high. Dee, Atkinson & Harrison, Driffield. Jul 04. HP: £90. ABP: £105.

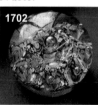

Paul Ysart Harland period Harlequin paperweight, partial label to base. Great Western Auctions, Glasgow. May 07. HP: £90. ABP: £105.

Paul Ysart Harland period millefiori paperweight, orange ground. Great Western Auctions, Glasgow. May 07. HP: £90. ABP: £105.

Italian glass paperweight, white latticinio, red and gold spiral canes, 3.5in wide. Fellows & Sons, Hockley, Birmingham. Oct 03. HP: £85. ABP: £99.

Three 19thC glass dumps, various heights and internal designs. Kent Auction Galleries, Folkestone. Oct 05. HP: £85. ABP: £99.

Glass dump paperweight with 3 tier plant to interior, 11.5cm. Boldon Auction Galleries, Tyne & Wear. Sep 05. HP: £85. ABP: £99.

Pair of North East, end of glass, novelty paperweights in form of turtles, 15.5cm. Boldon Auction Galleries, Tyne & Wear. Sep 05. HP: £85. ABP: £99.

Two green dumps, tapering form each with flower pot inclusions, 4.5in high and 6in high. Hartleys, Ilkley. Oct 07. HP: £85. ABP: £99.

Green glass dump weight/doorstop, 4in high. Sworders, Stansted Mountfitchet. Oct 01. HP: £80. ABP: £94.

Perthshire glass paperweight, floral canes, another similar paperweight and two others. Gorringes, Lewes. Jan 05. HP: £80. ABP: £94.

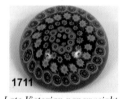

Late Victorian paperweight, concentric flower canes, 9cm dia. Charterhouse Auctioneers, Sherborne. Sep 06. HP: £80. ABP: £94.

Faceted glass paperweight, inset design of flowers within jardiniere, 3.5in. Gorringes, Lewes. Mar 03. HP: £75. ABP: £88.

Green 'End of Day' cased glass paperweight with four tiered stylised flower in a pot, 6.5in high. Tring Market Auctions, Herts. Jul 04. HP: £75. ABP: £88.

19thC Stourbridge tear drop dump, 7in. Dee, Atkinson & Harrison, Driffield. Feb 06. HP: £75. ABP: £88.

Victorian green glass dump, flowers enclosed, 5in high. Golding Young & Co, Grantham. Feb 06. HP: £75. ABP: £88.

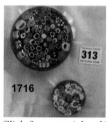

2 Clichy? paperweights, 3in and 1.5in dia. Kent Auction Galleries, Folkestone. Nov 06. HP: £75. ABP: £88.

Caithness Ltd Edn 'Christmas Rose' paperweight, designed by Colin Terris, No. 167/500, original presentation box. Cheffins, Cambridge. Feb 05. HP: £70. ABP: £82.

1718

Caithness Ltd Edn 'Heather' paperweight, designed by the Caithness Paperweight Studios, No. 54/500, original presentation box. Cheffins, Cambridge. Feb 05. HP: £70. ABP: £82.

1719

Pair of flower glass dumps. Great Western Auctions, Glasgow. Feb 06. HP: £70. ABP: £82.

1720

19thC Stourbridge green dump, opaque with floral inclusion, 4.5in high. Dee, Atkinson & Harrison, Driffield. Jul 08. HP: £68. ABP: £79.

1721

Kosta glass papperweight, bulb form, clear glass with internal bubble inclusions, 14cm high with a Kosta glass vessel, blue/orange swirled interior, 6.5cm high, both engraved marks to underside. Rosebery's, London. Mar 05. HP: £65. ABP: £76.

1722

1950s Strathearn spoked paperweight, 8 ribbon cane spokes dividing multiple canes in shades of pink/blue, 3.25in. Gorringes, Lewes. Apr 08. HP: £65. ABP: £76.

1723

Glass dump by J Kilner & Sons, central trumpet flowers, 8cm high. Boldon Auction Galleries, Tyne & Wear. Sep 04. HP: £60. ABP: £70.

1724

Mid 19thC French glass paperweight, scrambled canes in floral and spiral designs, 2.5in. Gorringes, Lewes. Jan 03. HP: £60. ABP: £70.

1725

Victorian cartwheel paperweight, and another similar paperweight. (2) Charterhouse Auctioneers, Sherborne. Sep 06. HP: £60. ABP: £70.

The illustrations are in descending price order. The price range is indicated at the top of each page.

1726

1727

Two green glass 'dump' paperweights both with internal bubbles. Great Western Auctions, Glasgow. Mar 08. HP: £60. ABP: £70.

Modern ruby flash glass paperweight, pentagonal form engraved with a dragonfly. Gorringes, Lewes. Dec 00. HP: £55. ABP: £64.

1728

19thC Stourbridge teardrop dump, 5.5in high. Dee, Atkinson & Harrison, Driffield. Feb 06. HP: £55. ABP: £64.

1729

Two Strathearn cartwheel paperweights, 8cm. Charterhouse Auctioneers, Sherborne. Sep 06. HP: £55. ABP: £64.

1730

Four paperweights, various sizes and styles and a green Victorian dump. (5) A F Brock & Co Ltd, Stockport. May 08. HP: £55. ABP: £64.

1731

Two 'End of Day' green cased glass paperweights, stylised three tier flowers in pots, 5.25 and 5.5in high. Tring Market Auctions, Herts. Jul 04. HP: £50. ABP: £58.

1732

Large clear glass dump with air bubbles. 15cm. Boldon Auction Galleries, Tyne & Wear. Sep 04. HP: £50. ABP: £58.

1733

Domed glass paperweight, floral internal decoration, 11cm. Gorringes, Bexhill. Jun 05. HP: £50. ABP: £58.

1734

Victorian green glass dump, squat form with bubble inclusions, 5in high. Hartleys, Ilkley. Aug 06. HP: £50. ABP: £58.

1735

Victorian dump weight on stand. Great Western Auctions, Glasgow. Sep 06. HP: £50. ABP: £58.

1736

Whitefriars glass paperweight, facet cut dome, six bands of coloured canes, single date cane, 5cm dia. Rosebery's, London. Apr 07. HP: £50. ABP: £58.

1737

Whitefriars millefiore Silver Jubilee paperweight, red, white and blue canes and '1952', '1977' and 'E II R' canes, 7.5cm dia, Whitefriars paper label and box. Rosebery's, London. Jul 07. HP: £50. ABP: £58.

Hammer: £50 - £15

Green glass dump. Great Western Auctions, Glasgow. Sep 07. HP: £50. ABP: £58.

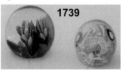

Domed millefiore glass paperweight and another. Gorringes, Bexhill. Sep 04. HP: £45. ABP: £52.

Millefiori paperweight, late 19th/early 20thC & another later floral paperweight, 4.5cm dia. Gorringes, Bexhill. Feb 06. HP: £45. ABP: £52.

Old glass paperweight, green, white, blue & yellow twisted stem decoration, 5cm high. Reeman Dansie, Colchester. Apr 06. HP: £45. ABP: £52.

Victorian green glass dump, flower enclosed, 4in tall. Golding Young & Co, Grantham. Feb 06. HP: £45. ABP: £52.

Two domed millefiori paperweights. Gorringes, Bexhill. Sep 04. HP: £40. ABP: £47.

Small multi cane glass paperweight, later gilt metal tripod stand, 2in. Gorringes, Lewes. Jul 02. HP: £40. ABP: £47.

Norfolk glass dump. Gorringes, Bexhill. Dec 04. HP: £40. ABP: £47.

White Friars Elizabeth II Silver Jubilee commemorative facet cut cane paper weight, 1952-1977, design centred with a crown, base 7.4cm dia. Thos Mawer & Son, Lincoln. Mar 04. HP: £40. ABP: £47.

Bacaraat paperweight, 3in dia. Kent Auction Galleries, Folkestone. Feb 06. HP: £40. ABP: £47.

Four paperweights. Golding Young & Co, Grantham. Nov 06. HP: £36. ABP: £42.

Paul Ysart ASC cap badge paperweight, ASC badge on a splatter ground, 7cm dia. Charterhouse Auctioneers, Sherborne. Sep 06. HP: £35. ABP: £41.

Three Strathearn style paperweights of ovoid form, green mound, coloured floral decoration, two smaller paperweights with 4 air bubbles, 7cm high, larger paperweight 14cm. Rosebery's, London. Apr 07. HP: £35. ABP: £41.

Caithness paperweights x 3, original boxes: 'Pink Champagne', 'Sea Dance' and 'Jack in the Box', a Ltd Edn No. 884/1,618, 1995 Collectors Club designed by Margot Thomson. Sandwich Auction Rooms, Kent. Jan 07. HP: £32. ABP: £37.

20thC Strathearn millefiore paperweight, pink cane central to four outer rings, radiating orange/red spirals, paper label, 7.5cm dia. Cheffins, Cambridge. Dec 00. HP: £30. ABP: £35.

Large millefiori glass paperweight set with various coloured glass canes, 13.5cm dia. Rosebery's, London. Aug 06. HP: £25. ABP: £29.

Selkirk glass paperweight 'Flower', 176/500, 1980. Great Western Auctions, Glasgow. May 08. HP: £22. ABP: £25.

Caithness paperweight, Festivity. Black Country Auctions, Dudley. Dec 05. HP: £22. ABP: £25.

Millefiori spoke wheel type paperweight, twisted multi-coloured canes within a flowerhead ground, 8cm dia. Rosebery's, London. Aug 06. HP: £20. ABP: £23.

Early 20thC Stourbridge glass paperweight, clear crystal cased in turquoise, cut back with plain printie panels, with a similar ruby cased example. Fieldings, West Hagley, Worcs. Jun 05. HP: £15. ABP: £17.

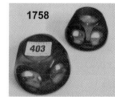

Early 20thC Stourbridge glass paperweight, clear crystal cased in green, cut back with plain printie panels, with similar amethyst cased example and an Oriental millefiori example. Fieldings, West Hagley, Worcs. Jun 05. HP: £15. ABP: £17.

PART V:
Figures & Car Mascots

'Modern Lalique figures are ubiquitous.....the market in Vistosi sculptures from the 1960s is volatile.....Marius Ernest Sabino was a Sicilian.... the John Derbyshire Landseer lion in the foreground is a red herring..... I would have paid more for the Michael Harris Mdina sculpture.....'

The Kiss at **1759**, by Libensky and Brychtora stands well above any of the other 100 lots in this Section. Art Czechoslovakia Glass rarely appears at auction. When it does it usually fetches four figures. A Vladimir Selinek, for Moser, blue glass vase sold for £2,450 hammer in 2006. This Section, as to be expected, is dominated by Lalique, with about thirty three entries ranging from **1760** at £2,300 hammer to a modern glass bird at **1821** and only £55 hammer. Modern Lalique figures are fairly ubiquitous, yet never that cheap and I would suggest this as a poor investment area with manufacturing still continuing. Resort to the old adage. Buy only the very best you can afford and ensure your purchases are not common collectibles. At **1765** are two examples of Vistosi sculptures from the 1960s. This is a volatile market. The example at **1765** and £1,050 hammer matched the £1,100 hammer paid for a further example at Bearnes, Exeter in 2006. Steady enough, but the *Orange* example at **1767** is all over the place. In April 2007 one raised £2,700 hammer, but by May 2008 another raised only £1,200, less than half as much. Further nationwide results in the last couple of years were two at a £1,000 hammer, our example at **1767** and then £600 hammer in Harrogate in 2007. The average hammer price for all Vistosi is just over £1,200. I am surprised the Almeric Walter pate-de-verre duck at **1770** fetched only £550 hammer at the end of 2007. This could be compared with the snail paperweight in that Section at **1605** which fetched £2,470 including premium in 2004. Stand alone figures tend to fetch between about £1,000 and £2,000, whereas at the lower end of the market their figural dishes fetch about £180 to £250. This swimming duck is rare enough to be a good buy. You are not going to come across one every day of the week. Recently a pair of rabbit bookends, which were cracked, fetched the same.
There are about six Sabino examples in these pages. See **1772, 1779, 1783, 1791, 1805** and **1823.** I believe **1772** and **1779** are the same group at £440 and £360 hammer respectively. Marius Ernest Sabino, 1878-1961 was a Sicilian whose French productions, during the art deco period of the 1930s, almost matched those of Lalique. Like Lalique they continue today and modern examples match in price, those of modern Lalique. The most I have seen paid at auction for Sabino was £1,700 hammer for a *Double Suzanne* statuette table lamp in 2006, so hardly a match for Lalique at the top end of the market. There are a similar number of Daum examples in these

pages. See **1775, 1799, 1806, 1807** and **1820** and all would appear modern. Specialists would know. We do not have this problem with English pressed glass. See **1774, 1786** and **1826.** I would suggest that the John Derbyshire *Landseer lion* in the foreground of **1774** is a 'blue' herring and the important piece is the classical maiden in the background. Derbyshire lions are not that uncommon and this is of medium size only at 12 cms in length. However at **1786** the pair of lions are bigger and desirable. Despite the severe downturn in the pressed glass market it is good to see these figures holding their value. As far as I know they have never been reproduced so you are not going to come across a seven inch pair of Derbyshire lions that often. At **1826** the Henry Greener lions, at only four and a half inches, with the added incentive of a Burtles & Tate swan failed to impress buyers in the north east at £40 hammer. To witness the depths to which prices have sunk see **1834** and **1835.**
There is a considerable amount of Italian glass, the best being a Fulvio Bianconi, Venice attribution at **1777**, and £446. There is more at **1813, 1817, 1827** etc. None is mind blowing and there is little of any quality or rarity, although the penguin at **1802** attracted £158 in 2005. It is unfortunate that more Mdina glass has not come to light but most of it has too low a value to appear at auction. This is not the case for the large sculpture at **1782,** standing at over twelve inches in height and undoubtedly very heavy indeed. Mdina was founded in 1969 by Michael Harris, who left after only three years because of the political situation, to found the Isle of Wight Glass factory. The early Harris pieces from this very short period are highly desirable, and particularly when signed, as with this sculpture. I would suggest that this was a good buy at only £317 in 2005 and if it were to appear on the market today, I would be prepared to pay more. There are a few more interesting lots. At **1797** is an Asprey & Co. attribution. These bookends are worth at least the £223 paid. Is it possible to confirm the maker and how would this affect the price? Bonzo (**1814**) has appeared in every other material so why not glass. Swarovski doesn't appear for obvious reasons but a group at **1811** fetched about £12 a piece. There is one frigger at **1818** with a Nailsea attribution but this is the generic use of the term. Surely it is not possible to ascribe a manufacturer. My favourite novelty piece is the boot match striker at **1828** and only £35. I think this is certainly a bargain as the only silver mounted piece in the Section, making it not the commonest piece around!

Hammer: £5,400 - £400

The Kiss, cast red glass sculpture by Stanislav Libensky & Jaroslava Brychtova, shaped square form, cast with features of stylised faces, signed BRYCHTOVA LIBENSKY, 16cm high, Art Czechoslovakia Glass export certificate, No. 3/10, signed by manager of glass works & Brychtova, dated 10th March 1969, in a paper wallet. Charterhouse Auctioneers, Sherborne. Jun 08. HP: £5,400. ABP: £6,351.

Lalique 'Sirene' statuette of a mermaid, opaline glass mermaid seated with arms to one side, moulded mark R Lalique, c1920, 4in. Gorringes, Lewes. Apr 03. HP: £2,300. ABP: £2,705.

Lalique topaz coloured Coq Nain car mascot, etched mark Lalique, France, 8in. Gorringes, Lewes. Oct 05. HP: £1,600. ABP: £1,882.

Renee Lalique, falcon, 1930s clear glass car mascot. Amersham Auction Rooms, Bucks. May 01. HP: £1,350. ABP: £1,587.

Faucon, R. Lalique clear and frosted glass car mascot as a standing falcon, etched and moulded marks, 6.5in high. Hamptons, Godalming. Jul 02. HP: £1,350. ABP: £1,587.

Lalique clear/frosted glass circular car mascot, 'The Archer' (No. 1126), flat disc with kneeling figure of an archer, 5in high, engraved mark 'R. Lalique, France', & numbered to base, complete with plated screw ring fitting, ring split. Canterbury Auction Galleries, Kent. Apr 07. HP: £1,300. ABP: £1,529.

Vistosi glass bird, 'Pulcini', designed by Alessandro Pianon, abstract striped blue body, wire legs, 8.5in long, c1965. Hartleys, Ilkley. Feb 07. HP: £1,050. ABP: £1,235.

Lalique frosted/clear glass falcon car mascot, moulded R Lalique in capitals, 6.25in. Gorringes, Lewes. Sep 00. HP: £1,000. ABP: £1,176.

'Pulcini' glass bird sculpture, designed by Alexander Pianon for Vistosi, c1960, textured globular body in bright orange, coloured murrine eyes, original copper legs, 20cm high. Rosebery's, London. Mar 08. HP: £950. ABP: £1,117.

Lalique amethyst coloured Tete de Coq car mascot, original chrome mount, fitted to an ebonised plinth, with a radiator cap, moulded mark, 12in. Gorringes, Lewes. Oct 05. HP: £900. ABP: £1,058.

Categories or themes can be followed through the colour coded Index which contains over 4500 cross references.

Pair of Lalique Faucon Presse Papiers, light amethyst tint, moulded marks, each 6in high. (1 af) Gardiner Houlgate, Corsham. Apr 05. HP: £600. ABP: £705.

Almeric Walter Pate-de-Verre figure of a swimming duck moulded in blue, green and a hint of yellow, 11.5cm long, impressed A.Walter Nancy, c1910-20. Bearne's, Exeter. Nov 07. HP: £550. ABP: £646.

Lalique glass model of a wart-hog, 'Sanglier', pre war, Cat Ref 1157, frosted glass, stencilled marks R. Lalique, France, 2.5in high. Gorringes, Lewes. Jan 04. HP: £440. ABP: £517.

Sabino opalescent glass group of two pumas, sharply modelled in Art Deco style, engraved mark to plinth, Sabino, France, 7.75in. long. Gorringes, Lewes. Jun 05. HP: £440. ABP: £517.

1930s Art Deco Lalique car mascot, St Christopher with Christ, base marked Lalique France, 4in, chip to top. Denhams, Warnham, Sussex. May 06. HP: £440. ABP: £517.

John Derbyshire and Co blue glass lion, modelled after Landseer, with a plain glass model of a seated classical female. Lion 12cm. Rosebery's, London. Sep 04. HP: £400. ABP: £470.

Modern Daum coloured glass figure, Isadora, by Andre Deluol, 16in. wide. Gorringes, Lewes. Nov 05. HP: £400. ABP: £470.

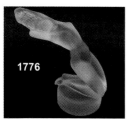

1776

Lalique frosted glass figure, Chrysis, Cat. Ref. 1670, nude female arched backward, engraved mark Lalique, France, 5.25in. Gorringes, Lewes. Mar 04. HP: £380. ABP: £446.

1777

Fulvio Bianconi (attributed) for Venini (Italy), Acrobat figure, white/black glass study of an acrobat in handstand position, 38cm high, unsigned. Rosebery's, London. Sep 04. HP: £380. ABP: £446.

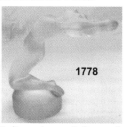

1778

Lalique glass nude figure of kneeling woman, out-stretched arms & hair, scratch marked to base Lalique, France. Kent Auction Galleries, Folkestone. Mar 08. HP: £380. ABP: £446.

1779

Sabino glass panther group, pressed in Art Deco-style, engraved mark Sabino, Paris, c1925, 5.75in. high. Gorringes, Lewes. Oct 05. HP: £360. ABP: £423.

1780

Lalique Leopard smoky grey glass No. 1167400, signed Lalique, France 14.5in long. Kent Auction Galleries, Folkestone. Feb 08. HP: £360. ABP: £423.

1781

Pair Sabino opalescent glass 'Dragonfly' car mascots, moulded mark to underside of body, one with engraved mark 'Sabino France' 15cm high. Rosebery's, London. Sep 04. HP: £300. ABP: £352.

1782

Large Maltese Medina glass sculpture by Michael Harris, typically coloured, signed, 31cm high. Cheffins, Cambridge. Apr 05. HP: £270. ABP: £317.

1783

Sabino opalescent glass model of a female torso, marked 'Sabino, Paris', 20cm. Woolley & Wallis, Salisbury. Jun 00. HP: £260. ABP: £305.

1784

Four miniature coloured glass Guinness characters. John Taylors, Louth. Jan 06. HP: £260. ABP: £305.

Hammer: £380 - £200

1785

Lalique clear/frosted glass bird bookend, etched in script R. Lalique, 6in. Gorringes, Lewes. Sep 00. HP: £240. ABP: £282.

1786

Pair of John Derbyshire pressed green glass lion models, recumbent, oval bases, moulded initials and anchor mark, PODR July 1874, 7in. Gorringes, Lewes. Mar 03. HP: £230. ABP: £270.

1787

Lalique model of a bird, 'Bellecoeur', clear glass bird seated upright, engraved mark R Lalique, 4.5in. Gorringes, Lewes. Jun 03. HP: £230. ABP: £270.

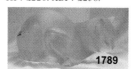

1788

White quartz crystal skull, carved and part polished features 6.5in high. Gorringes, Lewes. Jul 03. HP: £220. ABP: £258.

1789

Lalique Cat, No. 1160200, signed Lalique France, 10in long. Kent Auction Galleries, Folkestone. Feb 08. HP: £210. ABP: £247.

1790

Lalique glass bird, 'Moineau Hardi', pre-war, Cat. Ref. 1150, frosted glass, engraved mark R. Lalique, France 3.25in. Gorringes, Lewes. Jan 04. HP: £210. ABP: £247.

1791

Sabino opalescent glass figure of a dragonfly, 15cm. Sworders, Stansted Mountfitchet. Feb 03. HP: £200. ABP: £235.

1792

Lalique bird, 'Moineau Moqueur', frosted glass model arching upright, Cat. Ref. 1167, etched mark R Lalique, 3.25in high. Gorringes, Lewes. Jun 03. HP: £200. ABP: £235.

1793

Lalique model of a bird, 'Moineau Timide', Cat. Ref. 1151, frosted glass, etched mark R Lalique, 3in high. Gorringes, Lewes. Jun 03. HP: £200. ABP: £235.

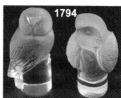

1794

Two Lalique owls, 'Chouette', Cat. Ref. 1667, and another, similar, both post-war, 3.5in. Gorringes, Lewes. Apr 05. HP: £200. ABP: £235.

Hammer: £200 - £70

Modern Lalique frosted glass Chinese dragon, 11.5in. Gorringes, Lewes. Mar 06. HP: £200. ABP: £235.

Modern Lalique frosted glass statuette, nude female with arms aloft, 9.5in. Gorringes, Lewes. Oct 06. HP: £200. ABP: £235.

Asprey & Co, (attrib.) pair of glass bookends, each with black glass bases surmounted by frosted and moulded glass bird figures, 12.5cm high. (2) Lyon & Turnbull, Edinburgh. Apr 08. HP: £190. ABP: £223.

Modern Lalique frosted glass car mascot, 'Tete Aigle', bold eagle's head, 4.5in high, engraved mark to base 'R. Lalique, France'. Canterbury Auction Galleries, Kent. Feb 07. HP: £180. ABP: £211.

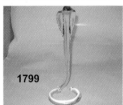

Daum Nancy crystal glass sculpture of a cobra. Gorringes, Bexhill. Dec 04. HP: £180. ABP: £211.

Studio glass model fish. Cotswold Auction Company, Cheltenham. Jul 07. HP: £160. ABP: £188.

Lalique frosted/clear glass Chouette or owl paperweight, stencilled Lalique France, 3.5in. Gorringes, Bexhill. Mar 02. HP: £140. ABP: £164.

Post war Italian glass figure of a penguin, circular base in white set, amethyst and white bird , tall drawn body and applied features, 15.5in high. Fieldings, West Hagley, Worcs. Jun 05. HP: £135. ABP: £158.

Lalique frosted glass toad, 4in. Gorringes, Lewes. Dec 00. HP: £130. ABP: £152.

Modern Lalique clear and frosted glass figure of an owl, clear cylindrical base, 3.5in high, engraved mark 'Lalique, France' to base. Canterbury Auction Galleries, Kent. Feb 07. HP: £110. ABP: £129.

Sabino opaline glass car mascot as a dragonfly, 5in high, inscribed 'Sabino France'. Hartleys, Ilkley. Oct 07. HP: £110. ABP: £129.

Daum clear glass study of a sitting cat, 20cm high, engraved Daum France, an opalescent glass cat study by Sabino, 5cm high, engraved mark and paper label, and a frosted glass study of a cat 9.5cm high. (3) Rosebery's, London. Sep 04. HP: £100. ABP: £117.

Art Deco glass model of a car, Daum, marble plinth, 17 x 7in. Golding Young & Co, Grantham. Nov 06. HP: £100. ABP: £117.

Lalique clear/frosted glass cendrier naiade, 4.25in. Gorringes, Lewes. Dec 00. HP: £90. ABP: £105.

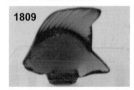

Small Lalique blue glass fish, 4.5cm high. Boldon Auction Galleries, Tyne & Wear. Sep 04. HP: £90. ABP: £105.

Lalique green glass duck, post war, engraved signature Lalique, France, 2.75in high. Gorringes, Lewes. Jun 03. HP: £80. ABP: £94.

Swarovski crystal animals & objects incl. daschund, elephant, 2 swans, chair, duck, chick, key ring & butterfly with some boxes. Kent Auction Galleries, Folkestone. Jun 06. HP: £80. ABP: £94.

Pair Venetian glass figures, male and female, pink, white and clear glass with gold dust inclusions, Murano paper labels, 11in tall. Golding Young & Co, Grantham. Feb 06. HP: £72. ABP: £84.

Murano glass figure of an owl, base signed, 8in. Denhams, Warnham, Sussex. Mar 06. HP: £70. ABP: £82.

Early 20thC glass inkwell, in the form of Bonzo the dog, with minor chips to chin, 9cm high. Charterhouse Auctioneers, Sherborne. Sep 06. HP: £70. ABP: £82.

Lalique figure of an owl, signed to side. Great Western Auctions, Glasgow. Jan 07. HP: £70. ABP: £82.

Pale blue Lalique crested bird No. 1203800, signed Lalique France. Kent Auction Galleries, Folkestone. Feb 08. HP: £70. ABP: £82.

Prices quoted are actual hammer prices (HP) and the Approximate Buyer's Price (ABP) includes an average premium of 15% + VAT.

Pair of Murano glass with aventurine figures. Great Western Auctions, Glasgow. Aug 07. HP: £65. ABP: £76.

Mid-19thC Nailsea green glass frigger, 4in. high. Gorringes, Lewes. Apr 04. HP: £65. ABP: £76.

Pair of early 20thC Venetian glass figures of a lady and gentleman. Black Country Auctions, Dudley. Sep 05. HP: £58. ABP: £68.

Daum clear glass model of a swan-neck, engraved mark Daum France, 17in. Gorringes, Lewes. Jul 04. HP: £55. ABP: £64.

Lalique glass bird. (modern) Orpington Salerooms, Kent. Nov 05. HP: £55. ABP: £64.

Modern Steuben glass eagle on a sphere, marked 'Steuben' to base, 16.5cm high, 32.5cm wide. Rosebery's, London. Oct 06. HP: £50. ABP: £58.

Sabino opalescent glass model of a cockerel, standing on a circular base, moulded maker's mark, 9cm high Cheffins, Cambridge. Feb 05. HP: £50. ABP: £58.

Langham glass cat, 6.5in high and an owl, 5.25in high. (2) Dee, Atkinson & Harrison, Driffield. Feb 06. HP: £50. ABP: £58.

Lalique style clear/frosted glass cockerel, moulded frosted body, clear glass comb, tiered base, unsigned, 19cm high. Rosebery's, London. Aug 06. HP: £50. ABP: £58.

Pair Greener & Co. amber glass seated lions, 11.5cm long & small Burtles & Tate opalescent glass swan, unmarked, 8.5cm long. Boldon Auction Galleries, Tyne & Wear. Sep 04. HP: £40. ABP: £47.

Six 1930s Murano faux fruits, with lustrous green Christmas bauble. (7) Dee, Atkinson & Harrison, Driffield. Feb 06. HP: £30. ABP: £35.

Edwardian moulded glass match striker, boot with silver rim, 3.25in wide, London 1903. Dee, Atkinson & Harrison, Driffield. Nov 07. HP: £30. ABP: £35.

Early 20thC Loetz style green glass apple form ornament, iridescent textured surface, clear glass stalk, 6in high. Diamond Mills & Co, Felixstowe. Jun 06. HP: £26. ABP: £30.

Murano glass cockerel, 8in. Gorringes, Lewes. Sep 00. HP: £20. ABP: £23.

Collection of art glass animals, bowl, mushroom, Murano amber glass, horses head. Kent Auction Galleries, Folkestone. Jul 05. HP: £18. ABP: £21.

Collection of six glass birds incl. swans, bird of paradise, etc. Kent Auction Galleries, Folkestone. Jul 05. HP: £15. ABP: £17.

Dartington Crystal Capredoni glass figurine depicting a horse & foal, boxed. Kent Auction Galleries, Folkestone. Dec 06. HP: £15. ABP: £17.

Greener dog, 2 Sowerby boots & 2 jugs, all jet glass. Boldon Auction Galleries, Tyne & Wear. Sep 04. HP: £12. ABP: £14.

Victorian pressed glass, two pairs of boots in polychrome splatter glass. Golding Young & Co, Grantham. Nov 06. HP: £12. ABP: £14.

Hammer: £3,800 - £1,750

Set of eleven stained glass panels, by repute from the Cafe Royale. Gorringes, Lewes. Jul 99. HP: £3,800. ABP: £4,469.

Stained glass pane, associated with work of Albrecht Durer, early 16thC, painted with an armour-clad St. George and a slain dragon, leaded frame, 5 x 3.25in. Gorringes, Lewes. Jun 07. HP: £2,900. ABP: £3,411.

Tiffany glass window, may have been a sample piece, yacht in full sail, arched top iron frame, wooden surround, original label 'Tiffany Glass & Decorating Company, Furnishers & Glassworkers, Domestic & Ecclesiastical Decoration, 333-441 Fourth Avenue New York USA'. Cotswold Auction Company, Cirencester. Apr 08. HP: £2,000. ABP: £2,352.

Collection of ten 16th/17thC stained glass panels, mostly depicting armorials with various attendants, sizes vary from 9.5 x 7.5in to 17 x 12in, one dated 1557, all re-leaded, 9 mounted into later stained/leaded glass panels, eight of which are in pine and white painted window frame panels. Canterbury Auction Galleries, Kent. Feb 07. HP: £1,950. ABP: £2,293.

Four 19thC stained/leaded glass panels, two damaged, each 38 x 20in. Sworders, Stansted Mountfitchet. Jul 01. HP: £1,850. ABP: £2,176.

Pair of late Victorian stained glass military portrait panels, one depicting .... of the Second West Riding Royal Engineers, surmounted by a crown, inscribed banner, foliate ground, arched foliate border studded with roundels, 81.5 x 19in, other depicting a member of Scottish Rifles, probably manufactured in Leeds. Hartleys, Ilkley. Jun 06. HP: £1,750. ABP: £2,058.

PART VI: Stained & Painted Glass

'For decorative use in the home there are stained glass panels and windows which can be found at auction for £100-£200.'

The juxtaposition of two contrasting techniques and functions can be justified on the basis that they represent flat art on a glass medium in picture form: at times and from distance it may be difficult to tell one from another. Stained glass may be made by constructing mosaics of coloured glass, but also by applying metal oxides onto the surface. Both techniques have been used to produce windows, panels, firescreens etc. Whilst we associate stained glass with medieval churches, during the nineteenth and the earlier twentieth century, the craft had many more uses, particularly in public and domestic architecture. Its popularity in Victorian and Edwardian times was pronounced. One of the finest pieces of stained glass I have seen was a large 264 x 122 cms panel in the arts and crafts style and possibly by Burns Jones which fetched £8,600 hammer back in 2004, whereas in 2007 a Guthrie & Wells, Glasgow, panel, in the medieval style, dating to 1930, at 80 x 47 cms sold for £4,200 hammer. As I write in 2008 a stained glass window, reputedly from Selby Abbey at 16 x 25 inches has sold for £3,600 hammer and four panels attributed to John Moyr Smith depicting multiple windows of flying birds surrounding roundels of Greek gods, sold for the same. For decorative use in the home there are panels and windows from the nineteenth and early twentieth centuries which can be found at auction for a £100-£200. They come in all shapes such as rectangles and as arched windows or roundels. Here the best is represented by eleven panels, reputedly from the *Cafe Royale* at **1836** and the Tiffany window at **1838**. For domestic use what better than the Victorian aesthetic window at **1850** and only £646, or the smaller panels at **1857** or **1863**. It would seem possible to buy art and good workmanship at a fraction of the cost of its production. Painting on glass relies on light reflected from its surface for its unique appearance. In stained glass the translucent colours are viewed by transmitted light. Glass paintings are inherently flawed because of the difficulty of bonding glass and paint. Ageing tends to leave a gap between. Reverse painting tended to function as a folk art and is alive and well today with specialist websites and books. A good example is the Victorian still life at **1860** for £300 hammer and also the small plaque at **1889** at an absurd £50 hammer. I admire the pair of reverse pictures at **1858** and under £400. The pair of pictures at **1843** suggests the top end of the market. Readers should note those examples that are printed as well as those that are painted.

Stained glass panel depicting a crowned and robed king with Celtic style attire. Humberts, Bourton on the Water. Mar 08. HP: £1,400. ABP: £1,646.

One of a pair of Georgian glass pictures, depicting women and children in land-scapes, inscribed Autumn, Winter, Spring and Summer, 9.5 x 13.5in stained frames. Andrew Hartley, Ilkley. Oct 99. HP: £1,350. ABP: £1,587.

Collection of ten 19thC painted and gilded leaded coloured glass hanging plaques, oval form and titled 'Richard I, II & III', 'Henry I, III, V & VII', 'Edward VI', 'Catherine of Aragon' and 'Phillip II', each approx 13 x 11in. Tring Market Auctions, Herts. Jan 04. HP: £1,000. ABP: £1,176.

Stained glass panel in style of Eglington Margaret Pearson, early 19thC, central panel depicting figures in a landscape, blue glass borders, later brass frame, 47 x 35cm. Sworders, Stansted Mountfitchet. Feb 07. HP: £780. ABP: £917.

Leaded stained glass panel, depicting a medieval style man within shield cartouches, oak frame, and another similar, 40 x 32cm. Cheffins, Cambridge. Dec 00. HP: £600. ABP: £705.

Stained glass panel, 25.75 x 43.25in. Hartleys, Ilkley. Apr 06. HP: £580. ABP: £682.

Set of four Georgian reverse printed glass pictures of the 4 seasons, inscribed mounts, published by John Fairburn, London 1796, 14.25 x 10.25in, ebonised frames. Hartleys, Ilkley. Jun 07. HP: £560. ABP: £659.

Pair of German leaded and stained glass panels of 16thC design, one depicting Kaiser Maximilian dated 1593, the other Maria von Burgund, 1880 in architectural setting with Coats of Arms, wood frames, 16.5 x 11.5in & 16 x 11.5 in. Gorringes, Lewes. Jul 03. HP: £550. ABP: £646.

Late Victorian aesthetic lead glazed window, stained panels, two roundels depicting an astronomer/artist, mahogany frame, 35 x 55.75in. Clarke Gammon, Guildford. Feb 03. HP: £550. ABP: £646.

Hammer: £1,400 - £340

Stained glass panel, with holyhocks and made around the turn of the last century by famous makers, Swaine, Bourne and Son of Birmingham and London. Thos Mawer & Son, Lincoln. Apr 08. HP: £520. ABP: £611.

Stained glass window of Pre-Raphaelite influence depicting a muse playing her violin, 127 x 54cm, pine frame. Lots Road Auctions, Chelsea. Jun 03. HP: £480. ABP: £564.

Set of three 19thC stained glass amorial panels, each of a family Coat of Arms with Latin mottos below, 16.25 x 11.5in. Gorringes, Lewes. Jul 03. HP: £460. ABP: £541.

Victorian stained glass fan light, depicting swallows in a landscape, red glass border and zig zag outer banding, 42in wide, 22in high. Andrew Hartley, Ilkley. Apr 04. HP: £420. ABP: £494.

Art Deco three piece stained glass panel, 53in overall x 34in high, and two narrow stained glass panels. (both damaged) Sworders, Stansted Mountfitchet. Apr 01. HP: £400. ABP: £470.

Pair of late Victorian stained and leaded glass window panels, each inset with a central bird decorated panel, 199 x 41cm. Sworders, Stansted Mountfitchet. Nov 04. HP: £390. ABP: £458.

The numbering system acts as a reader reference as well as linking to the Analysis of each section.

Stained glass panel, 94 x 51cm. Charterhouse Auctioneers, Sherborne. Nov 07. HP: £380. ABP: £446.

Pair of Georgian reverse printed glass pictures, The Reaper and The Shepherdess, inscribed mounts, 9.5 x 7.5in, ebonised frame. Andrew Hartley, Ilkley. Apr 05. HP: £340. ABP: £399.

Hammer: £320 - £200

Early 20thC stained glass window panel, depicting a bearded man and two ladies holding two doves in a cage, 110 x 52cm. Sworders, Stansted Mountfitchet. Apr 06. HP: £320. ABP: £376.

Oval Victorian glass painting of flowers, 23in high overall. Sworders, Stansted Mountfitchet. Apr 01. HP: £300. ABP: £352.

19thC stained leaded light glass panel, young lady in a landscape, 83 x 47cm. Henry Adams, Chichester. Jan 03. HP: £300. ABP: £352.

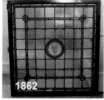

Five mahogany framed leaded stained glass panels (formerly from rear of a window display), each 37 x 36in. Canterbury Auction Galleries, Kent Dec 05. HP: £270. ABP: £317.

Late Victorian stained glass window, central circular portrait and various initials, 21 x 43in. Sworders, Stansted Mountfitchet. Jul 01. HP: £260. ABP: £305.

Four leaded coloured glass panels. Tring Market Auctions, Herts. Oct 04. HP: £260. ABP: £305.

> The illustrations are in descending price order. The price range is indicated at the top of each page.

Georgian reverse painted glass picture, Napoleon in battle and inscribed 'The French Army defeated ..... Buonaparte blowing up the Bridge at Leipsic', painted by W B Walker, Fox & Knot Court, Cow Lane, 10.25 x 14.25in, Hogarth frame. Hartleys, Ilkley. Apr 08. HP: £260. ABP: £305.

Late 19thC stained glass window panel, central panel decorated with the head of a young lady, 109 x 53cm. Sworders, Stansted Mountfitchet. Apr 05. HP: £250. ABP: £294.

Georgian reverse printed glass picture, family in an interior inscribed 'Saturday Night or the Reward of Industry', published London 1805, 10 x 14in, ebonised frame. Andrew Hartley, Ilkley. Jun 05. HP: £250. ABP: £294.

Victorian stained glass panel, incorporating a coat of arms with a cockerel, 52 x 43cm. Charterhouse Auctioneers, Sherborne. Oct 06. HP: £240. ABP: £282.

Stained glass window panel in the manner of Morris & Co, decorated with foliate motifs, later wooden frame, 3ft 8in x 1ft 11in. Gorringes, Lewes. Jul 08. HP: £240. ABP: £282.

Arts & Crafts stained glass panel, representing the four seasons, oak frame, 62.5cm high x 48cm wide. Sworders, Stansted Mountfitchet. Feb 07. HP: £240. ABP: £282.

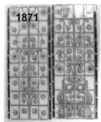

Early 20thC stained glass window panel, in two parts, lead glazed panels decorated in yellow with pair of stylised fish to base, trailing floral design throughout, 12 x 57in. Gorringes, Lewes. Sep 05. HP: £220. ABP: £258.

Four various stained glass panels, 16.5 x 11.5in. Ewbank Auctioneers, Send, Surrey. Dec 05. HP: £210. ABP: £247.

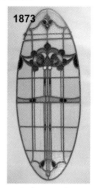

George Walton oval stained glass panel, with stylised floral design, 4ft 11 x 1ft 10in. Gorringes, Lewes. Jul 08. HP: £200. ABP: £235.

A Victorian painted glass panel depicting Queen Elizabeth I, on horseback with attendants, unsigned, 20.25 x 16.5in. Andrew Hartley, Ilkley. Dec 99. HP: £200. ABP: £235.

116   *Glass Prices*

1875

Stained glass mosaic panel, Head No.8, by Anthony Holloway A.R.C.A, c1962, 60 x 60cm, various mosaic glass tiles in colours, with provenance, original catalogue and bill of sale included. Rosebery's, London. Sep 04. HP: £200. ABP: £235.

1876

Stained glass roundel decorated with the crest of the City of Canterbury, 14in dia, and one other stained glass panel with a crest, lion's head and worded 'Lege et Labore', 18 x 15.75in. Canterbury Auction Galleries, Kent. Apr 07. HP: £200. ABP: £235.

1877

Two Victorian lead glass windows, stained armorial inserts and frames, another with Crimean armorial 'Crimea', no frame, 92.5 x 43.5cm. (3) Sworders, Stansted Mountfitchet. Feb 06. HP: £180. ABP: £211.

1878

Stained glass roundel of two Saints, 11.5in dia, edge damaged, need of repair, and 2 other stained glass armorial roundels, each 10in dia. Canterbury Auction Galleries, Kent. Apr 07. HP: £180. ABP: £211.

1879

Mid 19thC cut and etched stained glass portrait panel, possibly depicting Handel, 16 x 12in. Gorringes, Bexhill. Sep 02. HP: £160. ABP: £188.

1880

Pair of early 19thC leaded glass panels, one painted with the man's head wearing a gold brocaded hood the other man with close cropped curly hair wearing a toga, 21cm. Cheffins, Cambridge. Dec 00. HP: £150. ABP: £176.

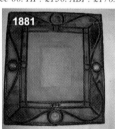

1881

Arts & Crafts leaded glass frame, coloured glass cabochons on a yellow, blue and pink ground, 10.5 x 9in. Hartleys, Ilkley. Feb 08. HP: £100. ABP: £117.

1882

Victorian stained glass roundel, decorated with a portrait bust of Queen Elizabeth I, 14in. Gorringes, Lewes. Sep 03. HP: £90. ABP: £105.

1883

Two stained glass panels, of stylized floral design, largest 20 x 30in. Gorringes, Lewes. Jul 08. HP: £90. ABP: £105.

1884

Leaded glass roundel, bearing date 1600 & painted with St John blessing a chalice and standing in a marbled hall, 23.5cm dia. Cheffins, Cambridge. Dec 00. HP: £80. ABP: £94.

1885

Reverse painted glass armorial panel, French, painted with a lion rampant in a shield, with script on a ribbon 'Essayez', mahogany frame. 38cm dia. Rosebery's, London. Sep 04. HP: £80. ABP: £94.

1886

J. Hombergen,19thC Continental, engraved glass panel decorated in gilt, 'Matin', view of a bull mastiff in a landscape, 8 x 10.5in, moulded ebonised frame. Canterbury Auction Galleries, Kent. Apr 06. HP: £60. ABP: £70.

1887

Three stained glass panels, decorated with coats-of-arms. Gorringes, Bexhill. Oct 05. HP: £60. ABP: £70.

1888

Oak barleytwist fire screen with stained glass centre, 1920s. Black Country Auctions, Dudley. Sep 05. HP: £58. ABP: £68.

1889

19thC glass plaque painted with a portrait of a young lady, 7.5in. Gorringes, Lewes. Apr 02. HP: £50. ABP: £58.

1890

Pair of lancet shaped stained glass leaded windows of multicoloured diamond pattern, 103cm high. (2). Rosebery's, London. May 06. HP: £20. ABP: £23.

Hammer: £3,200 - £880

Mallet shaped glass wine bottle, c1739, olive green metal with seal 'Wm Garnons 1739', applied with string rim. Sotheby's, Billingshurst. Jul 00. HP: £3,200. ABP: £3,764.

Green glass wine bottle, squat onion form, applied circular seal beneath a crown, kick-in base, prob. c1720, 8in high. Hy. Duke & Son, Dorchester. Jul 08. HP: £2,600. ABP: £3,058.

Categories or themes can be followed through the colour coded Index which contains over 4500 cross references.

Onion shaped sealed glass wine bottle, c1710-1720, dark green metal with an unidentified coat of arms, applied string rim. Sotheby's, Billingshurst. Jul 00. HP: £2,100. ABP: £2,470.

George II mallet shape green glass bottle, seal inscribed Wm. Rendal 1739, 7.75in. Gorringes, Lewes. Dec 02. HP: £1,700. ABP: £1,999.

18thC onion shaped wine bottle. Sworders, Stansted Mountfitchet. Nov 00. HP: £1,600. ABP: £1,882.

18thC deep green free blown onion seal bottle, domed base, circular body, low shoulder, tapered neck, ring collar, body detailed with applied lozenge bearing initials 'R.C', damage to neck, 5.5in high. Fieldings, Stourbridge. Oct 05. HP: £1,500. ABP: £1,764.

Mallet shape bottle, dated 1789, high kick in base, string rim, seal inscribed 'I. Chubb 1789', 35cm high. Hampton & Littlewood, Exeter. Jul 04. HP: £920. ABP: £1,082.

Mammoth sealed wine bottle, seal of David Manser, Rye, Sussex, c1780, onion shape, deep green colour, 15in. Gorringes, Lewes. Jun 07. HP: £900. ABP: £1,058.

English green glass seal bottle, early 18thC, onion shape, applied seal depicting bird of prey 20cm high. Halls Fine Art, Shrewsbury. Dec 06. HP: £880. ABP: £1,035.

PART VII: Georgian Wine Bottles

'It took another 1500 years before the bottle as we know it, with its string rim and reinforced lips to facilitate corking, appeared in about 1630.'

The subject of bottle collecting could fill this book. My purpose is to introduce the idea of good utility bottles and for those who might take an interest to focus the mind on the worthwhile in bottle collecting terms and avoid the trap of collecting the dross from the refuse dumps of the Victorian and later period.

As utility serves a much more demanding master than art, thus developed the glass bottle by the core forming technique in about 1500BC. It took until about 50BC before glass blowing was invented, a technique that has remained unchanged to the present. It took another 1500 years before the bottle as we know it, with its string rim and reinforced lips to facilitate corking, appeared in about 1630. By 1632 the shaft and globe had arrived. So began the modern bottle industry in Europe. By 1650 we had produced the first authentic dated seal known which reads 'WE-1650'. The second half of the century saw the development of 'glass of lead' by George Ravenscroft. By 1697 there were 37 bottle houses in England and Wales. Nine were in London, five in Bristol, five in Stourbridge and four in Newcastle. The earliest English bottle (onion) bearing a date was sealed '1702' and the first full provenance of an English onion was sealed 'Ann Tomlinson, the Three Tuns Tavern, Oxford, 1713'. By the 1760s Belgium was producing 1.5 million bottles a year and by 1789 five Bordeaux bottle-houses produced 3.2 million. The standard litre (100cl) was introduced in France in 1793. By 1814 William Hamilton had patented his egg shaped bottle which, by storing on its side kept the cork moist and in 1821 Henry Ricketts of Bristol invented the three part mould. This left the lip of the bottle to be hand tooled. Bottles were still pontilled and hand blown. Hiram T Codd. invented a captive glass marble closure in 1872 and semi automated production evolved in the 1870s. Coca-Cola was first bottled in 1886. The 'crown cork' and 'swing stopper' appeared in 1892 and fully automated production, which included bottle blowing followed. All of the bottles shown are from the Georgian period and are handmade including the Ricketts examples at **1904** and **1905**. These are highly collectible, hence the £500 price tags. The top end of the market is shafts and globes and early seals. This covers the seventeenth century and through to, at the latest 1850. the period where examples are worth collecting.

The bible is *Antique Glass Bottles, Their History and Evolution (1500-1850)* by Willy Van der Bossche, Antique Collectors Club, 2001.

1900

Sealed bottle, dated 1770, large mallet shape, high kick in base, string rim, applied with circular seal, inscribed 'I. Salkeld 1770', 31cm high. Hampton & Littlewood, Exeter. Jul 04. HP: £860. ABP: £1,011.

1901

George I sealed wine bottle, onion shape with basal kick, seal named Welman, dated 1723, 6.75in. (seal chipped) Gorringes, Lewes. Jan 03. HP: £700. ABP: £823.

Prices quoted are actual hammer prices (HP) and the Approximate Buyer's Price (ABP) includes an average premium of 15% + VAT.

1902

Large George III wine bottle, sealed and dated 1786, blown construction in deep-green, seal inscribed H Hopper Esq. 1786, 12in. Gorringes, Lewes. Jun 06. HP: £600. ABP: £705.

1903

Early 18thC sealed wine bottle, 1721, onion shape, string rim & high basal kick, seal with name 'E Herbert' & date, 7.5in. Gorringes, Lewes. Sep 04. HP: £480. ABP: £564.

1904

Ricketts sealed wine bottle, early 19thC, shouldered form, moulded 'patent' on shoulder, on base 'W. Ricketts & Co, Glassworks, Bristol', applied circular seal inscribed 'W. Williams, Surgeon, Llandover', 27.5cm high. Hampton & Littlewood, Exeter. Jul 04. HP: £480. ABP: £564.

1905

Ricketts sealed wine bottle, dated 1771, shouldered form, moulded on shoulder 'patent' and on the base 'H. Ricketts & Co, Glassworks, Bristol', applied circular seal inscribed 'W Leman, Chard, 1771', 24cm high. Hampton & Littlewood, Exeter. Jul 04. HP: £440. ABP: £517.

1906

19thC etched wine bottle, commemorating marriage of John & Margaret Eadie 1851, 27cm high. Great Western Auctions, Glasgow. May 05. HP: £430. ABP: £505.

1907

George I sealed wine bottle, mallet shape, seal named J.Fenn and dated 1725, 7in (reduced) and another onion-shape without seal, 6.25in. Gorringes, Lewes. Jan 03. HP: £400. ABP: £470.

1908

Two large early 19thC Dutch wine bottles, deep green and hand blown, 22.75in. Gorringes, Lewes. Jun 06. HP: £400. ABP: £470.

1909

Seal bottle, English 18th/19thC, shouldered form with initials 'H.C.' beneath a crest in form of an open hand, 26cm, & second seal bottle marked 'SIR WILL STRICKLAND BART 1809.' within circular seal (cracked), 24cm, and a tall necked green glass bottle and 2 bellarmine fragments. Rosebery's, London. Jun 05. HP: £270. ABP: £317.

1910

Late 17th/early 18thC green glass rugby ball bottle with kick up base and pontil scar, 7.5in high. Tring Market Auctions, Herts. Apr 05. HP: £260. ABP: £305.

1911

Mallet shaped green glass seal bottle, second half of the 18thC, mallet shaped body with spreading neck, kick up foot, seal impressed 'I. Watson Efqr. Bilton Park', 22cm high, with two 20thC green glass bottles. (3) Rosebery's, London. Mar 06. HP: £250. ABP: £294.

1912

Two early 19thC chemists shop bottles, one amethyst, indistinct inscription, other green, inscribed on one side 'Berkshire Gem', on the other P:ACACIÆ, tallest 35cm. Sworders, Stansted Mountfitchet. Feb 06. HP: £240. ABP: £282.

1913

Queen Anne onion shape wine bottle, green glass with string rim, high basal kick, 7.5in. Gorringes, Lewes. Apr 06. HP: £190. ABP: £223.

1914

Early 18thC onion shaped green glass wine bottle, kick base, 17cm. Locke & England, Leamington Spa. Jan 03. HP: £130. ABP: £152.

1915

19thC green glass wine bottle, trailed rim, slender neck, cylindrical body, 30cm high with an 18thC green glass spa water flask, 26.5cm high. (2) Cheffins, Cambridge. Apr 05. HP: £100. ABP: £117.

PART VIII:
Georgian Glass

'The tazzas could have a dessert use.....expect anything Irish to be expensive.....this is not a vase, it is a serving bottle.....the 'ships' decanters were more likely to have been engraved for use at the Anchor Inn..... dealers sometimes mistakingly insert stoppers in carafes.....'

Attributing glass to an ill-defined period is not easy. For example the 'Georgian' period is under way during the reign of James II, William and Mary and fully established by Queen Anne. Similarly at the other end of the period William IV glass might also be given a Georgian attribution. Additionally not all auctions have an expert and sometimes descriptions may be optimistic. Working from photographs is also difficult so at times I have used my judgement to include glass that didn't have a Georgian attribution and to exclude glass where the attribution was suspect. Glass, with or without a Georgian attribution may well appear in earlier Sections.

Georgian glass was the wonder of its day and the new lead crystal matched the table silver to perfection. It shimmered in the lights of many candles, adding sophistication to fine dining. Today there are collectors who seek period silver and glass and the other accoutrements of dining and put them to use in their homes. This is entirely what collecting should be about, for what is the point of buying fine period glass or anything else for that matter, and leaving it in a cupboard?

Georgian table centres are rare, hence the price achieved at **1917**. Very few of us will ever be able to afford such a luxury, but the pair of candlesticks at **1920** or the taper at **1927** will certainly come within the range of more collectors. See also **1942, 1949, 1957** and **1980** and note the enhanced values of pairs. The tazzas at **1958** or **1972** could certainly have a dessert use although I wouldn't advise the pyramids of sweetmeats which were a feature of the eighteenth century. Always expect Irish anything to be expensive and glass is no exception, see **1918, 1921, 1922, 1926** and **1931**. Proving an Irish attribution is difficult, as English manufacturers used the same raw materials. A pinch of salt would be appropriate at times when you come across an Irish attribution, otherwise an intense knowledge of Georgian glass might suffice. The attribution of a 'vase' at **1928** is incredibly naive. This is clearly a rare serving bottle of the kind that preceded decanters, and of course it would never have had a stopper. It fetched over a £1,000, much to the auction's surprise and is probably worth more. On the subject of decanters, as with candlesticks, pairs are good, as in the example at **1933**. Regardless of the engraved anchors and the possibility only, that they were used at sea, these more likely were made for an 'Anchor Inn' and are not ship's decanters at all. For similar examples of pairs see also **1935, 1938, 1948** and **1950** etc. Good pairs should always fetch at least £500 but condition is important.

Watch out for ill-fitting stoppers which are unlikely to be original. Related to wine drinking, are Georgian carafes, as decanters were more for spirits. These are rarer and fewer have survived. Sometimes unknowingly dealers add stoppers and present the collector with a bargain. Smaller personal carafes were also used. The examples at **2010** are not 'decanters'. These would also be used to take a nightcap to the bedroom and larger versions were used for water. There is a nice set of four at **1928** which are attributed to the Victorian period. I think they date to 1810-20 and are worth more than the £200 paid. Good Georgian jugs are uncommon because survival would be precarious. Here, apart from **1926**, there are fine examples at **1952**, two for under £300 at **1965**, which is a very good price, and a further example at **1971**, which is good value at £235. One of the nicest here is the late Georgian example at **1989**, which, if in good condition was undersold. This also applies to the silver mounted, fluted ewer at **1991** where I cannot understand the low price unless there are undisclosed faults.

There are other pieces of fine tableware in this Section which may easily be used in dining situations. Browse through the bowls and urns and cruet sets commencing opposite. Note the later silver mounts on the trio of urns at **1924** and the famous Isaac Jacobs of Bristol fame, at **1934**. Silver mounted cruets are, I am afraid, going to set you back £500 at least. See **1943, 1944** and **1954**. The essential element is to ensure the originality of everything in the set. The silver mounted biscuit box at **1939** is a rarity and accordingly fetched more than £600. Similarly a set of four cut boat-shaped salts must have been fought over to achieve the same price. However note the pair at **1987** for a £140. Singles may be bought for about £25 to £50, so where money is tight you could put together a harlequin set. There are some interesting novelties, including the eighteenth century lacemaker's lamp at **1979**. At under £200 this is uncommon enough to have just about been worth the money and would add to the interest in a Georgian setting. The flask at **2003** in the form of bellows is less appealing and at £50 hammer I would have left it alone. There are better ways to spend the money. See also a further lamp at **1993** and a fly trap at **2007**, best displayed in the kitchen!

With Georgian glass, damages, repairs and mis-labelling are worries. Even if in no doubt, ensure that you request the three elements in the invoice, that is the description, the age and condition. After all someone may inherit your glass when you no longer need it!

Gilt bronze/cut glass ceiling light, Regency, c1820, formerly with oil reservoir, 64cm dia. Sotheby's, Billingshurst. Apr 01. HP: £6,400. ABP: £7,528.

Antique facet cut glass table centre piece, central diamond cut glass bowl above eight hanging sweetmeat baskets, 47cm. Stride & Son, Chichester. Jul 03. HP: £5,200. ABP: £6,116.

The numbering system acts as a reader reference as well as linking to the Analysis of each section.

Pair neo-classical cut glass 'Ice' urns and covers, hob-cut decoration, square bases, probably Waterford, c1800, 18in. high. Hy. Duke & Son, Dorchester. Jan 08. HP: £2,800. ABP: £3,293.

Hookah base, Moghul Indian, early 18thC, bell-shape engraved/gilded with sun-bursts and leaf borders, 7.5in. Gorringes, Lewes. Jun 07. HP: £1,700. ABP: £1,999.

Pair of cut glass candlesticks, late 18thC. Sotheby's, Billingshurst. Oct 99. HP: £1,700. ABP: £1,999.

Late Georgian cut/moulded fruit bowl centrepiece, poss. Waterford, 12in wide, 8.5in high. Tring Market Auctions, Herts. May 02. HP: £1,300. ABP: £1,529.

Irish canoe shaped cut glass pedestal bowl, possibly Cork, 35cm wide, c1800, some rim chips. Dreweatt Neate, Newbury. Jun 03. HP: £1,300. ABP: £1,529.

George III silver cruet set, silver mounted spiral cut glass oil/vinegar ewers and central mustard, boat shaped stand with scroll ends, fluted rims, reeded legs, bun feet, Richard Cooke, London 1803, 12.5in. Gorringes, Lewes. Feb 07. HP: £1,300. ABP: £1,529.

Georgian glass hobnail cut candy jar/cover, square foot, later silver mounted by George Fox, London 1898, cover with pineapple finial, 27.5cm with two smaller similar jars and covers, 18cm high. (3) Cheffins, Cambridge. Apr 05. HP: £1,200. ABP: £1,411.

Pair of early 19thC cut glass and ormolu table lustres, 13in. Gorringes, Lewes. Dec 03. HP: £1,200. ABP: £1,411.

Pair of Irish cut glass jugs. George Kidner Auctioneers, Lymington. Jul 05. HP: £1,200. ABP: £1,411.

Taperstick, c1740, octagonal sconce above knop with air tears, moulded pedestal, an annular knop and base knop with air tears, domed/ribbed foot, 6.75in. Gorringes, Lewes. Jun 07. HP: £1,200. ABP: £1,411.

Late Georgian English transparent glass vase, unusually large proportions, 39cm. Rosebery's, London. Jun 08. HP: £880. ABP: £1,035.

Glass ogee shaped bowl, un-dulating rim, cut diamond, facet/diagonal bands, knopped stem, stepped base, 24.8cm, c1810. Dreweatt Neate, Newbury. Apr 00. HP: £820. ABP: £964.

Pair of glass bowls, covers/stands, ovoid knops, cut with diamond/horizontal bands, star cut bases, 20.5cm, c1820. Dreweatt Neate, Newbury. Apr 00. HP: £720. ABP: £846.

Georgian Irish cut glass salad bowl, c1780, knopped stem, square foot, 33cm wide. Rosebery's, London. Dec 03. HP: £700. ABP: £823.

Late 18thC Nailsea flagon spotted/flecked in white, 24cm, and a bottle green flask, white clouded trailed neck, 27cm. (2) Cheffins, Cambridge. Feb 05. HP: £700. ABP: £823.

Pair of glass ships decanters/stoppers, c1800, triple ring necks, engraved swags and anchors, chips, 29cm. (4) Sworders, Stansted Mountfitchet. Feb 05. HP: £680. ABP: £799.

Set of three George III glass decanters by Isaac Jacobs of Bristol, blue glass, pear-shape, gilded with simulated labels for Hollands, Brandy & Rum, signed beneath in gilt, original stoppers, 9.5in. Gorringes, Lewes. Sep 05. HP: £650. ABP: £764.

Hammer: £600 - £380

Pair of George III cut glass decanters, engraved crest, c1780, 31cm high. (possibly Irish) Sworders, Stansted Mountfitchet. Dec 02. HP: £600. ABP: £705.

George III Warwick cruet stand, central spiral turned stem, shell and scroll handle, leaf capped shell feet, floral cartouche engraved with a crest, London 1772 by Thomas Whipham, 28cm dia, 31oz, 4 associated cut glass bottles. Dreweatt Neate, Donnington. Nov 04. HP: £550. ABP: £646.

Facon de Venise flask, late 16thC, flattened spherical body, trailed band to neck, stem with ribbed, hollow knop and folded foot, 10.5in. Gorringes, Lewes. Jun 07. HP: £550. ABP: £646.

Pair of late George III mallet shaped decanters, slice cut necks, cartouches engraved with initials 'J.W.', 8.25in, cut tear shaped stoppers, and a pair Regency black papier-mâché/gilt decorated coasters, 4.5in dia, decanters forced into coasters. Canterbury Auction Galleries, Kent. Jun 07. HP: £520. ABP: £611.

George III silver mounted cut glass biscuit box, later finial and conflicting marks, 6in. Gorringes, Lewes. Jan 03. HP: £520. ABP: £611.

Set of four boat shaped salts, shaped and diamond cut rim above fluted band, lobed oval foot, 7.6cm high. Dreweatt Neate, Newbury. Apr 00. HP: £500. ABP: £588.

George III glass decanter, prob. Irish, prismatic cuts to neck, 3 horizontal bands to body, c1810, stopper odd, 11.5in. Gorringes, Lewes. Apr 05. HP: £500. ABP: £588.

Pair cut glass candlesticks, early 19thC, cut glass drops, baluster shaped column, square canted corner bases, 26.5cm. (2) Sworders, Stansted Mountfitchet. Sep 07. HP: £500. ABP: £588.

George III silver cruet stand, reeded loop handle, 7in wide, five original cut glass cruets, London 1810. Hartleys, Ilkley. Aug 00. HP: £500. ABP: £588.

William IV silver 8 division glass cruet set. Locke & England, Leamington Spa. Mar 02. HP: £500. ABP: £588.

Gilt decorated glass part table service, early 19thC: water jug, jar/cover, footed bowl, 6 beakers and 5 wine glasses, decorated foliate swags, 2 other gilt decorated glass beakers. Rosebery's, London. Mar 06. HP: £480. ABP: £564.

Late 18th/early 19thC mallet shaped decanter engraved swag ornament and 'Claret', 8.5in high, 3 19thC rummers, partly slice cut bodies & cut banding, 5.5in high, 3 Dutch wine glasses, engraved bowls, plain stems, fold-over footrims, 5.75in high. Canterbury Auction Galleries, Kent. Apr 07. HP: £460. ABP: £541.

Set of twelve Bristol green wine flutes. Tring Market Auctions, Herts. Jan 02. HP: £450. ABP: £529.

Pair of George III decanters and stoppers, mallet shapes facetted between triple rings, engraved flowering vines and basal fluting, 25cm high. (W) (4) Cheffins, Cambridge. Apr 05. HP: £440. ABP: £517.

George III candlestick, c1770, ribbed sconce on moulded pedestal stem, shoulder/base knops with air-tears, domed and faceted foot, 8.75in. Gorringes, Lewes. Jun 07. HP: £440. ABP: £517.

Pair of heraldic decanters, Silesian, c1770, mallet shape, fluted/gilded necks, engraved with armorial crests, possibly Von Moltke, gilded/faceted stoppers, 11.5in. Gorringes, Lewes. Jun 07. HP: £440. ABP: £517.

Early 19thC Irish (Cork) glass decanter, mallet shape, finger-rings, engraved with leaf garlands/ribbons, bull's-eye stopper, c1810, 11.5in. Gorringes, Lewes. Dec 07. HP: £400. ABP: £470.

Early 19thC water jug, panel cut body, engraved fruiting vines, 9in, & pair of matching glasses, faceted knopped stems, star cut bases, 6.25in. Canterbury Auction Galleries. Feb 07. HP: £400. ABP: £470.

Set of 3 early 19thC 'Bristol Blue' barrel shaped decanters labelled in gilt, Rum, Brandy and Hollands, 6.5in high. Canterbury Auction Galleries. Aug 02. HP: £380. ABP: £446.

1954

George IV silver cruet set, six cut glass cruets, 8in wide, London 1823. Andrew Hartley, Ilkley. Apr 01. HP: £340. ABP: £399.

1955

18thC onion bottle vase in deep celadon blue. Great Western Auctions, Glasgow. May 08. HP: £330. ABP: £388.

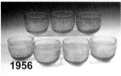

1956

Seventeen 19thC clear glass rinsers, hobnail cut bands, star cut bases, each 12cm dia. (17) Sworders, Stansted Mountfitchet. Feb 05. HP: £320. ABP: £376.

1957

George III glass candlestick, late 18thC, dome holder above triple knopped faceted stem, domed foot, 20cm high. Rosebery's, London. Mar 08. HP: £300. ABP: £352.

1958

Glass tazza, short turned up rim, octagonal moulded stem, 2nd half 18thC, 20.5cm. Woolley & Wallis, Salisbury. Mar 00. HP: £300. ABP: £352.

1959

Set of 3 'Bristol' blue glass decanters, gilded labels for Brandy, Rum and Hollands, gilded stoppers, and set of 6 blue glasses, knopped stems, decanters 8.75in. Gorringes, Lewes. Oct 04. HP: £280. ABP: £329.

1960

Continental glass flask, pewter screw top, painted with gentleman raising his glass, incised verso, 19thC, 7.75in high. Hartleys, Ilkley. Jun 06. HP: £270. ABP: £317.

The illustrations are in descending price order. The price range is indicated at the top of each page.

1961

Georgian Irish glass fruit bowl, c1780, strawberry cut banding, fluted rim, 23cm high. Rosebery's, London. Sep 03. HP: £260. ABP: £305.

1962

Set of 4 19thC Bristol blue square glass decanters and stoppers marked Rum, Brandy and Hollands. Denhams, Warnham. Oct 04. HP: £260. ABP: £305.

1963

George III oval glass pedestal bowl, scalloped rim, cut detail, square base, probably Irish, 9in long, base chipped. Gorringes, Lewes. Apr 02. HP: £260. ABP: £305.

Hammer: £340 - £190

1964

Three bottle cruet, English early 19thC, amber glass, each with applied gilt label for rum, brandy & hollands, each with foliate border and chain motif, brass bound ebonised wood frame, brass mounts, 40cm high. Rosebery's, London. Jun 05. HP: £260. ABP: £305.

1965

Two early 19thC cut glass jugs, one of baluster shape, diamond cut band, 18cm, and other with bellied cylindrical, ribbed body, 18.5cm. (W) (2) Cheffins, Cambridge. Apr 05. HP: £250. ABP: £294.

1966

Set of six Continental glass decanters, early 19thC, square section, domed shoulders, wheel cut decoration, 26cm, matching set of 5 smaller decanters, 19cm, and a set of eleven wine labels, unmarked Continental silver. (22) Rosebery's, London. Jun 08. HP: £250. ABP: £294.

1967

Georgian mallet shaped stooper & dish poss. Irish, floral sprays beneath a triple ring of oval flutes, slice cut lozenge stopper, 29cm, and 19thC oval footed fruit bowl, probably Irish, cut diamond/geometric decoration, 25cm long. Hampton & Littlewood, Exeter. Jul 04. HP: £240. ABP: £282.

1968

Late 18thC preserve jar and cover engraved with swags between fluting, square lemon squeezer foot, 29cm high. (2) Cheffins, Cambridge. Apr 05. HP: £240. ABP: £282.

1969

Pair Georgian mallet shaped decanters/stoppers, c1800, triple ring necks, bullseye stoppers, 18.5cm high. Rosebery's, London. Sep 03. HP: £230. ABP: £270.

1970

Geo. III Irish glass decanter, twin neck rings, engraved with ribbon drapes/flowers, bull's eye stopper, 11.5in. Gorringes, Lewes. Dec 06. HP: £220. ABP: £258.

1971

Cut glass jug, Irish early 19thC, shaped/scalloped rim, fluted neck, body cut alternate bands of diamonds, horizontal fluting, 19cm high. Rosebery's, London. Jun 05. HP: £200. ABP: £235.

1972

18thC glass tazza, raised rim, moulded pedestal stem, folded foot, c1760, 13.25in. Gorringes, Lewes. Jan 05. HP: £190. ABP: £223.

Hammer: £190 - £100

Pair of 'Bristol' blue glass sauce bottles and stoppers, inscribed 'Cayenne' & 'Soy' within gilt simulated labels, 12.5cm. Phillips, Bath. May 00. HP: £190. ABP: £223.

Early 19thC Bristol blue glass bottle, 10.5in high, Bristol blue glass finger bowl, 4.25in dia and a squat Bristol blue bottle, raised collar, stopper, 6in high. (3) Dee, Atkinson & Harrison, Driffield. Nov 05. HP: £190. ABP: £223.

Categories or themes can be followed through the colour coded Index which contains over 4500 cross references.

19thC Venetian glass milk jug with spiralling opaque threads and blue rim, 4in. Gorringes, Lewes. Oct 00. HP: £180. ABP: £211.

Silesian engraved glass bottle, early 18thC, faceted pear form engraved with figure of hope & wounded stag, scroll/strapwork borders, later stopper, 11cm. Rosebery's, London. Dec 04. HP: £180. ABP: £211.

Pair of Georgian three ring facet cut decanters, circular 'bull's eye' stoppers, 12in high overall. Tring Market Auctions, Herts. Jul 04. HP: £180. ABP: £211.

Set of four Victorian glass carafes, bulbous shape cut with diamond bands, 7.5in. Gorringes, Lewes. Jul 04. HP: £170. ABP: £199.

18thC 'Lace Maker's' lamp, circular font & drip catcher, blown stem, 10.75in high. Tring Market Auctions, Herts. Apr 05. HP: £170. ABP: £199.

18thC Irish pillar glass candlestick, facet cut stem & domed foot, shaped rim, 11.5in, chipped, and two other heavy slice cut pillar candlesticks, 9in & 8.5in. Canterbury Auction Galleries, Kent. Mar 05. HP: £170. ABP: £199.

George III glass carafe, cut fish scale neck and engraved floral drapes, 7.75in, and a George III drinking glass, wrythen bowl, folded foot, 4in. Gorringes, Lewes. Jul 04. HP: £170. ABP: £199.

One of pair of late Georgian glass oval baskets, 9.5 x 6.75 x 4.75in high, & one matching stand, 11.5 x 7.75in, chips/ flakes to rim. Canterbury Auction Galleries, Kent. Aug 02. HP: £140. ABP: £164.

Early 19thC glass bowl, foot with unground pontil, body etched with a fly fisherman in a landscape, 23cm high. Thos Mawer & Son, Lincoln. Sep 04. HP: £140. ABP: £164.

Two central European milchglas items, one a cylindrical tankard, 17cm, other a canted rectangular section flask, 13cm. Woolley & Wallis, Salisbury. Mar 00. HP: £130. ABP: £152.

Pair club-shaped decanters, mushroom stoppers, engraved with initials GFA and floral garlands, between bands of flutes, 21cm high, c1825. Dreweatt Neate, Donnington. Nov 02. HP: £130. ABP: £152.

Late Georgian circular bowl, cut serrated rim, panel cut body and star cut octagonal base, 4in high, similar sweetmeat jar, steeple cover, 12in high, late Georgian panel cut glass jug, 5.5in high and two plates with cut serrated rims, 7in, all chipped. Canterbury Auction Galleries, Kent. Apr 05. HP: £120. ABP: £141.

Pair of Late George III cut glass boat shaped salts, pedestal stems, 3in high. Gorringes, Lewes. Mar 04. HP: £120. ABP: £141.

Early 19thC jug, baluster shape facetted at its base, petal foot, 19.5cm high. (W) Cheffins, Cambridge. Apr 05. HP: £120. ABP: £141.

Late Georgian water jug, prismatic/diamond cutting, 7.5in. Gorringes, Lewes. Jul 03. HP: £120. ABP: £141.

Geo. III blown glass decanter/ stopper, 3 neck rings, with two cut glass rummers, each with a band of small diamond cutting and fluting. Decanter 24cm. Rosebery's, London. Apr 05. HP: £120. ABP: £141.

George III silver mounted fluted glass ewer, reeded handle, unmarked, 8.25in. Gorringes, Lewes. Apr 08. HP: £100. ABP: £117.

Early 19thC cut and moulded glass fruit bowl, strawberry cut band, plain column and spreading star cut base, 8in dia, 5.25in high. Tring Market Auctions, Herts. May 02. HP: £100. ABP: £117.

Georgian lace maker's lamp, loop handle, baluster stem and dished base, 5.25in high. Hartleys, Ilkley. Dec 06. HP: £100. ABP: £117.

Early 19thC green glass carafe, mallet shape, 3 ringed neck, 22.5cm high & an early 19thC decanter/stopper, clear glass body cut with diamond band, ringed neck, 25cm high. (3) Cheffins, Cambridge. Apr 05. HP: £100. ABP: £117.

Early 19thC Bristol blue coloured sugar bowl, plain stem, domed circular foot, gilded with the inscription 'Be Canny with the Sugar', (possibly Yarmouth), 4.5in high. Dee, Atkinson & Harrison, Driffield. Feb 06. HP: £95. ABP: £111.

George III ring necked decanter, target-shaped stopper, 27cm. Reeman Dansie, Colchester. Apr 06. HP: £85. ABP: £99.

Heavy cut crystal elliptical footed bowl, hobnail cut, 7in high. Golding Young & Co, Grantham. Feb 06. HP: £85. ABP: £99.

Early 19thC single decanter, three ring neck, kick in base, blown ball stopper, 8in high overall. Tring Market Auctions, Herts. Sep 02. HP: £75. ABP: £88.

Glass vase, hobnail-cut, turn-over rim, knopped pedestal stem, 8.5in. Gorringes, Lewes. Jul 04. HP: £75. ABP: £88.

Early 19thC Cork 'pilgrim bottle' decanter cut with shallow oval facets, domed circular facet cut foot, flat disk stopper, small chip to underside of foot rim, 13in high overall. Tring Market Auctions, Herts. Jul 04. HP: £65. ABP: £76.

English cut glass bowl, roll top rim cut with flowers and foliage, 2 bands of geometric decoration, octagonal faceted stem, square base, 18cm high. Rosebery's, London. Jan 08. HP: £65. ABP: £76.

Hammer: £100 - £30

Late Georgian heavy slice cut mallet shaped claret jug, deep cut loop handle, moulded base, 10.25in high, hexagonal cut stopper, and heavy slice, panel/diamond cut waisted vase, shaped rim, 10.5in. Canterbury Auction Galleries. Jun 07. HP: £50. ABP: £58.

Georgian footed glass flask, applied glass decoration, etched with floral & foliate design & initials. Great Western Auctions, Glasgow. Mar 08. HP: £50. ABP: £58.

Prices quoted are actual hammer prices (HP) and the Approximate Buyer's Price (ABP) includes an average premium of 15% + VAT.

Cut glass pepper, diamond cut body, 10cm and a cylindrical glass bottle, mushroom stopper, panel cut sides, 18cm. Woolley & Wallis, Salisbury. Sep 00. HP: £50. ABP: £58.

Late Regency heavy cut glass claret jug, faceted mushroom stopper, slice cutting to neck, star cut base, 11.5in high. Kent Auction Galleries, Folkestone. Mar 06. HP: £45. ABP: £52.

19thC soda glass jug, applied trailing to rim, strawberry prunt to handle, engraved longboat to body, 8.25in. Gorringes, Lewes. Jan 05. HP: £45. ABP: £52.

Fly or wasp bottle trap. Black Country Auctions, Dudley. Sep 05. HP: £44. ABP: £51.

Three cut glass decanters and stoppers in a distressed walnut box. Ewbank Auctioneers, Send, Surrey. Dec 05. HP: £40. ABP: £47.

Early 19thC blue glass flagon, metal mounts, 21cm. Boldon Auction Galleries, Tyne & Wear. Sep 04. HP: £35. ABP: £41.

Pair late Georgian decanters, split cut bands and facet cut shoulders, three ring necks, 5.25in high, one with slight rim chip. Tring Market Auctions, Herts. May 02. HP: £30. ABP: £35.

PART IX:
Georgian Drinking Glasses

'By about 1690 lead glass was being widely used, fashion finally turning away from Venice. The different handling properties of lead glass brought it to the tables and the taverns of England, an ever-increasing market promoting a truly English style, now known as Georgian glass.'

A Brief History of Glass

Glass is eminently functional and remains one of the few materials unsuperseded. When molten it may be manipulated, when cool subjected to any process. Such a nature offers considerable aesthetic potency. In its natural state it exists as obsidian, a dark vitreous lava, or as rock crystal, a form of quartz. In manufacture it is made from various forms of silica. In practice fluxes of carbonate of potash, from burnt vegetation or carbonate of soda from minerals were added. Generally potash glass was manufactured in Northern Europe where there were abundant forests. Potash glass has a greenish tint. Soda glass usually came from the Mediterranean, for example Venetian, a clear glass called *cristallo*. The manufacture began in the Middle East over 3,500 years ago. All the basic manufacturing techniques have been in existence since then with the exception of blowing, which appears to have been invented in Syria c50BC.

Glass in England

The earliest manufacture can be traced to French immigrants starting with *Lawrence Vitrearius* in 1226 at Chiddingfold. Production up to the fifteenth century was of window glass for churches/monasteries with some glass for medical use. In 1567 *John Le Carré*, a gentleman glassmaker, arrived in London. He obtained a license to make the Venetian *cristallo*, popular amongst the nobility. After his death in 1572 his glassmaker *Jacob Verzelini* revived the patent and established quality glassmaking in England. He is buried in Downes Church in Kent. Glassmaking spread north and west. By 1615 *Sir Robert Mansell* had gained control of the patent. He made *crystall* in the *façon de Venise* using soda from barilla imported since Le Carré's days. Under Mansell the industry became structured. He offered licenses based on loyalties and market restrictions. Now with coal-fired furnaces, production settled into areas where fuel was available and the sea offered cheap transport to the markets for the finished products, namely London, Bristol and Newcastle. The retailers began to organise themselves, gaining a Charter in 1635 for the incorporation of the Glass Sellers Company, a Guild in 1664. Glasses bearing engravings with English names and dates are attributable to the Verzelini period but none to Mansell. Hence they are known as *façon de Venise*; that is a Northern European style derived from Venice. Earlier in 1612 *Antonio Neri* had published his treatise *L'Arte Vitrearia*. Its translation into English in 1662 by *Dr Christopher Merrett*, was significant for the

history of English glass. From the 1670s the term *flint* appears. Merrett's translation mentions *flint* as being associated with an 'incomparable pure and white crystal metal'. Flint was the term used to describe Ravenscroft's new 'glass of lead' resembling 'rock crystall' and perfected by 1676, the most important development in the history of English glassmaking. Calcined flint was used as an alternative form of silica to Spanish barilla. As lead oxide was a commercial secret, Ravenscroft's new glass could be described as improved flint.

The benefits were a glass of greater transparency, whiter colour and greater refractive properties than the Venetian *cristallo*. Now, glass of considerable thickness could be made which retained the transparency of the thinly blown *cristallo*, and its softness was an attraction for the decorators. By about 1690 lead glass was being widely used, fashion finally turning away from Venice. The different handling properties of lead glass brought it to the tables and the taverns of England, an ever-increasing market promoting a truly English style, in antique terms now known as Georgian glass.

Summary of Types

After Ravenscroft's 'glass of lead' the last 30 years of the seventeenth century, saw an English style develop, particularly after 1685 through to 1710 characterised by the heavy baluster. These glasses rarely fetch less than £1,000 and often much more. The period from 1710-15 to about 1750 is that of lighter glasses called balusters which copied all of the complex stem formations of the heavy balusters, followed by the balustroids, typified by kit kat glasses which always included a baluster in the stem. The latter part of this period saw moulded pedestal stems and two and three-piece plain stemmed glasses.

Air twist and incised twist stems follow from the 1740s to 1760s which also saw composite stems introduced. Opaque twists follow from c1755-1780 with mixed and colour twist stems produced during this period. Most Georgian drinking glasses sell in the hundreds of pounds. Colour twists fetch thousands of pounds. Glasses engraved with the symbolism of the Scottish Jacobite movement are also desirable. The most expensive glasses of all are usually enamelled and traceable to the Beilby output of Newcastle upon Tyne. Faceted stems follow from about 1770-1800. The early nineteenth sees only rudimentary stems including the common rummer, except for the reproductions of earlier stemmed glasses. By about 1830 the greatest period in the history of English glass was coming to an end.

Georgian Drinking Glasses
A Market Survey

'These glasses are wines, not ales.....after the eighteenth century exhausted their stem varieties.....these become fakes when sold as genuine .....94% of eighteenth century 'Jacobites' have later engraving.....the makeover was so good, the auction had no chance of spotting the deception.....'

Here are 355 lots making this the most extensive market survey in print. The quantity reflects the needs for a large sample. Analysis will raise important issues. Any readers interested should buy the bible, L M Bickerton's *Eighteenth Century English Drinking glasses*, by the Antique Collector's Club. The original work was 1971 and the latest reprint was in 2000. In this monograph readers will find 1,200 illustrations, with the types, the bowls, stems and feet identified. Its importance cannot be overstated.

Descriptive errors are common. Whilst the various names that attach to bowl capacities can never be a science the guidelines and the tradition are clear. The glasses at **2031** are wines and not ales, which are flute shaped. These are in fact decorated with grapes, which seems to have escaped the notice of the auction. Ales are frequently engraved with hops and barley, if not always contemporaneously! See **228**. Wines, which are the most common Georgian drinking glass, often pose as cordials, one of the periods rarest glasses, whose capacity should be no more than one ounce. See **2040** for a good example and **2178** for a misdescribed lot. See also the *Glossary of Terms*. The pair of glasses at **2167** are wines and not cordials. Note also that true cordials are worth a lot of money and at least £500 to £800 is not unusual. Rummers and goblets are also, if not exactly misdescribed (because even Bickerton plays fast and loose with these two terms) a confusing area. Goblets on long stems that are clearly eighteenth century, are not an issue. See **2037** and **2070**, which has been misdescribed as a wine. True goblets are also expensive, from £500 upwards at least in today's market; they are ideal for wine drinking which adds to their appeal. However, after about 1790, along came rummers, a large capacity, short-stemmed glass, which was used for rum-grog concoctions. There are three examples in the foreground of **2301**. These are what most experts would designate as rummers. Their bowls, with the characteristic double ogee S-shape are well known. However the eighteenth century, having exhausted stem varieties, continued to produce goblet-sized capacities with old goblet shaped bowls and there lies the confusion. Check out **2041**, **2049**, **2069**, **2111**, **2132** and **2184** and see what I mean. Whilst the rummer/goblet debate isn't solved by Bickerton and, as in general, prices would normally be unaffected by the issue, for practical purposes, the argument may remain academic. As far as I am aware this is the first time it has been aired in public.

A further concern is the need to be able to distinguish between lead crystal and the much lighter soda glass. Holding the foot and tapping the bowl should produce the characteristic ring where this is appropriate. If you get it wrong you could end up paying about twice as much at least, as the glass is worth.

The more important issues today are the reproductions and fakes, and those insidious glasses altered to deceive. If a Dutch engraved and valuable Newcastle baluster, has a minute rim chip sensitively ground, then repolished, this is acceptable. Indeed at the lower end this can not be censured. However let us examine some of the more contentious fakes in the market. At the milder end there are plenty of reproduction rummers around and it doesn't take long before they get misdescribed. Similarly eighteenth century glasses have also been reproduced throughout the twentieth century and it is clear these become fakes when sold as genuine glasses. Even more insidious, genuine period glasses, with ground bowls and feet are common, with no mention of 'restoration'. A worrying fact, which has been with us for years is later or modern engraving on genuine period glasses. Where serious money can be made by forgers is the Jacobite market. 94% of genuine period glasses, often described in euphemistic terms, as of Jacobite significance, have been engraved at a later date. Despite this the market accepts their presence, but at the serious money end, never buy a Jacobite unless it comes with credentials, unless you're the expert. A growing worry are glasses that are made from genuine period glass and genuine bowls, stems and feet, but where the three parts of the glass never began life together. They have been married by trade restorers and are now finding their way onto the market as original. As these have been hot-metalled and reworked, I have noticed wear, apparent on all genuine glasses, is missing and I have seen some quite incongruous matching of parts that would never have been put together in the eighteenth century. Again, there is nothing wrong with the practice in the interests of restoration but it is obvious that motives are not always entirely honest. I viewed a sale where upwards of thirty glasses bore the characteristics of a makeover and were so good that the auction had no chance of spotting the deception. Many collectors feel competent about buying from all sources but there are dangers. Even if you have this confidence, if you are buying at the serious end of the market, such as heavy balusters, buy from specialists who will guarantee their authenticity.

Hammer: £10,000 - £980

Facon de Venise goblet, honey-comb moulded knop, flared folded foot, probabl. Hall in Tyrol, 2nd half 16thC, 21.5cm high, 13.5cm wide. Woolley & Wallis, Salisbury. May 02. HP: £10,000. ABP: £11,762.

Early 18thC glass, central European screw goblet/cover, engraved with 6 oval scenes in German wishing success to their new Queen, 43.5cm. Cheffins, Cambridge. Mar 01. HP: £3,600. ABP: £4,234.

Deceptive Jacobite cordial glass, c1750, 3-piece glass, bowl engraved with rose and single bud, double-series air-twist stem, spiral column & four threads, conical foot, 6.75in. Gorringes, Lewes. Jun 07. HP: £3,400. ABP: £3,999.

Knopped wine glass, c1755, flared bucket bowl, air-twist stem,5 knops, conical foot, 6.5in. Gorringes, Lewes. Jun 07. HP: £3,100. ABP: £3,646.

Colour twist wine glass, bell bowl, shouldered knop stem, opaque corkscrew spiral, purple edged, conical foot, 17cm high, c1770, footrim polished.) Dreweatt Neate, Newbury. Jun 01. HP: £2,500. ABP: £2,940.

Rare tartan-twist wine glass, 3 colours, c1770, bell bowl above stem with shoulder & centre knops, central gauze encircled by red, blue and green spiral canes, 6.75in. Gorringes, Lewes. Jun 07. HP: £2,300. ABP: £2,705.

Pair air twist wine glasses, c1770, each ogee bowl with spiral rib moulding, alternating engraved flower and insect panels, single opaque spiral stems, moulded panel conical feet, 15cm. Sworders, Stansted Mountfitchet. Jul 05. HP: £1,900. ABP: £2,234.

Dutch-engraved goblet, bobbin knopped stem, bead inclusions, conical foot, 19cm, c1750, minute foot rim chip. Dreweatt Neate, Newbury. Jun 02. HP: £1,850. ABP: £2,176.

German enamelled glass Reichsadlerhumpen, dated 1700. 21cm, poss. Franconian. Mellors & Kirk, Nottingham. Apr 03. HP: £1,600. ABP: £1,882.

Ceremonial goblet/cover, rare with homosexual significance, Thuringian, c1730, bowl engraved 3 cartouches, embracing David & Jonathon, goblet on table and heart on pedestal, and script, knopped moulded pedestal stem, engraved/folded foot, cover with moulded handle, 12.5in. Gorringes, Lewes. Jun 07. HP: £1,500. ABP: £1,764.

Large Dutch engraved wine glass, mid 18thC. Sotheby's, Billingshurst. Oct 99. HP: £1,250. ABP: £1,470.

Goblet, engraving attributed to Elias Rosbach, Potsdam, Germany, c1725, design of dancing putti, knopped stem, conical foot engraved a stiff leaf border, 8.5in, some crizzling. Gorringes, Lewes. Jun 07. HP: £1,200. ABP: £1,411.

Opaque-twist wine glass, c1760, round funnel bowl, lower half wrythen/moulded with a trellis design, double-series opaque-twist stem, conical foot, 6.25in, foot chipped. Gorringes, Lewes. Jun 07. HP: £1,200. ABP: £1,411.

Pair of engraved airtwist wine glasses, bucket bowls engraved & polished with fruiting vine, double knopped stems filled spiral threads, conical feet, 19.5cm, c1770, one with footrim chip. Dreweatt Neate, Newbury. Jun 01. HP: £1,050. ABP: £1,235.

Rare colour-twist wine glass, c1765, ogee bowl, double-series colour-twist, two red/white spiral canes around central white gauze, conical foot, 5.75in. Gorringes, Lewes. Jun 07. HP: £1,000. ABP: £1,176.

Engraved opaque twist wine or cordial glass, ogee bowl, sprays of stylised flowers/foliage, double series stem, domed foot, 17cm, c1770. Dreweatt Neate, Newbury. Jun 01. HP: £980. ABP: £1,152.

2027

Glass goblet, engraved bowl, double opaque twist stem, 9in. Gorringes, Lewes. Dec 00. HP: £980. ABP: £1,152.

2028

Baluster goblet, funnel bowl with solid lower section on a swelling knopped stem with basal knop, enclosing 2 tears, folded conical foot, 17cm high, c1715, paper label for Churchill Glass. Dreweatt Neate, Newbury. Jun 01. HP: £950. ABP: £1,117.

The numbering system acts as a reader reference as well as linking to the Analysis of each section.

2029

Deceptive wine glass, c1740, conical bowl, broad knop with air tear, folded foot, 5in. Gorringes, Lewes. Jun 07. HP: £950. ABP: £1,117.

2030

Cordial glass, c1750, trumpet bowl, high shoulder knop, fine, single series opaque-twist stem, conical foot, 6in. Gorringes, Lewes. Jun 07. HP: £950. ABP: £1,117.

2031

Set of ten 18thC ale glasses, bell-shaped bowls, wheel engraved with butterflies, double series opaque twist stems and two similar ales engraved with birds and grapes. Edgar Horn, Eastbourne. Nov 99. HP: £900. ABP: £1,058.

2032

Tumbler, finely engraved with Masonic devices, with monogram CD within a leaf scroll cartouche, 9cm high, c1820, contemporary leather case. Dreweatt Neate, Newbury. Apr 00. HP: £850. ABP: £999.

2033

18thC cordial glass, white enamelled floral swag bowl, opaque twist stem. Gorringes, Lewes. Jul 00. HP: £850. ABP: £999.

2034

Mixed-twist wine glass, c1765, ogee bowl engraved with flowers/leaves, lower section wrythen-moulded, stem with central air-twist cable and double-series opaque-twists, conical foot, 6in. Gorringes, Lewes. Jun 07. HP: £850. ABP: £999.

Hammer: £980 - £680

2035

Sweetmeat glass, c1740, ribbed, double ogee bowl with flared rim, air-twist stem with applied ring collar, on wrythen, domed foot, 5.75in, foot chipped. Gorringes, Lewes. Jun 07. HP: £850. ABP: £999.

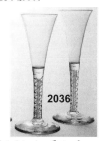

2036

Airtwist wine flute, drawn trumpet bowl, double series stem, conical foot, 20cm high, footrim chip, and another similar, 19.5cm high, c1750. Dreweatt Neate, Newbury. Jun 01. HP: £800. ABP: £941.

2037

Wine goblet, George II, c1750, ogee bowl, double-series air-twist stem, conical foot, 8.5in. Gorringes, Lewes. Jun 07. HP: £800. ABP: £941.

2038

Pair of opaque twist wine glasses, c1765. Sotheby's, Billingshurst. Oct 99. HP: £780. ABP: £917.

2039

Dutch baluster stem goblet, c1750, trumpet shaped bowl engraved with huntsman and hounds, twin baluster stem, spreading foot, 18cm high. Rosebery's, London. Mar 06. HP: £750. ABP: £882.

2040

Opaque-twist cordial glass, c1760, round funnel bowl, stem with central gauze and cotton-twist spiral, conical foot, 6.5in. Gorringes, Lewes. Jun 07. HP: £750. ABP: £882.

2041

Pair heavy cut glass goblets, engraved within a crowned shield Richard Scott 1844, other Elizabeth Scott 1849, both engraved with Masonic symbols, 5.75in high. Wallis & Wallis, Lewes. May 02. HP: £750. ABP: £882.

2042

Airtwist cordial glass, solid lower section, engraved with flowers, inscribed Jap(?) Johnson, double series mercury twist stem, spiral cables outside central column, conical foot, 16.5cm, c1760. Dreweatt Neate, Newbury. Jun 01. HP: £680. ABP: £799.

Hammer: £650 - £540

Baluster wine glass, c1730. Sotheby's, Billingshurst. Oct 99. HP: £650. ABP: £764.

Jacobite-type airtwist wine glass, mid 18thC. Sotheby's, Billingshurst. Oct 99. HP: £650. ABP: £764.

Jacobite wine glass, ogee shaped bowl engraved with a rose, two buds and leaves, multi-opaque spiral twist stem, with two tapes outside gauze, 14.5cm high, c1770. Dreweatt Neate, Newbury. Apr 00. HP: £650. ABP: £764.

Wine glass, pointed funnel shaped bowl, multi-spiral air twist stem, shoulder and domed foot, 16.5cm high, c1750. Dreweatt Neate, Newbury. Apr 00. HP: £650. ABP: £764.

Mixed twist wine glass, round funnel bowl, stem with an entwined opaque tape and an airtwist gauze cable, conical foot, 15.5cm high, c1770. Dreweatt Neate, Newbury. Jun 01. HP: £650. ABP: £764.

George II, rare mammoth ale glass, c1750, large capacity bowl, double-cable air-twist stem, 19in. Gorringes, Lewes. Jun 07. HP: £650. ABP: £764.

Early 19thC armorial goblet, partly diamond cut body, short knopped stem, star cut base, rim engraved fruiting vines and a coat of arms, thought to be of the Duke of Stirling, initial 'M' in oval cartouche, 8.75in x 6in dia. Canterbury Auction Galleries, Kent. Feb 07. HP: £620. ABP: £729.

Large glass hunting goblet, with inscription, 19thC, 27.5cm. Woolley & Wallis, Salisbury. Sep 00. HP: £620. ABP: £729.

Wine glass, pointed round funnel shaped bowl, multi-opaque spiral twist stem, two tapes outside a cable, 16cm high, c1770, and 2 other wine glasses, opaque twist stems. Dreweatt Neate, Newbury. Apr 00. HP: £600. ABP: £705.

Pair of engraved glasses, English 18thC, each ogee bowl engraved with chino-iserie figures in a landscape, opaque twist stems, 14cm. Rosebery's, London. Jun 05. HP: £600. ABP: £705.

The illustrations are in descending price order. The price range is indicated at the top of each page.

Wine glass, bell shaped bowl on stem with shoulder, central and basal knops, folded foot, 16.5cm high, c1750, another with trumpet shaped bowl, annular shoulder knop, folded foot, 15.2cm, c1750. Dreweatt Neate, Newbury. Apr 00. HP: £580. ABP: £682.

Pair of airtwist ale glasses, c1750. Sotheby's, Billingshurst. Oct 99. HP: £550. ABP: £646.

Wine glass, flared bucket shaped bowl engraved with a vine band, multi-spiral air twist stem, shoulder knop, 16cm high, c1755. Dreweatt Neate, Newbury. Apr 00. HP: £550. ABP: £646.

Cordial glass, pan topped bowl engraved with vine band, plain multi-spiral air twist stem, 12.8cm high, c1750. Dreweatt Neate, Newbury. Apr 00. HP: £550. ABP: £646.

Opaque twist cordial glass, c1770, perhaps of Jacobite significance, bowl engraved with moth/rosebud, double series stem, conical foot, 16cm, small foot-rim chip. Dreweatt Neate, Newbury. Jun 01. HP: £550. ABP: £646.

Wine glass, Jacobite design, engraved bell bowl, multi spiral airtwist double knopped stem, high conical foot, 7.25in high. Dee, Atkinson & Harrison, Driffield. Nov 01. HP: £540. ABP: £635.

Wine glass, bell shaped bowl, solid base with a tear, teared knop above a basal knop, folded foot, 16cm high, c1740. Dreweatt Neate, Newbury. Apr 00. HP: £520. ABP: £611.

Wine flute glass, trumpet shaped bowl, multi-spiral opaque corkscrew stem, 17.5cm high, c1770. Dreweatt Neate, Newbury. Apr 00. HP: £520. ABP: £611.

Balustroid wine glass, bell bowl, annular knop, baluster stem with tear inclusion and small basal knop, domed and folded foot, 16cm high, c1740. Dreweatt Neate, Newbury. Jun 01. HP: £520. ABP: £611.

Opaque twist punch glass, round bowl with everted rim, applied with auricular handle, stem with pair of spiral threads, 11.5cm, c1770. Dreweatt Neate, Newbury. Jun 01. HP: £520. ABP: £611.

Wine glass, c1730, drawn type with trumpet bowl, elongated air tear above annular knop and domed foot, 6.5in. Gorringes, Lewes. Jun 07. HP: £520. ABP: £611.

Wine glass, drawn trumpet shaped bowl, stem with tear knop, folded foot, 17.2cm, c1750. Dreweatt Neate, Newbury. Apr 00. HP: £500. ABP: £588.

Balustroid wine glass, bell bowl, solid lower section, tear inclusion pulled through into the baluster stem, basal knop, 15.5cm high, c1735. Dreweatt Neate, Newbury. Jun 01. HP: £500. ABP: £588.

Wine glass, bell shaped bowl, stem with shoulder and basal knops, folded foot, 14.5cm high, c1740, another with pointed round funnel shaped bowl, tear stem with shoulder, annular and basal knops, folded foot, 15.2cm, c1730. Dreweatt Neate, Newbury. Apr 00. HP: £480. ABP: £564.

Wine glass with round funnel shaped bowl, opaque 'corkscrew' stem and round foot, 16cm high, c1765. Dreweatt Neate, Newbury. Apr 00. HP: £480. ABP: £564.

Mid 18thC wine glass, bell shaped bowl finely engraved with a wide band of fruiting vines, plain stem, 2 ball knops, domed footrim with open pontil, 6.5in, c1750. Canterbury Auction Galleries. Aug 00. HP: £460. ABP: £541.

Large engraved rummer, 19thC. Sotheby's, Billingshurst. Oct 99. HP: £450. ABP: £529.

Wine glass, large ogee shaped bowl engraved with vines/leaves, multi-opaque spiral twist stem, ply bands outside spiral threads, 18.5cm high. Dreweatt Neate, Newbury. Apr 00. HP: £450. ABP: £529.

Pair engraved opaque twist wine glasses, slender funnel bowls with ears of barley/hops, double series stems, conical feet, 20.5cm high, c1770, one with footrim chip. Dreweatt Neate, Newbury. Jun 01. HP: £450. ABP: £529.

Mid 18thC glass. Henry Adams, Chichester. Jul 06. HP: £450. ABP: £529.

George II wine glass, bell bowl above shoulder knop with air-tears, inverted baluster stem with air tear, conical foot, c1740, 6.5in. Gorringes, Lewes. Sep 07. HP: £450. ABP: £529.

George II wine glass, bell bowl above true-baluster stem, conical, folded foot, c1735, 6.5in. Gorringes, Lewes. Sep 07. HP: £450. ABP: £529.

Two ale glasses, one with tapering bowl, other with a bowl engraved with hops and barley, both raised opaque twist stems, 2nd half 18thC, 18.5cm & 17.8cm. Woolley & Wallis, Salisbury. Sep 00. HP: £430. ABP: £505.

Engraved wine glass, mid 18thC. Sotheby's, Billingshurst. Oct 99. HP: £420. ABP: £494.

Opaque twist cordial glass c1765. Sotheby's, Billingshurst. Oct 99. HP: £420. ABP: £494.

Wine glass, pan topped round funnel shaped bowl, multi-spiral air twist stem, central swelled knop, 16.5cm high, c1750. Dreweatt Neate, Newbury. Apr 00. HP: £420. ABP: £494.

Four Jacobite style wine glasses, 18thC, all with chipped bases. Woolley & Wallis, Salisbury. Sep 00. HP: £420. ABP: £494.

Wine glass, bucket shaped bowl, multi-spiral air twist stem, shoulder and central swelling knops, 15.2cm high, c1750. Dreweatt Neate, Newbury. Apr 00. HP: £420. ABP: £494.

Wine glass with round funnel shaped bowl, plain stem with shoulder knop, folded foot, 16cm high, c1750. Dreweatt Neate, Newbury. Apr 00. HP: £420. ABP: £494.

'Tom Noel - Foxhunter', 19thC tumbler with a fox and 'Tallyho' engraved at the base, 9.5cm high, with six other various engraved and incised tumblers, smallest 5.5cm high. (D) (8) Cheffins, Cambridge. Apr 05. HP: £420. ABP: £494

Airtwist wine glass, tapered bucket bowl, shoulder knopped stem filled with spiral threads, conical foot, 16cm high, c1750. Dreweatt Neate, Newbury. Jun 01. HP: £420. ABP: £494.

Opaque twist wine or cordial glass, round funnel bowl with vertical ribs, double series stem, conical foot, 13cm high, c1770. Dreweatt Neate, Newbury. Jun 01. HP: £420. ABP: £494.

18thC wine glass, bell bowl moulded Lynn Rings, airtwist stem with domed foot, 5.25in high. Dee, Atkinson & Harrison, Driffield. Jul 02. HP: £420. ABP: £494.

Two similar air twist wine glasses, c1750, rounded funnel bowls, double-knopped, multiple twist stems, conical feet, 14.25cm high. Sworders, Stansted Mountfitchet. Jul 05. HP: £420. ABP: £494.

Five 18thC drinking glasses, one with facet cut stem, 15.5cm high, three with white cotton twist stems, 15cm high, and another with ruby and white cotton twist stem and seven air bubbles in the base of the bowl, 15.5cm high. Rosebery's, London. Oct 06. HP: £420. ABP: £494.

George II ale glass, bell bowl, air-twist stem with shoulder and centre knops, conical foot, c1750, 7.75in. Gorringes, Lewes. Sep 07. HP: £420. ABP: £494.

> Categories or themes can be followed through the colour coded Index which contains over 4500 cross references.

Three Dutch 19thC wine glasses. Gorringes, Bexhill. Sep 04. HP: £420. ABP: £494.

George II wine glass, pan-top bowl engraved with flowers, single-series air-twist stem with centre swelling knop, conical foot, c1755. Gorringes, Lewes. Sep 07. HP: £420. ABP: £494.

2091

Set of three opaque airtwist wine glasses, 19thC, bell shaped bowls, knop stems, 17cm, with a trumpet shaped wine glass, 19thC, opaque airtwist stem, 18cm, cordial airtwist glass, 19thC, bell shaped bowl, double knop stem, conical foot, 15cm, set of 4 late 19thC wine glasses, diaper/animal engraved bowls baluster stem, 14.5cm, and a cordial glass, late 19thC, engraved bowl, baluster stem, 9cm. (chips to rims) (10) Rosebery's, London. Mar 08. HP: £420. ABP: £494.

2092

Airtwist wine glass, c1750. Sotheby's, Billingshurst. Oct 99. HP: £400. ABP: £470.

2093

Pair ale glasses, tall tapering bowls engraved (probably later) in Jacobite style with a rose spray, mercury twist stems, 20.5cm. Woolley & Wallis, Salisbury. Sep 00. HP: £400. ABP: £470.

2094

Wine glass, inverted baluster stem, tear drop, plain foot, c1730. Eastbourne Auction Rooms, Sussex. Apr 04. HP: £400. ABP: £470.

2095

Wine glass, trumpet shaped bowl, annular shoulder knop, inverted baluster stem, folded foot, 19cm high and another, drawn trumpet shaped bowl, beaded tapering stem, 16.5cm. Dreweatt Neate, Newbury. Apr 00. HP: £400. ABP: £470.

2096

Wine glass, drawn trumpet shaped bowl with solid base, inverted baluster stem, 17.2cm high, c1750. Dreweatt Neate, Newbury. Apr 00. HP: £400. ABP: £470.

2097

Wine glass, bell shaped bowl, multi-spiral air twist stem, shoulder central knops, 16cm high, c1750. Dreweatt Neate, Newbury. Apr 00. HP: £400. ABP: £470.

2098

Wine glass, bell shaped bowl, multi-spiral air twist stem with vermiform collar, 16cm high, c1750. Dreweatt Neate, Newbury. Apr 00. HP: £400. ABP: £470.

2099

Wine glass, bell shaped bowl, multi-spiral air twist stem with shoulder knop, folded foot, 18cm high, c1750. Dreweatt Neate, Newbury. Apr 00. HP: £400. ABP: £470.

2100

Wine goblet, George II, c1740, 'drawn trumpet' type with air tear, conical folded foot, 7.75in. Gorringes, Lewes. Jun 07. HP: £400. ABP: £470.

2101

Wine glass, pointed funnel shaped bowl, multi-spiral air twist stem, 15.2cm, c1750. Dreweatt Neate, Newbury. Apr 00. HP: £400. ABP: £470.

2102

Engraved baluster wine glass, c1730, trumpet shaped bowl engraved with fruiting vines, knopped stem, spreading foot, 17cm. Rosebery's, London. Mar 06. HP: £400. ABP: £470.

2103

Dutch wine goblet, baluster shaped bowl engraved with a wide band of fruiting vines, plain stem and footrim with open pontil, 7.5in high, and 2 other Dutch wine glasses, one with flared bowl, both with plain knopped stems, folded footrims, 6in and 5.25in high. Canterbury Auction Galleries, Kent. Feb 06. HP: £400. ABP: £470.

2104

18thC cordial glass, bucket bowl above knopped stem, dome folded foot, 17.5cm high, with four matched opaque multi airtwist trumpet cordial glasses, 2 with leaf engraved bowls, and 2 further engraved cordial dome footed glasses. (7) Rosebery's, London. Mar 08. HP: £390. ABP: £458.

2105

Baluster wine glass, c1750. Sotheby's, Billingshurst. Oct 99. HP: £380. ABP: £446.

2106

Wine glass, pointed round funnel shaped bowl, multi-spiral air twist stem, central and shoulder knops, 17.2cm high, c1755. Dreweatt Neate, Newbury. Apr 00. HP: £380. ABP: £446.

Balustroid wine glass, bell bowl, solid lower section and small tear inclusion, inverted baluster, folded conical foot, 15.5cm high, c1740. Dreweatt Neate, Newbury. Jun 01. HP: £380. ABP: £446.

19thC Irish/Scottish cut glass goblet, cut thistle decoration. Denhams, Warnham. Aug 03. HP: £380. ABP: £446.

Opaque twist wine glass, round funnel bowl with honey-comb moulded lower section, stem with multi-ply corkscrew, conical foot, 15cm, c1765. Dreweatt Neate, Newbury. Jun 01. HP: £380. ABP: £446.

Facet stemmed wine glass, ogee bowl, everted rim and fluted and foliate cut lower section, fluted/notched waist knopped stem, panel cut conical foot with scalloped rim, c1790. Dreweatt Neate, Newbury. Jun 01. HP: £380. ABP: £446.

Late Georgian rummer, partly slice cut bowl engraved with a working horse, wheat and barley, oval cartouche with initialled monogram, squat knopped stem, plain footrim, 6.5in high. Canterbury Auction Galleries, Kent. Feb 07. HP: £380. ABP: £446.

Glass goblet, conical bowl wheel cut with rose and tree, domed foot with folded edge, 19thC, 9.5in high. Andrew Hartley, Ilkley, W Yorks. Feb 06. HP: £380. ABP: £446.

Mixed-twist cordial glass, George II, c1755, waisted bucket bowl, fine multi-spiral air-twist core surrounded by an opaque twist, conical foot, 6.25in. Gorringes, Lewes. Jun 07. HP: £380. ABP: £446.

George II wine goblet, ogee bowl with lower rib-moulding, single-series air-twist stem, conical foot, c1750, 7.5in. Gorringes, Lewes. Sep 07. HP: £380. ABP: £446.

George III goblet, large-capacity ogee bowl, lower ribbed moulding, single-series opaque-twist stem with fine/thick canes, conical foot, c1760, 8.75in. Gorringes, Lewes. Sep 07. HP: £380. ABP: £446.

Wine glass, bell shaped bowl, double knopped multi-spiral air twist stem, 16.5cm, c1750. Dreweatt Neate, Newbury. Apr 00. HP: £360. ABP: £423.

Mid 18thC wine glass, bell shaped bowl finely engraved with a band of fruiting vines, stem with swelling knop, plain footrim, open pontil, 6.75in high, c1750. Canterbury Auction Galleries, Kent. Aug 00. HP: £360. ABP: £423.

Early 19thC Masonic rummer, partly sliced body engraved Masonic symbols, initialled 'J.A.G.', short bulbous knopped stem, star cut base, 5.75in high. Canterbury Auction Galleries, Kent. Aug 03. HP: £360. ABP: £423.

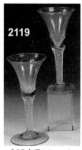

Pair of 18thC air twist glasses, 17cm high. Cheffins, Cambridge. Feb 05. HP: £360. ABP: £423.

George II wine glass, bell bowl, single-series air-twist stem with applied vermicular collar, conical foot, c1750, 6.75in. Gorringes, Lewes. Sep 07. HP: £360. ABP: £423.

> Prices quoted are actual hammer prices (HP) and the Approximate Buyer's Price (ABP) includes an average premium of 15% + VAT.

Wine glass with ogee shaped bowl, multi air twist cork-screw stem, 12cm high, c1755 and two other small glasses. Dreweatt Neate, Newbury. Apr 00. HP: £350. ABP: £411.

Wine glass, bell shaped bowl, multi-spiral air twist stem, shoulder knop, folded foot, 18cm high, c1750. Dreweatt Neate, Newbury. Apr 00. HP: £350. ABP: £411.

Wine glass, pointed round funnel shaped bowl, multi-spiral air twist stem, 15.2cm high, c1755, and another with flared bucket shaped bowl, multi-spiral air twist stem, 14.5cm high, c1755. Dreweatt Neate, Newbury. Apr 00. HP: £350. ABP: £411.

Two similar wine glasses, 20thC, each trumpet bowl with knopped opaque twist stem, possibly Continental, pair of air twist wine glasses and two more glasses tallest 16.75cm. (6) Sworders, Stansted Mountfitchet. Jul 05. HP: £350. ABP: £411.

Large wine glass, ogee shaped bowl, multi-spiral opaque twist stem, ply bands outside gauze, 19.5cm high, c1770. Dreweatt Neate, Newbury. Apr 00. HP: £350. ABP: £411.

Wine glass, flared bucket shaped bowl, spiral cable air twist stem, 15.2cm high, c1750. Dreweatt Neate, Newbury. Apr 00. HP: £350. ABP: £411.

18thC glass goblet, wheel cut engraved bowl, faceted knop with an inverted tear, wide foot, c1760. Sworders, Stansted Mountfitchet. Jun 03. HP: £350. ABP: £411.

Wine glass, rounded funnel shaped bowl, stem with shoulder and annular knops, folded foot, 14cm high, c1750, and another with dimple moulded ogee shaped bowl, teared inverted baluster shaped stem. Dreweatt Neate, Newbury. Apr 00. HP: £340. ABP: £399.

Wine glass, pointed funnel shaped bowl, multi-spiral air twist stem, central swelled knop, 15.2cm high, c1750. Dreweatt Neate, Newbury. Apr 00. HP: £340. ABP: £399.

Two wine glasses, opaque twist stems, 18thC, 15.5cm & 14.5cm. Woolley & Wallis, Salisbury. Sep 00. HP: £340. ABP: £399.

18thC wine glass, bucket shaped bowl, folded foot, 5cm high with another example with ogee shaped bowl and another with double airtwist stem, foot ground down. Rosebery's, London. Sep 03. HP: £340. ABP: £399.

Early 19thC Sunderland drinking glass engraved with the Wear Bridge and various sailing vessels, reverse with garland design and initials ALD 13.5cm. Boldon Auction Galleries, Tyne & Wear. Sep 04. HP: £340. ABP: £399.

19thC opaque double twist wine glass, 16cm high. Gorringes, Bexhill. Sep 04. HP: £340. ABP: £399.

Set of six late Georgian wine glasses, engraved with festoons, short cylindrical stems, square 'lemon-squeezer' bases, 5.5in, and a set of four similar rummers, 5in. Gorringes, Lewes. Jul 04. HP: £340. ABP: £399.

Late 18thC European soda glass coloured twist wine, bell bowl on red/opaque twist stem, 16.5cm high, with a similar later pan topped liqueur glass engraved with grapes on the rim, cranberry twist baluster stem, folded foot, 10.5cm high. (2) Cheffins, Cambridge. Apr 05. HP: £340. ABP: £399.

Two rummers, c1800, each bowl with an engraved band, moulded 'lemon squeezer' bases, a glass with a notched rim & similar foot, with three further glasses, tallest 14.25cm. (6) Sworders, Stansted Mountfitchet. Jul 05. HP: £340. ABP: £399.

Three large glass beakers, c1800, largest engraved with 6 individual flower specimens and triangular cutting, other 2 engraved with hops/flowers, tallest 14cm. Sworders, Stansted Mountfitchet. Jul 05. HP: £340. ABP: £399.

George III bell-shaped wine glass, airtwist stem, a George III liqueur glass, double air-twist stem, another airtwist stem glass, & a bubble stem glass, 17cm, 13.5cm, 20cm & 20.5cm. Gorringes, Bexhill. Feb 06. HP: £340. ABP: £399.

Hammer: £320

Airtwist wine glass, c1750. Sotheby's, Billingshurst. Oct 99. HP: £320. ABP: £376.

Opaque twist wine glass, c1765. Sotheby's, Billingshurst. Oct 99. HP: £320. ABP: £376.

Firing glass, trumpet shaped bowl engraved with Neptune and seahorses, numbered 22, knopped stem, round foot, 10cm high, c1820. Dreweatt Neate, Newbury. Apr 00. HP: £320. ABP: £376.

Wine glass, bell shaped bowl, multi-spiral air twist stem, shoulder knop, 16cm high, c1750 and another the stem with shoulder & central knops, 16cm high, c1750. Dreweatt Neate, Newbury. Apr 00. HP: £320. ABP: £376.

Wine glass, drawn trumpet shaped bowl, teared stem with inverted baluster at base, folded foot, 16cm high, c1750. Dreweatt Neate, Newbury. Apr 00. HP: £320. ABP: £376.

Wine glass, pointed round funnel shaped bowl, multi-ply opaque corkscrew stem, 15.2cm high, c1770, and another, multi-spiral opaque twist stem, two tapes outside gauze, 16cm high, c1770. Dreweatt Neate, Newbury. Apr 00. HP: £320. ABP: £376.

Wine glass, bell shaped bowl, solid teared base, multi-spiral air twist stem, shoulder knop, 16.5cm high, c1750. Dreweatt Neate, Newbury. Apr 00. HP: £320. ABP: £376.

Plain stemmed sweetmeat glass, bowl with inverted rim, supported on waist knopped stem, domed foot, 16.5cm high, c1740. Dreweatt Neate, Newbury. Jun 01. HP: £320. ABP: £376.

Opaque twist wine glass, ogee bowl with flared rim, stem with a multi-ply corkscrew, conical foot, 16cm high, c1765. Dreweatt Neate, Newbury. Jun 01. HP: £320. ABP: £376.

18thC ale glass, elongated bell bowl with fruiting vine decoration in gilt, (rubbed) (Giles) 1765, double airtwist stem, domed circular foot, 6.9in high. Dee, Atkinson & Harrison, Driffield. Jul 02. HP: £320. ABP: £376.

Near pair of 19thC ale flutes, 19.5cm high. Gorringes, Bexhill. Sep 04. HP: £320. ABP: £376.

Two similar Jacobite wine glasses, bowls engraved with two rose fronds on one side and a bird on other, facetted stems, 14cm high. (2) Cheffins, Cambridge. Apr 05. HP: £320. ABP: £376.

Air twist wine glass, c1760, bucket bowl engraved with vines and a bird, multiple opaque twist stem, 15cm. Sworders, Stansted Mountfitchet. Jul 05. HP: £320. ABP: £376.

Collection of glassware, incl: two 18thC cordial glasses & 2 wine glasses, 7.25in & pair of early Victorian goblets, 6in. Gorringes, Lewes. Jan 03. HP: £320. ABP: £376.

18thC wine glass, bucket shaped bowl, white opaque double twist stem, plain foot-rim, 6.75in, bowl engraved with view of a frigate, 'Success to the Eagle Frigate. Privateer', engraving poss. of a later date. Canterbury Auction Galleries, Kent. Apr 06. HP: £320. ABP: £376.

Pair of documentary clear glass tumblers, wheel cut with floral and foliate wreath containing initials 'WPI 1783' and verso with an exotic bird in flight, slice cut base, rim with a band of printies, 9.5cm high. Bearne's, Exeter. Nov 07. HP: £320. ABP: £376.

Large engraved rummer, dated 1808. Sotheby's, Billingshurst. Oct 99. HP: £300. ABP: £352.

Wine glass, pointed round funnel shaped bowl, double knopped multi spiral air twist stem 15.2cm high, c1750 and another, large pointed round funnel shaped bowl, 13.5cm high, c1770. Dreweatt Neate, Newbury. Apr 00. HP: £300. ABP: £352.

Wine glass with ogee shaped bowl, multi-opaque spiral twist stem with ply bands outside a cable, 14.5cm high, c1760 and another, pointed round funnel shaped bowl, multiple opaque corkscrew stem, 16cm high, c1760. Dreweatt Neate, Newbury. Apr 00. HP: £300. ABP: £352.

Large wine glass, drawn trumpet shaped bowl, plain stem, folded foot, 23.5cm high. Dreweatt Neate, Newbury. Apr 00. HP: £300. ABP: £352.

Airtwist cordial glass, funnel bowl, stem with basal knop and filled with spiral threads, 15cm, c1750, footrim chip. Dreweatt Neate, Newbury. Jun 01. HP: £300. ABP: £352.

19thC goblet, large proportions, deep bowl engraved with a fox hunting scene, bulbous knopped centre column, plain footrim, bowl 7in dia, 12in high overall. Canterbury Auction Galleries, Kent. Apr 05. HP: £300. ABP: £352.

Late 18thC wine glass, trumpet bowl, teared stem, folded foot, 15cm high, with two similar conical bowled glasses, hollow stems, domed feet, 16cm high. (3) Cheffins, Cambridge. Apr 05. HP: £300. ABP: £352.

Sweetmeat bowl, ogee shaped bowl, dentated rim, multi-spiral opaque twist stem, shoulder knop, radially moulded foot, 10cm high, c1760. Dreweatt Neate, Newbury. Apr 00. HP: £300. ABP: £352.

George III wine glass, pan-top bowl, fine double-series opaque-twist stem, conical foot, 6in. Gorringes, Lewes. Sep 07. HP: £300. ABP: £352.

Set 4 Regency glass rummers, 19thC, part fluted bowls, octagonal stem, stepped square feet, 15.5cm, with a Regency glass rummer, bowl with s-shaped swirls, stepped square foot, 16cm, bell shaped glass rummer, 11cm, faceted cordial glass, knop stem, 11cm, and a circular hob nail decorated glass bowl,10.5cm. (8) Rosebery's, London. Mar 08. HP: £300. ABP: £352.

The numbering system acts as a reader reference as well as linking to the Analysis of each section.

Opaque twist wine glass, c1765. Sotheby's, Billingshurst. Oct 99. HP: £290. ABP: £341.

Opaque twist sweetmeat glass, c1765. Sotheby's, Billingshurst. Oct 99. HP: £290. ABP: £341.

Pair 18thC cordial glasses, engraved bowls, double-series opaque twist stems, conical feet, 5.75in Gorringes, Lewes. Jun 03. HP: £290. ABP: £341.

Small light baluster wine glass, c1730. Sotheby's, Billingshurst. Oct 99. HP: £280. ABP: £329.

Wine glass, drawn trumpet shaped bowl diamond point engraved 'J Hands', multi-spiral air twist stem, folded foot, 18cm high, c1750. Dreweatt Neate, Newbury. Apr 00. HP: £280. ABP: £329.

Wine glass, pointed round funnel shaped bowl, multi-ply opaque corkscrew stem, 16cm high, c1770, another, with rounded funnel shaped bowl, multi-spiral opaque twist stem, central knop, 15.2cm, c1760. Dreweatt Neate, Newbury. Apr 00. HP: £280. ABP: £329.

Wine glass, pointed funnel shaped bowl, stem with shoulder and central knops, folded foot, 16.5cm high, c1750. Dreweatt Neate, Newbury. Apr 00. HP: £280. ABP: £329.

Sweetmeat bowl, ogee shaped bowl, dentated rim, multi-spiral opaque twist stem, shoulder knop, radially moulded foot, 8.2cm high, c1760. Dreweatt Neate, Newbury. Apr 00. HP: £280. ABP: £329.

Wine glass, lipped ogee shaped bowl, multi-spiral twist stem, central swelled knop, 16cm high, c1770. Dreweatt Neate, Newbury. Apr 00. HP: £280. ABP: £329.

18thC Dutch wine glass deeply engraved with French mottoes and amorini panels, 6.5in and another similar glass. Gorringes, Lewes. Jun 00. HP: £280. ABP: £329.

Three matching wine glasses, part panel moulded bowls, folded feet, 14.5cm. Woolley & Wallis, Salisbury. Sep 00. HP: £280. ABP: £329.

18thC wine glass, bell shaped bowl, 5.75in high, a trumpet shaped glass, 7in, af, and a goblet on an 8 sided Silesian stem, 6.25in. Dee, Atkinson & Harrison, Driffield. Apr 01. HP: £280. ABP: £329.

Engraved facet stemmed wine glass, round funnel bowl engraved/polished with a bee and flower spray, shoulder knopped stem with diamond facets, conical foot, 14.3cm high, c1790. Dreweatt Neate, Newbury. Jun 01. HP: £280. ABP: £329.

Cordial glass, rare bucket bowl, multi spiral airtwist stem, conical foot, 2in dia x 5.75in high, c1750. Dee, Atkinson & Harrison, Driffield. Nov 01. HP: £280. ABP: £329.

18thC wine glass, 15cm high. Gorringes, Bexhill. Sep 04. HP: £280. ABP: £329.

Near-pair of mid-18thC wine glasses, round funnel bowls, twin-knopped air-twist stems, conical feet, 6.25in. Gorringes, Lewes. Jan 05. HP: £280. ABP: £329.

> The illustrations are in descending price order. The price range is indicated at the top of each page.

Three glasses, 19thC, one of trumpet form, knopped air twist stem, another of trumpet form, knopped stem, fluted bowl, third with knopped stem. Tallest 21cm. Rosebery's, London. Jun 05. HP: £280. ABP: £329.

Pair of late 18thC air twist wine glasses, trumpet bowls, tapering stems, 16.5cm and another similar, 17cm. (D) (3) Cheffins, Cambridge. Apr 05. HP: £280. ABP: £329.

Set of six George III cordial glasses, ogee bowls engraved with grapes and vine leaves, faceted stems, 5.25in. Gorringes, Lewes. Dec 06. HP: £280. ABP: £329.

Early 19thC commemorative glass rummer, tapered bowl engraved/dated 1820, short knopped stem, plain footrim, 5.75in high. Canterbury Auction Galleries, Kent. Aug 02. HP: £270. ABP: £317.

Dutch glass beaker vase or druivenspoeler engraved with a shield shaped cartouche with 'VOC' monogram surmounted by 'A' and marquis's coronet, dated Ao. 1741, 21cm high, minor rim chip. Bearne's, Exeter. Nov 07. HP: £270. ABP: £317.

Sweet meat glass, compressed ribbed bowl, flanged rim, hollow circular stem with 4 tears and shoulders, 4 tails giving appearance of pedestal stem, c1745, 4in high. Dee, Atkinson & Harrison, Driffield. Nov 01. HP: £265. ABP: £311.

2187

Wine flute, drawn trumpet shaped bowl, plain stem, 16cm high and a wine glass, bell shaped bowl, stem with shoulder and basal knops, folded foot, 13cm high, c1750. Dreweatt Neate, Newbury. Apr 00. HP: £260. ABP: £305.

2188

Mid 18thC Norwegian glass, wheel engraved cartouches, c1750, 7.25in. Gorringes, Lewes. Jul 08. HP: £260. ABP: £305.

2189

Wine glass, ogee shaped bowl, basal flutes, multi-spiral opaque twist stem, ply bands outside tapes, 14cm high, c1765. Dreweatt Neate, Newbury. Apr 00. HP: £260. ABP: £305.

2190

Six various wine glasses, two with faceted stems, two with engraved bowls, two with folded feet, one with a bell bowl, opaque twist stem and one with a facet cut funnel shaped bowl, 18thC & later, tallest 15.5cm. Woolley & Wallis, Salisbury. Sep 00. HP: £260. ABP: £305.

2191

Toasting glass, typical drawn trumpet, plain stem, conical foot, 20cm high, mid 18thC. Dreweatt Neate, Newbury. Jun 01. HP: £260. ABP: £305.

2192

Pedestal stemmed sweetmeat glass, ogee bowl, octagonally moulded tapering stem with basal collar, domed/folded foot, 16cm high, mid 18thC. Dreweatt Neate, Newbury. Jun 01. HP: £260. ABP: £305.

2193

Set of five Regency rummers, semi fluted tapering bowls, vine engraved borders, knopped stem, 14.5cm high. (5) Rosebery's, London. Dec 03. HP: £260. ABP: £305.

2194

Sunderland Bridge rummer, c1800, engraved with a ship sailing under the bridge, inscribed 'Sunderland Bridge over the Wear', back with initials JSW under a basket of flowers, between hops and barley, 16.5cm. Sworders, Stansted Mountfitchet. Jul 05. HP: £260. ABP: £305.

Hammer: £260 - £240

2195

Glass 'Sunderland' tankard, c1800, engraved with a ship under the Sunderland Bridge, inscribed 'Charles William, Sunderland Bridge over the River Wear', back with initials 'GH' under basket of flowers, 11cm. Sworders, Stansted Mountfitchet. Jul 05. HP: £260. ABP: £305.

2196

Pair 18thC bell shaped wine glasses, faceted stems, domed/folded foot, 7in. Denhams, Warnham, Sussex. Aug 07. HP: £260. ABP: £305.

2197

Engraved facet stemmed wine glass, tall bowl engraved and polished with band of flower heads with scale cut basal section, stem with hexagonal facets, conical foot, 15.5cm high, c1790. Dreweatt Neate, Newbury. Jun 01. HP: £250. ABP: £294.

2198

Seven 19thC rummers, part slice cut bowls engraved with fruiting vines, knopped stems, plain footrims, 5.75in high, 2 other similar rummers, 5.5in & 6in high and finger bowl. Canterbury Auction Galleries, Kent. Feb 04. HP: £250. ABP: £294.

2199

Wine glass, pointed funnel shaped bowl, multi-spiral air twist stem, shoulder/central knops, 16cm, c1750, and another, bell shaped bowl, double knopped multi-spiral air twist stem, 16.5cm, c1750. Dreweatt Neate, Newbury. Apr 00. HP: £240. ABP: £282.

2200

Nine green wine glasses, late 18thC, conical bowls, bladed knop stems, 13cm. Sworders, Stansted Mountfitchet. Jul 05. HP: £240. ABP: £282.

2201

Wine glass, drawn trumpet shaped bowl, multi-spiral air twist stem, 18cm high, c1750, and another, bell shaped bowl, double knopped multi-spiral air twist stem, 18cm high, c1750. Dreweatt Neate, Newbury. Apr 00. HP: £240. ABP: £282.

2202

Wine glass, ogee shaped bowl, multi-spiral opaque twist stem 14.5cm high, c1765, and another, pointed round funnel shaped bowl, multi-spiral opaque twist stem, ply bands outside tapes, 15.2cm high, c1770. Dreweatt Neate, Newbury. Apr 00. HP: £240. ABP: £282.

Hammer: £240 - £220

Sweetmeat glass, honeycomb moulded pointed round funnel shape bowl, shaped rim, 8 sided pedestal stem between collars, honeycomb moulded domed foot, 15.2cm high, c1750. Dreweatt Neate, Newbury. Apr 00. HP: £240. ABP: £282.

Opaque twist ale flute, slender ogee form, double series stem conical foot, 19cm, c1770. Dreweatt Neate, Newbury. Jun 01. HP: £240. ABP: £282.

Two double-series opaque-twist wine glasses, c1775, funnel bowl, central spiral core, one with spiral threads, other with a single spiral thread, 15cm. (2) Sworders, Stansted Mountfitchet. Nov 04. HP: £240. ABP: £282.

Set of 8 early 19thC green glasses, tulip bowls, tapering stems, circular feet, 12cm. (8) Cheffins, Cambridge. Apr 05. HP: £240. ABP: £282.

Two George III wine glasses, folded feet, one basally fluted tapering bowl rounding above the swollen and tear knopped stem, other unornamented, similar shaped bowl, 14.5cm. (2) Cheffins, Cambridge. Apr 05. HP: £240. ABP: £282.

English 18thC wine glass, bell shaped bowl, multi spiral air twist stem, conical foot, 7in high. Fellows & Sons, Hockley, Birmingham. Oct 03. HP: £240. ABP: £282.

Early 19thC goblet, bowl wheel cut and engraved, opaque twist stem, 7in high. Dee, Atkinson & Harrison, Driffield. Apr 01. HP: £240. ABP: £282.

18thC German glass engraved with figures in gilt cartouche, foot restored, 7in. Gorringes, Lewes. Apr 02. HP: £240. ABP: £282.

Pair early 19thC rummers, plain deep wide bowls, plain stems and footrims, 5in high x 4in dia, and 6 other 19thC plain glass rummers, various. Canterbury Auction Galleries, Kent. Apr 06. HP: £230. ABP: £270.

Wine glass, large honeycomb moulded bucket shaped bowl, plain stem, round foot, 15.2cm high, c1755. Dreweatt Neate, Newbury. Apr 00. HP: £230. ABP: £270.

> Categories or themes can be followed through the colour coded Index which contains over 4500 cross references.

18thC wine glass, plain bell shaped bowl, white opaque double twist stem, plain footrim, 6.75in high, c1770. Canterbury Auction Galleries, Kent. Apr 06. HP: £230. ABP: £270.

18thC wine glass, trumpet shaped bowl, fine air twist stem, plain footrim with open pontil, 6.5in high, and three similar with bell shaped bowls, 6.5in/6.25in high. c1760, all footrims somewhat chipped. Canterbury Auction Galleries, Kent. Jun 07. HP: £230. ABP: £270.

Opaque twist wine glass, c1765. Sotheby's, Billingshurst. Oct 99. HP: £220. ABP: £258.

Wine glass, bell shaped bowl, multi-spiral air twist stem, shoulder and central knops, 18cm high, c1750. Dreweatt Neate, Newbury. Apr 00. HP: £220. ABP: £258.

Wine glass, rounded funnel shaped bowl, plain stem with shoulder knop, folded foot, 15.2cm high, c1750. Dreweatt Neate, Newbury. Apr 00. HP: £220. ABP: £258.

Opaque twist wine glass, drawn trumpet form, stem filled with spiral threads, conical foot, 17cm high, c1770, possible polished area to footrim. Dreweatt Neate, Newbury. Jun 01. HP: £220. ABP: £258.

Facet stemmed wine glass, ogee bowl with faceted lower section cut stylised foliage above circles, waist knopped stem with diamond facets, conical foot with shaped rim, 14.2cm high, c1790, occasional minute chips to facets. Dreweatt Neate, Newbury. Jun 01. HP: £220. ABP: £258.

Seven green wine glasses: two pairs with conical bowls and knopped stems and three with ovoid bowls and plain stems, 12.5cm approx. Woolley & Wallis, Salisbury. Sep 00. HP: £220. ABP: £258.

Masonic jelly or firing glass, flared bowl engraved with Masonic symbols, glass probably Continental, 10.5cm high, mid 18thC. Dreweatt Neate, Newbury. Jun 01. HP: £220. ABP: £258.

Pair Masonic firing glasses, conical bowls engraved with Masonic symbols, 9.5cm high, 19thC. Dreweatt Neate, Newbury. Jun 01. HP: £220. ABP: £258.

18thC wine glass, ogee bowl, multiple spiral airtwist stem, central knop, domed foot, 7in high, minute chip to base of foot rim. Tring Market Auctions, Herts. Jul 04. HP: £220. ABP: £258.

Late 18thC European soda glass opaque twist firing glass, trumpet bowl on double helix stem, thickened foot, 10cm, with a similar opaque twist glass, rounded bowl, 12cm. Cheffins, Cambridge. Apr 05. HP: £220. ABP: £258.

Pair of late 18thC soda glass opaque twist wines, each of the rounded bowls on double helix stems and circular feet, 14.5cm high. (2) Cheffins, Cambridge. Apr 05. HP: £220. ABP: £258.

George III air twist wine glass, bell bowl on double knopped stem, folded foot, 17cm high. Cheffins, Cambridge. Apr 05. HP: £220. ABP: £258.

Five late 18th/early 19thC wine glasses, bead engraved bowls, 3 with facet cut stems and the other pair with plain stems, largest 12.5cm high. (5) Cheffins, Cambridge. Apr 05. HP: £220. ABP: £258.

18thC ale glass, plain tapered bowl engraved with hops and ears of wheat, white opaque double twist stem, plain foot-rim, 7.75in high. Canterbury Auction Galleries, Kent. Apr 06. HP: £220. ABP: £258.

Georgian wine glass, ovoid bowl wheel cut with baskets of flowers above band of ovals, faceted baluster stem, spreading foot, 5.75in high, a glass etched with 'E. Aston', another with a crest and a half fluted baluster tankard, 19thC. (4) Hartleys, Ilkley. Feb 08. HP: £220. ABP: £258.

Three pieces of 18thC and later glassware: cotton twist stemmed ale glass, trumpet glass with tear drop stem and folded foot, and a facet cut rummer with leopard head crest to base. Locke & England, Leamington Spa. Nov 05. HP: £220. ABP: £258.

Twelve various green wine glasses, 19thC and later, 14cm tallest. Woolley & Wallis, Salisbury. Sep 00. HP: £220. ABP: £258.

Opaque twist wine glass, c1765. Sotheby's, Billingshurst. Oct 99. HP: £210. ABP: £247.

Double series opaque twist cordial glass, c1775, 19cm. Sworders, Stansted Mountfitchet. Nov 04. HP: £210. ABP: £247.

18thC cordial glass, c1780, small ogee shaped bowl, airtwist stem with spiral gauze around a central core, spreading foot, 16cm high. Rosebery's, London. Sep 04. HP: £210. ABP: £247.

Hammer: £210 - £200

Early 18thC wine glass, ogee pattern bowl, double knopped stem, plain footrim, 6in high. Canterbury Auction Galleries, Kent. Apr 06. HP: £210. ABP: £247.

Ale glass, English 18thC, trumpet bowl, opaque twist stem with an air twist stem glass with trumpet bowl. Ale glass 16cm. Rosebery's, London. Jun 05. HP: £210. ABP: £247.

Three 18thC drinking glasses, two of trumpet form, cotton twist stems and another with large bowl and double series stem, each with spiral twist, 14cm and 15cm. Sworders, Stansted Mountfitchet. Dec 03. HP: £210. ABP: £247.

18thC wine glass, bell shaped bowl, inverted baluster stem, domed/folded foot, 16cm. Brown & Co, Brigg. May 07. HP: £210. ABP: £247.

Two small Monteiths, each with ogee shaped honeycomb moulded bowl, 7.6cm high, c1760, and another with panel moulded ogee shaped bowl, 8cm high. Dreweatt Neate, Newbury. Apr 00. HP: £200. ABP: £235.

Wine glass, pointed round funnel shaped bowl with basal flutes, multi-opaque spiral twist stem, two tapes outside a cable, 16cm high, c1765, and another, round funnel shaped bowl with basal flutes, multi-spiral stem, 16cm high. Dreweatt Neate, Newbury. Apr 00. HP: £200. ABP: £235.

Pair of Regency rummers, c1810, bowls engraved and initialled cartouche, lemon squeezer base. Rosebery's, London. Sep 03. HP: £200. ABP: £235.

Wine flute, trumpet shaped bowl, multi-opaque spiral twist stem, two tapes outside gauze, 19cm high, c1760. Dreweatt Neate, Newbury. Apr 00. HP: £200. ABP: £235.

Gin glass, bell shaped bowl, plain stem, round foot, 14cm high, c1750. Dreweatt Neate, Newbury. Apr 00. HP: £200. ABP: £235.

Two air twist stem glasses, English 18thC, one with trumpet bowl, other with bell shaped bowl. Tallest 16.5cm. Rosebery's, London. Jun 05. HP: £200. ABP: £235.

Air twist wine glass, tall conical bowl with flared rim, double helix stem, 17.5cm high, with an opaque twist wine glass, base of the bell bowl teared above the double helix stem and circular foot, 17cm high. (D) (2) Cheffins, Cambridge. Apr 05. HP: £200. ABP: £235.

Small pair Continental glass decanters/stoppers, mallet shaped bodies engraved with vines, 20cm, a wine goblet, U-shaped bowl, a set of four wine glasses with red/ opaque white twist stems, 18thC, all with chipped bases. (9) Woolley & Wallis, Salisbury. Sep 00. HP: £200. ABP: £235.

Drawn trumpet wine glass and glass millefiori paper-weight, 2in dia. Louis Taylor, Stoke on Trent. Sep 03. HP: £200. ABP: £235.

Three facet stem wine glasses, late 18thC, 2 with engraved bowls, third with faceted knop, tallest 14.5cm. Sworders, Stansted Mountfitchet. Jul 05. HP: £200. ABP: £235.

Prices quoted are actual hammer prices (HP) and the Approximate Buyer's Price (ABP) includes an average premium of 15% + VAT.

18thC wine glass, conical bowl, heavy base and air bubble, double knopped stem also with air bubble, 15cm high. Rosebery's, London. Oct 06. HP: £200. ABP: £235.

19thC large glass rummer, engraved with hunting scene of hounds and a huntsman jumping a fence, 21cm. Sworders, Stansted Mountfitchet. Jul 05. HP: £200. ABP: £235.

Hammer: £195 - £180

18thC wine glass, fluted bowl, rim trailing flora, double airtwist stem, 5.5in high. Dee, Atkinson & Harrison, Driffield. May 02. HP: £195. ABP: £229.

Small wine glass, drawn trumpet shaped bowl, multi spiral air twist stem, folded foot, 14.5cm high, c1750. Dreweatt Neate, Newbury. Apr 00. HP: £190. ABP: £223.

Two folded foot glasses, English 18thC, each with an ogee shaped bowl, one with engraved rim, each set on a plain stem and broad folded foot. Tallest 14cm. Rosebery's, London. Jun 05. HP: £190. ABP: £223.

Six large plain glass rummers, 19thC, tallest 16cm. Sworders, Stansted Mountfitchet. Jul 05. HP: £190. ABP: £223.

Squat wine glass, drawn trumpet shaped bowl, multi-spiral air twist stem, 12cm high, c 1750. Dreweatt Neate, Newbury. Apr 00. HP: £190. ABP: £223.

Wine glass, drawn trumpet shaped bowl, plain stem with inverted baluster knop, 17.2cm high, c1740. Dreweatt Neate, Newbury. Apr 00. HP: £190. ABP: £223.

Mixed twist wine or dram glass, ogee bowl, stem with central elongated tear within three opaque spiral threads, conical foot, 11.5cm high, c1770. Dreweatt Neate, Newbury. Jun 01. HP: £190. ABP: £223.

Pair of early 19thC bucket rummers engraved, plain stems, domed circular bases, 5.5in high. Tring Market Auctions, Herts. May 02. HP: £190. ABP: £223.

18thC soda glass opaque and air twist wine, tapering bowl on helical stem, 15.5cm high. Cheffins, Cambridge. Apr 05. HP: £190. ABP: £223.

Masonic glass tumbler, c1820, engraved with emblems incl. pillars, squares, compasses etc, and a Continental cut glass goblet, c1840, engraved with a coat of arms and a view of Marianbad, tallest 15cm. (2) Sworders, Stansted Mountfitchet. Jul 05. HP: £190. ABP: £223.

Mid-18thC Lynn cordial glass, stepped bowl, double-series opaque-twist stem, conical foot, 5.5in. Gorringes, Lewes. Oct 06. HP: £190. ABP: £223.

Pair of wine glasses, bell shaped bowls, double cotton twist stems, spreading foot, 19thC, 7in high. Hartleys, Ilkley. Feb 07. HP: £190. ABP: £223.

Six clear glass tumblers, 19thC, bulbous bottomed tumblers engraved with Masonic set square, ruler and dividers, 10cm, and 10 faceted liqueur glasses, gilt rims, 11cm high. (16) Rosebery's, London. Jan 08. HP: £190. ABP: £223.

19thC ale glass, tapered bowl engraved with hops/barley, air twist stem, open pontils, 8in, c1770, 2 small chips to foot-rim, and a 18thC cordial glass, moulded bowl, double white opaque twist stem, open pontil, 6in, c1760, rim slightly chipped. Canterbury Auction Galleries, Kent. Jun 07. HP: £190. ABP: £223.

Tumbler, engraved with a daisy and a lesser spray to reverse, 12cm, early 19thC, paper label for Parkington Collection. Dreweatt Neate, Newbury. Jun 01. HP: £180. ABP: £211.

Three George III drinking glasses, one with round funnel bowl, faceted stem 6.25in, another with ovoid bowl, 5.75in, & an engraved cordial glass with folded foot, 4.5in, bowl chipped. Gorringes, Lewes. Jan 04. HP: £180. ABP: £211.

George III opaque-twist drinking glass, bell bowl, double-series opaque-twist stem, c1760, 6.75in. Gorringes, Lewes. Jan 04. HP: £180. ABP: £211.

George III drinking glass, ovoid cut bowl, faceted stem with central knop, cut conical foot, 6.25in. Gorringes, Lewes. Jan 04. HP: £180. ABP: £211.

Seven various 18thC & later soda glasses, prob. Dutch, incl. a near pair with bell bowls and triple knopped air-twist stem, tallest 7in. Gorringes, Lewes. Mar 03. HP: £180. ABP: £211.

Five late 18th/early 19thC liqueur glasses, folded feet and three others with similar bowls and stems, largest 11.5cm high. (8) Cheffins, Cambridge. Apr 05. HP: £180. ABP: £211.

Pair facet stem firing glasses, late 18thC, round funnel bowls with base facets, 12cm high. Sworders, Stansted Mountfitchet. Jul 05. HP: £180. ABP: £211.

Three trumpet bowl glasses, 2 c1740, one with tear drop, tallest 17.5cm. Sworders, Stansted Mountfitchet. Jul 05. HP: £180. ABP: £211.

Wine glass, conical bowl, multi air twist stem, plain conical foot, 19thC, 6in high, a wine glass, conical bowl engraved with roses, buds and leaves, plain pulled stem, conical foot, 6.25in high. (2) Hartleys, Ilkley. Apr 08. HP: £180. ABP: £211.

Opaque twist wine glass, round funnel bowl, double series stem, conical foot, 15cm, c1770. Dreweatt Neate, Newbury. Jun 01. HP: £170. ABP: £199.

Bell shaped firing glass, bowl inscribed 'Britannic' and numbered '57', 9cm high, c1820 and two other firing glasses. Dreweatt Neate, Newbury. Apr 00. HP: £170. ABP: £199.

Wine glass, trumpet bowl, tear drop plain stem, folded foot, 18thC, 15.5cm. Woolley & Wallis, Salisbury. Sep 00. HP: £170. ABP: £199.

Pair of engraved/cut glass footed tumblers, English early 19thC, each engraved with a fox leaping a fence between words 'GONE AWAY' and 'TALLIO', above a band of small diamond cutting, stepped square base, 13cm. Rosebery's, London. Jun 05. HP: £170. ABP: £199.

18thC engraved bucket bowl glass, 6.5in, two 18thC engraved cordial glasses, 3.75in tallest, an 18thC wine glass with air tear, 6.5in and two further 19thC engraved glasses, 4.5in. (minor chips) Gorringes, Lewes. Jan 03. HP: £170. ABP: £199.

Pair of 18thC wine glasses, air twist stems, 17.5cm high. Rosebery's, London. Oct 06. HP: £170. ABP: £199.

Four green wine glasses, 3 with facet cut bowls & stems, 12cm, fourth with ovoid bowl engraved with three crests inscribed 'By Faith We Are Saved', I Hope to Speed' and 'March 11 1857', 12.5cm. Woolley & Wallis, Salisbury. Sep 00. HP: £160. ABP: £188.

The numbering system acts as a reader reference as well as linking to the Analysis of each section.

Two wine glasses, double opaque twist stems. Gorringes, Lewes. Dec 00. HP: £160. ABP: £188.

Pair of cordial glasses, half panelled bowls, one wheel cut with fruiting vines, other with roses/thistles, faceted baluster stem and spreading foot, 19thC, 6in high. Hartleys, Ilkley. Dec 06. HP: £160. ABP: £188.

Hammer: £160 - £150

Wine glass, square bucket shaped bowl with basal flutes, multi-spiral opaque twist stem, tapes outside a corkscrew, 14cm high, c1765. Dreweatt Neate, Newbury. Apr 00. HP: £160. ABP: £188.

Two 19thC drinking glasses, plain slightly tapering stems, 14.5cm high. Rosebery's, London. Oct 06. HP: £160. ABP: £188.

Wine flute glass, drawn trumpet shaped bowl, slender stem, 18.5cm high, c1765-70. Dreweatt Neate, Newbury. Apr 00. HP: £160. ABP: £188.

18thC wine glass, bucket bowl, opaque twist stem, 6in. Gorringes, Lewes. Jun 00. HP: £160. ABP: £188.

Engraved plain stemmed firing glass, ogee bowl with a band of stylised flowers, terraced foot, 9cm, mid 18thC. Dreweatt Neate, Newbury. Jun 01. HP: £160. ABP: £188.

Balustroid gin glass, bell bowl, inverted baluster stem with basal knop, folded conical foot, 13cm, c1740. Dreweatt Neate, Newbury. Jun 01. HP: £160. ABP: £188.

Engraved tumbler, tapered cylindrical form, engraved with monogram PMW within a floral wreath, reverse with a bird in flight, reserved on a star ground, beneath a star and dot band, 12.5cm high, c1800. Dreweatt Neate, Newbury. Jun 01. HP: £160. ABP: £188.

18thC English wine glass, drawn trumpet bowl, slightly tapering air twist stem, conical foot, 16.5cm high. Wintertons Ltd, Lichfield. Feb 02. HP: £160. ABP: £188.

Mid-18thC wine glass, round funnel bowl, double-series opaque twist stem, conical foot, 6in. Gorringes, Lewes. Jan 05. HP: £160. ABP: £188.

Wrythen ale glass, English late 18thC, conical shape, wrythen knopped stem, folded circular foot, conical fluted later ale glass, 3 Georgian style rummers with a glass bowl. Ale glass 13cm. Rosebery's, London. Dec 05. HP: £160. ABP: £188.

18thC cordial glass, ogee bowl, c1760. 5.5in high. Dee, Atkinson & Harrison, Driffield. Dec 00. HP: £150. ABP: £176.

Hexagonal section jelly glass, tapered form, domed foot, 9cm high, late 18thC. Dreweatt Neate, Newbury. Jun 01. HP: £150. ABP: £176.

Early 19thC Masonic glass vase, wheel engraved armorial and cut lozenge shape border to base 6.5in. Gorringes, Lewes. Jan 03. HP: £150. ABP: £176.

Engraved ale flute, conical bowl with hops and barley, stem on a folded conical foot, 14.5cm high, and another similar, 14cm high. Dreweatt Neate, Newbury. Jun 01. HP: £150. ABP: £176.

Cordial glass, half fluted engraved bowl, double opaque twist stem. Gorringes, Lewes. Dec 00. HP: £150. ABP: £176.

18thC English cordial glass, round funnel bowl acid etched with foliage, plain straight stem, conical folded foot, 6.5in high. Wintertons Ltd, Lichfield. Feb 02. HP: £150. ABP: £176.

Two wine glasses, plain bell shaped bowls, white opaque twist stems, plain footrims, 6.25in, footrims chipped, and three other wine glasses with rims and facet cut stems, plain footrims, 5.75in and 6in high. Canterbury Auction Galleries, Kent. Jun 07. HP: £150. ABP: £176.

18thC English wine glass, drawn trumpet bowl, straight stem with two internal tears, folded conical foot, 6.25in high. Wintertons Ltd, Lichfield. Feb 02. HP: £150. ABP: £176.

Three Georgian glass rummers, an engraved goblet, and another rummer. (5) Sworders, Stansted Mountfitchet. Jul 01. HP: £150. ABP: £176.

Four Georgian glass boot stirrup glasses, late 18th/ early 19thC, 3 with spirally fluted bowls and plain feet, one plain, tallest 13cm, and a glass lacemaker's lamp, early 19thC, spirally turned column and a slightly domed foot, 9cm high, with a related letter. (6) Sworders, Stansted Mountfitchet. Nov 04. HP: £150. ABP: £176.

Five late 18thC small wine glasses, each of the conical bowls engraved, tapering cylindrical stems and one of the circular feet folded, tallest 11.5cm high. Cheffins, Cambridge. Apr 05. HP: £150. ABP: £176.

19thC wheel etched glass, bell shaped bowl, cotton twist stem, 15cm and another wine glass, wheel etched with fruiting grape and a bird, unground pontil, 12cm. Thos Mawer & Son, Lincoln. Sep 04. HP: £140. ABP: £164.

Firing glass, trumpet shaped bowl engraved with a Masonic device, 9cm high, c1810. Dreweatt Neate, Newbury. Apr 00. HP: £140. ABP: £164.

Tapering sided tumbler, rim applied with a blue tinted band, 8cm high, c1800, and a similar small straight sided tumbler. Dreweatt Neate, Newbury. Apr 00. HP: £140. ABP: £164.

Four early 19thC green glasses, conical bowls, five green bowled wine glasses, clear stems and feet, with a green glass finger bowl. (10) Cheffins, Cambridge. Apr 05. HP: £140. ABP: £164.

18thC flute with semi hollow stem and folded circular foot, 7.5in high. Dee, Atkinson & Harrison, Driffield. May 02. HP: £140. ABP: £164.

Large 18th/19thC cut glass goblet, faceted stem, 10in. Denhams, Warnham. Aug 03. HP: £140. ABP: £164.

George III wine glass, bell bowl, clear stem and folded foot, 16cm high. Cheffins, Cambridge. Apr 05. HP: £140. ABP: £164.

Folded foot glass, English 18thC, ogee bowl and plain stem, with an ale glass of characteristic form, air twist stem. Tallest 16cm. Rosebery's, London. Jun 05. HP: £140. ABP: £164.

Nine glasses, c1840, tallest 14cm. Sworders, Stansted Mountfitchet. Jul 05. HP: £140. ABP: £164.

The illustrations are in descending price order. The price range is indicated at the top of each page.

Large glass goblet and a small wine glass. Gorringes, Bexhill. Dec 04. HP: £140. ABP: £164.

Late 18thC wine glass, tall conical bowl five ball swags above facetted stem and another similar with unornamented bowl, 17cm high. (D) (2) Cheffins, Cambridge. Apr 05. HP: £140. ABP: £164.

Early 18thC North German or Dutch glass roemer, with fronted stem, c1700, 10in. Gorringes, Lewes. Jul 08. HP: £130. ABP: £152.

Large crested glass goblet, engraved round funnel bowl, faceted knop and single series opaque-twist stem, 11.75in. Gorringes, Lewes. Mar 03. HP: £130. ABP: £152.

Four glass rummers, c1840, tallest 14cm. Sworders, Stansted Mountfitchet. Jul 05. HP: £130. ABP: £152.

George III opaque twist wine glass, double elliptical twist and three piece construction, 6.5in. Gorringes, Lewes. Apr 08. HP: £130. ABP: £152.

George III wine glass, ogee bowl, double series opaque twist stem, conical foot, 18thC, 6in high, sold with a receipt dated 1997. Hartleys, Ilkley. Apr 08. HP: £125. ABP: £147.

18thC trumpet shaped ale glass, air twist stem, 8in. Denhams, Warnham. Aug 03. HP: £120. ABP: £141.

18thC cordial glass, round funnel bowl and spiral gauze air twist stem, conical foot. Gorringes, Lewes. Jun 03. HP: £120. ABP: £141.

Georgian wine glass, tapering bowl, thick tapering stem, folded foot, wheel cut with initials P.F.P, late 18thC. Hartleys, Ilkley. Dec 06. HP: £120. ABP: £141.

Two plain-stem wine glasses, 18thC, each of trumpet form, tear inclusions, conical feet, tallest 16.5cm. (2) Sworders, Stansted Mountfitchet. Nov 04. HP: £120. ABP: £141.

Pair of 18thC jelly glasses, tapering hexagonal bowls on bun knops, domed circular feet, 9.5cm high. (W) (2) Cheffins, Cambridge. Apr 05. HP: £120. ABP: £141.

Small Monteith, ogee shaped honeycomb moulded bowl, lobed foot, 6.5cm high, c1750 and a similar larger Monteith, 7.6in high. Dreweatt Neate, Newbury. Apr 00. HP: £120. ABP: £141.

18thC opaque twist wine glass, slightly tapering cylindrical bowl, double helix stem, circular foot, 15cm. (W) Cheffins, Cambridge. Apr 05. HP: £110. ABP: £129.

Jelly glass, bell bowl, fluted form, gadroon-moulded foot, rudimentary stem, 10cm high, mid 18thC. Dreweatt Neate, Newbury. Jun 01. HP: £110. ABP: £129.

Pair of amethyst coloured wine glasses, trumpet bowls, plain stems, 13cm. Woolley & Wallis, Salisbury. Sep 00. HP: £110. ABP: £129.

Small monteith with blue rim and petal foot, 3in high. Dee, Atkinson & Harrison, Driffield. May 02. HP: £110. ABP: £129.

19thC large pedestal glass, knopped stem, 7.5in and a smaller glass with engraved patterned rim, square lemon squeezer base, 5in. Gorringes, Lewes. Mar 04. HP: £110. ABP: £129.

19thC Masonic glass rummer decorated with six Masonic symbols. Denhams, Warnham. May 04. HP: £110. ABP: £129.

Engraved tumbler, barrel shaped form, engraved and polished with a long tailed bird and stylised sprigs of foliage, 12cm high, early 19thC. Dreweatt Neate, Newbury. Jun 01. HP: £110. ABP: £129.

18thC drinking glass, plain bowl, airtwist stem, circular foot ring, 6in high. Diamond Mills & Co, Felixstowe. Dec 04. HP: £110. ABP: £129.

'Lynn' firing glass, round funnel shaped bowl, plain stem, 10.8cm high, c1790-1800. Dreweatt Neate, Newbury. Apr 00. HP: £110. ABP: £129.

George III wine glass, trumpet bowl, clear stem and circular foot, 14.5cm high, an ale flute similar, 14.5cm high & a soda glass ale, base of the conical bowl & stem spirally fluted, 13.5cm high. (D) (3) Cheffins, Cambridge. Apr 05. HP: £100. ABP: £117.

Five early 19thC wine glasses, conical bowls, largest 13cm high. Cheffins, Cambridge. Apr 05. HP: £100. ABP: £117.

Floral engraved cordial glass, faceted stem, another with plain bowl and stem, folded foot. Gorringes, Lewes. Dec 00. HP: £100. ABP: £117.

Three early 19thC rummers, fluted bowls, largest 8cm dia & 2 ales with lemon squeezer feet, taller 13.5cm high. (D) (5) Cheffins, Cambridge. Apr 05. HP: £100. ABP: £117.

Plain stemmed firing glass, drawn trumpet bowl with initials JW, 10cm, mid 18thC. Dreweatt Neate, Newbury. Jun 01. HP: £95. ABP: £111.

Sweetmeat dish, ogee shaped bowl, everted rim, multi-opaque spiral twist stem and radially moulded foot, 8.2cm high, c1760. Dreweatt Neate, Newbury. Apr 00. HP: £95. ABP: £111.

Plain stemmed wine glass, bell bowl, solid lower section & tear inclusion, slender stem, conical foot, 18cm, c1750. Dreweatt Neate, Newbury. Jun 01. HP: £95. ABP: £111.

Plain stemmed wine glass, ogee bowl and folded conical foot, 15.5cm high, c1740. Dreweatt Neate, Newbury. Jun 01. HP: £95. ABP: £111.

Facet stemmed wine glass, engraved and polished with an 'oxo' band, above a basal scale section, stem with hexagonal facets, conical foot, 12cm high, c1790. Dreweatt Neate, Newbury. Jun 01. HP: £95. ABP: £111.

Georgian wine glass, mildly fluted bowl wheel cut with flowerheads, plain stem, folded foot, 6in high. Hartleys, Ilkley. Jun 07. HP: £95. ABP: £111.

18thC opaque twist wine glass, double helix stem and circular foot, 15cm high. (W) Cheffins, Cambridge. Apr 05. HP: £90. ABP: £105.

Georgian wine glass, conical bowl, stem with clear spiral twists, spreading foot, 6.75in high. Hartleys, Ilkley. Aug 06. HP: £90. ABP: £105.

Categories or themes can be followed through the colour coded Index which contains over 4500 cross references.

Pair engraved plain stemmed short wine or firing glasses, 10cm high, mid 18thC. Dreweatt Neate, Newbury. Jun 01. HP: £85. ABP: £99.

Facet stemmed wine glass, round funnel bowl with scale cut lower section, hexagonal faceted stem, conical foot, 14cm high, c1790. Dreweatt Neate, Newbury. Jun 01. HP: £85. ABP: £99.

2349

Pair of cordial glasses, ovoid bowl wheel cut with lily of the valley, cotton twist stem, spreading foot, 19thC, 5.5in high. Hartleys, Ilkley. Jun 07. HP: £85. ABP: £99.

2350

Early 18thC Bohemian glass goblet, engraved a bird cage & couple in a garden, c1700, 8.25in. Gorringes, Lewes. Jul 08. HP: £80. ABP: £94.

2351

Clear glass goblet commemorating the Golden Jubilee of George III, etched design of a crown amongst a wreath, 16cm. Rosebery's, London. Jul 07. HP: £80. ABP: £94.

2352

Bucket rummer engraved with fruiting vine & arched bridge with sailing ship, inscribed 'SPAN 236ft, height 100ft', 8in. Tring Market Auctions, Herts. Apr 05. HP: £80. ABP: £94.

2353

18thC English glass Hogarth type rummer, thick circular base and short stem, 4.75in. Gorringes, Lewes. Jul 08. HP: £75. ABP: £88.

2354

Late 18th/early 19thC ale glass, plain tapered bowl engraved with hops/barley, 5.5in high, two other plain ale glasses, 5.5in high, and five champagne flutes with part slice cut bowls, various. Canterbury Auction Galleries, Kent. Apr 06. HP: £75. ABP: £88.

2355

Engraved rummer, ogee bowl with a swag band, capstan stem and circular foot, 13cm high, early 19thC. Dreweatt Neate, Donnington. Nov 02. HP: £70. ABP: £82.

2356

Three conical ale glasses wheel etched with barley and vine leaves, two with folded feet, all with unground pontils. Thos Mawer & Son, Lincoln. Sep 04. HP: £70. ABP: £82.

2357

18thC cordial glass, cotton twist stem, English c1765, round funnel bowl, double series opaque twist stem, , central solid vertical cable surrounded by a pair of spiral tapes, plain conical foot, approx. 5in high. A F Brock & Co Ltd, Stockport. Feb 07. HP: £70. ABP: £82.

Hammer: £85 - £28

2358

Near pair of champagne flutes, and a wine glass. Gorringes, Bexhill. Sep 04. HP: £70. ABP: £82.

2359

18thC wine glass, English c1765, round funnel bowl set, double series opaque twist stem, central solid vertical cable surrounded by a pair of spiral tapes, plain conical foot, approx 6.5in high. A F Brock & Co Ltd, Stockport. Feb 07. HP: £65. ABP: £76.

2360

18thC engraved wine glass, English c1760, ogee bowl, vertical moulding to bottom half of bowl, engraved floral band to rim, plain stem, folded foot, approx 5in high. A F Brock & Co Ltd, Stockport. Feb 07. HP: £50. ABP: £58.

2361

Set of eight 19thC drinking glasses, strawberry cut cylindrical bowls upon a facet cut knopped stem, foot with radiating cutting to underside, 10cm high. (8) Rosebery's, London. Aug 06. HP: £45. ABP: £52.

2362

Jelly or firing glass, knop stem and substantial circular foot, 10.5cm high, mid 18thC. (scratches) Dreweatt Neate, Newbury. Jun 01. HP: £45. ABP: £52.

2363

18thC engraved wine glass, English c1760, trumpet bowl with engraved floral design to front, small rising Phoenix to back, engraving appears to be of a later date, plain stem, folded foot, approx 4.75in high. A F Brock & Co Ltd, Stockport. Feb 07. HP: £40. ABP: £47.

2364

18thC wine glass, plain tapering stem, base of flared conical bowl with single large air bubble, 16.5cm high. Rosebery's, London. Jan 07. HP: £35. ABP: £41.

2365

19thC green flared ale glass, ring turned stem, pontil, 4in high. Golding Young & Co, Grantham. Feb 06. HP: £28. ABP: £32.

Glossary of Terms

acid etching Use of hydrofluoric acid to ornament the surface of nineteenth century glassware. Cheaper than real engraving.

air twist Spiralling threads of air in the stems of eighteenth century drinking glasses, and later copies.

ale glass From the eighteenth century drinking glass with a deep funnel or flute shaped bowl, used for strong ale and frequently engraved with hops and barley ornament.

alexandrite glass Late nineteenth century translucent glass reheated to show a range of colours from amber to rose blue.

amberina glass Translucent glass containing air bubbles with reddish to yellow colour shadings. Late nineteenth century.

amen glass Drinking glass c1745, diamond point engraved with the Jacobite 'God save Great James our King' and amen below cypher of James III of England and VIII of Scotland. See also Jacobite.

annealing Toughening by slow cooling or tempering glass, by the eighteenth century using a tunnel lehr.

aventurine glass Glass containing brass filings for decorative purposes in imitation of early Venetian glass.

Baccarat, France From the late eighteenth century and especially famous for their millefiori paperweights in the nineteenth century.

Bacchus Important Birmingham manufacturers of coloured glassware, millefiori paperweights and pressed glass.

back painting Painting on the underside of glass.

baluster Swelling vase shape on the stem of drinking glasses and associated with such glasses known as balusters from the late seventeenth to the early eighteenth century, c1680-1740.

balustroid A stem containing knops of small and insignificant character, c1730-50.

beaker Ancient style of drinking vessel with straight, slightly tapering sides and plain base, like a tumbler.

Beilby glass The decorators in enamels, William and his sister Mary working in Newcastle-Upon-Tyne c1762-78.

Blanc-de-Lait An opalescent pressed glass developed by Sowerby in 1880.

blown glass See also free blown glass. The 2000 year old technique, when a gather of molten glass was inflated into a bubble by blowing down a metal tube and then tooled to the required shape.

blown-moulded glass Vessels shaped and relief patterned achieved by blowing into a mould. From the seventeenth century with one-piece moulds until the 1800s, then two piece moulds and then three piece moulds from the 1820s. Not to be confused with pressed glass.

blue glass Made in Mesopotamia as early as 2000BC and in the UK at Bristol, Newcastle, Sunderland etc in the eighteenth and nineteenth centuries.

blue tint See Waterford glass.

Bohemian glass From central Europe, part of the Austrian Empire. Lacks the resonance and lustre of English flint.

bottle glass Unrefined, cheaply taxed glass in green amber and brownish tones.

Bristol blue A generic term coined from a Bristol dealers brief monopoly, around 1760, of Saxony smalt blue.

Bristol glass May be clear blue, red or green, from c1740s-1850s. Bristol also renowned for its dense white opaque glass often painted like china.

broad glass Early window glass. Cheaper and inferior to crown glass. Blown and shaped into cylinders then cracked with a cold iron and opened into flat sheets.

bull's eye Roughly shaped boss in the centre of a sheet of crown glass. Any lens-shaped glass.

Burmese glass See Queen's Burmese.

cameo glass Using a colour contrast by casing white glass over dark then cutting through with tools or acid to produce varying intensities of white against a dark background.

canes Slender glass rods drawn out for use as flowers in millefiori paperweights or as twisted stems in drinking glasses.

cased glass Up to five layers of coloured and clear glass fused and blown into decanters etc to be ground away to produce decorative effects. Made in England mainly after 1845. See overlay glass and acid etching.

champagne glass A glass of 4-6 oz capacity. From the 1670s. Usually a flute as was customary for strong ale, but some early Georgian use of a tazza shaped glass, almost hemi-spherical, on a Silesian stem then a return to this shape occurred from the late 1820s. From the 1850s tulip shaped. Occasionally hollow stemmed.

Clutha glass Patented by James Couper & Son, Glasgow, c1890.

collar A sharp edged flange in the stems of drinking glasses.

colour twist An eighteenth century drinking glass containing colour twisted canes in the stem. See also air twist.

cordial glass A Georgian tall stemmed drinking glass of no more than one ounce capacity for strong aromatic alcoholic drinks.

crackle glass Glass given a deliberate crazing effect for decorative purposes.

cranberry glass The English name, probably adopted from the USA for glass of that colour and on the Continent known as gold ruby.

crizzling The defect in early flint glass in the seventeenth century, which gradually became opaque.

crown glass The early process of blowing then flattening by spinning into a large circular sheet.

crystal i.e. the modern term for lead crystal which was earlier known as flint glass.

cucumber glass Slender bottle without a base to make a cucumber grow straight.

cullet Broken and discarded glass added to the batch during glass making, which acted as a flux to reduce the melting temperature.

custard glass dessert glass in a cup shape with or without a handle.

cut class Glass ornamented by wheel cutting to enhance its refractive brilliance. Improvements in the annealing process and the softer nature of lead glass lead to deeper cutting from the end of the eighteenth century.

decanter From the 1670s a vessel with stopper for the decanting of wine.

demijohn Large bottle with a narrow neck and swelling body, frequently encased in wicker.

dessert glasses Includes jelly glasses, custard cups and syllabubs. In the eighteenth century guests were offered a range of wet and dry sweetmeats arranged on pyramids of glass salvers or tazzas.

diamond point Engraving on glass using a diamond topped hand tool as distinct from wheel engraving but much finer.

double scent bottle Victorian. Two glass tubes welded together at the base with lids at either end to hold smelling salts and a handkerchief scent.

dram glass Short glass with a thick stem or none, and a heavy foot for holding two ounces of spirit.

enamel Basically glass, opacified and/or coloured using pigments from metal oxides and heat fused onto glassware.

enamel glass Objects opacified with tin oxide to appear like translucent white porcelain.

enamelled glass Glass so ornamented such as Beilby or Mary Gregory.

enamel twist So called stem ornament in drinking glasses consisting of spirals of opaque white or colours.

end-of-day glass A name coined from the inclusion of blast furnace slag in cheap pressed objects. In fact this would seem in the main to be a misnomer and certainly this is the case with the various coloured pressed glass malachites as these would certainly have been made to a strictly controlled formula.

engraved glass Wheel and diamond point engraving occurs from c1730.

etched glass Cheap shallow substitute for hand cutting when hydrofluoric acid applied to patterns scratched through acid-resistant wax.

facet cutting The grinding of shallow hollows to make a pattern of diamonds etc on various objects.

facon de venise. Literally in the style of Venice and referring to the glass and the period in England and on the Continent before the development of lead crystal by Ravenscroft. This would usually predate c1780 or so but this style of glass certainly disappears with emergence of flint glass or lead crystal.

Favrile glass The American Long Island glassworks of Louis Comfort Tiffany, established in 1893.

finger bowl For rinsing the finger tips at dinner. From c1760 as a wash hand glass, and not to be confused with a wine glass cooler.

fire or mercury gilding Gold applied in an amalgam of mercury which was removed as a vapour by heating, leaving a film of pure gold.

fire polishing Reheating at the mouth of the furnace to remove mould marks, hence disguising a moulded or pressed piece.

firing glass A stumpy dram with a short thick stem and a heavy disc (firing) foot to approve a toast by a volley of rapping on the table. Supposed to be from c1760 but I have seen earlier examples from about c1730-40.

flammiform Literally flame like. Protruding spikes of glass usually at the termination of writhen moulding.

flashed glass Cheap substitute for cased glass with tinted molten glass skimmed over clear blown glass before being reheated and shaped.

flint glass Now called lead crystal, developed by George Ravenscroft. (1618-81) Contained lead oxide from 1675 instead of lime and crushed flints although after c1730 the silica was obtained from sand.

flute Drinking glass with a long deep bowl, from the 1680s, to allow for the sediment usual in cider.

fly catcher C1780-1860. Resembling a decanter on three feet with an open base curved in to form a gutter for holding a sweet strong ale which attracted insects which were then stupefied and drowned.

folded foot Wine glass foot folded back on itself to form a strong rim. From the late seventeenth century to about 1750 and after 1800 with reproductions.

free blown Shaped by a glass blower without moulds. The 2000 year old technique which implies quality.

frigger An original design by a glass-maker and a term now applied to novelty glass such as walking sticks.

frit Glass makers basic mixture of sand and alkalis.

gadrooning A decorative effect achieved by pinching the glass into ribs, at the base of a bowl for example.

gather Glass makers blob of hot molten glass gathered onto the end of the blowing iron for inflating into a vessel.

gemel Twin flasks joined together as in Nailsea glass.

gin glass A miniature wine glass for the consumption of neat gin.

glass A basic mixture of sand and carbonate of lime with an alkali flux of soda or potash to lower the melting point. See also flint glass, broad glass, cased glass, crown glass, plate glass, rock crystal and obsidian.

goblet A glass with a large capacity bowl.

gold ruby The European term for cranberry glass.

green glass Flint glass in a dark green from about the 1750s. Wider colour range in the nineteenth century. Cheap, dark bottle glass was cleared to a pale green by the 1800s.

hobnail In deep cutting, each projecting diamond shape is cross cut and the four points further cut into eight pointed stars.

hollow stem In a wine glass a stem drawn from the bowl to retain sediment. 1760s-1770s then revived c1830s-1840s for champagne glasses.

iridescent glass Glass which reflects light in interchanging colours.

Irish glass Exported to England particularly between 1784 and 1825 when it escaped the English glass tax by weight, hence heavy decanters, kettle drum bowls etc. Rarely distinguishable from English glass except when marked with wholesalers and retailers marks such as Cork Glass Co.

Jacobite glass Engraved drinking glasses supporting the cause of the Old and Young Pretender, especially the 1745 rebellion. Because of their high values there has been much modern engraving on old glasses.

jelly glass Small footed glasses with bell or trumpet shaped bowls from c1700. Unusual for Georgian glasses the foot diameter is small for close placing on the dessert pyramid or tazza.

kick In a glass bottle or decanter, a hollow rounded dome in the base to aid annealing, mainly pre 1760 but stylistically still present in modern wine bottles, particularly champagnes.

king's blue Strong purplish blue glass of the 1820s-30s coloured with refined cobalt and named after George IV. See also zaffre.

King's Lynn See Norwich glass.

Kit-Cat glass A particular form of early eighteenth century baluster as depicted by Kneller in portraits of members of a Whig Club (founded 1703) at a London tavern run by Christopher (Kit) Catling.

knop In stemmed glassware a swelling more pronounced than a baluster, with various names such as acorn, mushroom, cushion knop etc.

Lalique, Rene 1860-1945. Glassware in the art nouveau and art deco styles. The factory and the styles continued by his son, Marc.

lead crystal See flint glass.

leer, lehr Glassmaker's oven for slowly toughening wares in the process known as annealing.

liquid gold gilding A brilliant gold substitute as gilding on glass from the second half of the nineteenth century. On cheap glass and easily worn.

Lyn glasses Seemingly arbitrary title given to tumblers and wine glasses that are horizontally ribbed or grooved or banded in the belief that they are associated with Kings Lyn and Norwich glass although there seems no evidence to support this theory.

malachite glass Imitates the stone with veining and marbling, produced by most of the pressed glass manufacturers, particularly in the north east from c1880.

Mary Gregory glass Mainly Bohemian from the 1870s onwards. Cheap glass associated particularly with cranberry.

mead glass An early glass with a cup shaped bowl, attributed for mead but of dubious authenticity, gadrooned at the base.

mercury twist a flattened rather than a circular cross section air twist which produces a particularly brilliant effect.

milk glass See enamel glass.

millefiori glass Literally a thousand flowers. An ancient Roman process revived in sixteenth century Venice. Used particularly in paperweights where patters of concentric circles etc are made up using multi-coloured canes.

montieth Large bowl with a notched or undulating rim. Or a small glass with double ogee or cup shaped bowl, wider than a jelly glass and attributed as a salt or as a sweetmeat.

moulded glass See blown moulded and pressed glass.

Murano The Venetian island famous for its glassware from the sixteenth century.

Nailsea glass Mainly a generic term associated with a range of highly coloured, flecked and striped gemel flasks and rolling pins etc made at the Nailsea works near Bristol. In fact such objects were widely made at Sunderland, Newcastle Stourbridge and Alloa etc.

Newcastle-on Tyne Important glass-making centre and noted in particular for Newcastle light balusters and other glasses between 1730 and 1780. See also Beilby.

nipt diamond waies A decorative effect formed by pinching the glass into diamond shaped compartments. The phrase is taken from Ravenscroft's usage in 1675 and refers only to glasses of the seventeenth century which are extremely rare today and exceedingly valuable.

Norwich glass See Lyn glasses.

obsidian A black, glassy volcanic rock with a glossy sheen. Along with rock crystal the only naturally occurring glass.

opal glass From the early Victorian period a semi opaque glass with a fiery glow when held to the light.

opaline glass A pressed glass development by Sowerby also known as a vitro porcelain, from about 1877.

opalescent glass A further pressed glass development by Sowerby from May, 1880. See Blanc de Lait.

opaque twist An eighteenth century drinking glass in which the stem contains single or double twists of canes of opaque glass. Later copies.

orange glass A large top glass for a dessert pyramid in eighteenth century dining, holding an orange or orange chip sweetmeats. Williamite glasses are also sometimes given this name. (William of Orange)

overlay glass See cased glass.

pate de verre Late nineteenth century French technique: glass paste, coloured and moulded into figures etc.

patent glass See Queen's Burmese glass; Queen's ware glass.

pontil mark Also called a punty. Scar on base of an object when a glass vessel is broken off the iron pontil rod. From the late eighteenth century it is common to see the pontil scar ground out but unground pontils occur as late as c1850 on cheaper glass.

posset glass A low cylindrical vessel with handles and a spout.

pressed glass Cheap substitute for free blown cut glass but became an art in itself after about 1870. The first machines were operating in the late 1830s. Molten glass was forced by a plunger into a patterned mould to create the outside pattern which was then finished or improved by fire polishing.

prismatic cutting The deep cutting of the 1800s. Parallel grooves cut in a V section. Elaborated into blazes.

prunts Small glass bosses attached to glass objects for decorative purposes, sometimes tooled as strawberry prunts. From the late seventeenth century.

punty See pontil mark.

purled Ribbing added around the base of a drinking glass bowl.

Queen's Burmese glass From the late nineteenth century. Heat shaded from a pale yellow to deep pink. Used for tablewares and lightshades.

Queen's ware glass Patented in 1878 by Sowerby to imitate carved Japanese ivory in an opaque yellowish tinted colour.

ratafia glass A small capacity eighteenth century flute for the almond flavoured cordial. About one to one and a half ounce capacity.

Ravenscroft, George Associated with the important Savoy Glasshouse, London, from 1673 and credited with the development of flint glass, now known as lead crystal.

registration marks The lozenge marks from 1842 to 1883 and the later serialised registration numbers are particularly relevant to the study of pressed glass. See Appendix.

rock crystal A naturally occurring natural glass with a semi-precious status.

rock crystal glass Introduced by Thomas Webb & Sons in 1878 and characterised by deep cutting of flint glass which was then polished to a limpid clarity.

roemer, romer From the 1670s, the English version of the German pale green hock glass, often with prunts. The style re-emerged in around 1810-1820. Not to be confused with the rummer.

ruby glass A deep red, from the late seventeenth century, coloured with expensive gold chloride.

rummer Distinct from the roemer. From the late eighteenth century a goblet for long drinks such as rum and water grog with a large, deep bowl on a short stem and small foot, the bowl typically of ogee form.

satin glass A Victorian fancy glass in many colours given a satiny surface with hydrofluoric acid.

scent bottle See smelling bottle.

sealed bottle From the seventeenth century until c1830 vintners supplied bottles embossed with the crest or cypher of their wealthy customers.

sham dram Deceptive, short and sturdy spirit glass for a tavern keeper.

shank In drinking glasses where the stem is drawn out from the bowl. In the stuck shank it is fused to the bowl under heat.

ship's glass Decanters had a wide heavy base with the sides slanting sharply to the neck. Drinking glasses had an extremely wide and substantial foot.

silesian stem On early eighteenth century drinking glasses. The modern name for a pedestal stem tapering downwards from a pronounced shoulder. Early versions are four sided then six and finally eight sided by about c1740 at which time they have lost their distinctive cross section.

slag glass See end-of-day glass.

smelling bottle The early name for a scent bottle. From the Victorian period a substitute for some for the Georgian vinaigrette, to contain a reviving scent based on liquid ammonia perfumed with lavender, clove etc.

soda-lime glass Silica and carbonate of lime fluxed with sodium carbonate. The quick cooling glass of early Venetian fame. Its fragility and thinness meant that it could be decorated only with wrought work whereas the softer lead crystal was clear enough to be thickly proportioned and could therefore be engraved and cut.

spatter glass Items mottled with bright specks of various colours of enamel glass against an opaque body.

spun glass Cheap ornaments made with a bunsen lamp and coloured glass rods by street corner showman. In the Victorian period much more elaborate models were produced such as ships and lighthouses and birds around a fountain. See also friggers.

stained glass Glass may be stained with metal oxides, fixed by firing. Also mosaics of coloured glass for windows, firescreens etc.

step cut Typically on decanters as a series of sloping steps.

sucket glass For dry sweetmeats such as candied fruits. Included among the fashionable dessert glasses. Has a wide shallow bowl and, usually a fancy rim on a tall stems.

Sunderland glass Typically rummers or goblets engraved with views of the Wearmouth Bridge and pressed glass made by the firm of Henry Greener.

surfeit water glass A very narrow eighteenth century flute on a wide foot completely different from other cordial glasses. Possibly intended for a potent brandy concoction. Sometimes now called a ratifia.

sweetmeat A glass similar in form to early 'champagnes' but but with an indented or cut rim making them unsuitable as a drinking glass.

syllabub A stemmed Georgian glass for a dessert of sweetened wine topped with whipped cream. Again a small foot allowed for the close arrangement of such glasses on a pyramid.

tazza From the Georgian period a wide shallow stand, the earlier versions frequently having a Silesian stem and a folded foot. Used for the dessert pyramid or singly.

tear In glass a tear of air, for example in a system which also could be drawn out into an elongated drop.

three piece glass The bowl, stem and foot are made separately and then fused together. Sometimes joins can be difficult to detect whereas others have a clear joining line.

Tiffany, Louis Comfort. 1848-1933. Founder of the famous glass works from 1893 and noted for his iridescent glass. See Favrille.

toasting glass Late seventeenth and early eighteenth century to about 1750. For drinking a lady's health. The stem was only one eighth to perhaps a quarter of an inch in diameter so that it could be snapped rather than have the glass demeaned by lesser toasts.

toastmaster's glass A Georgian and later glass with a deceptively small bowl so that the toastmaster could remain sober. See also sham dram.

toddy glass A sturdy type of rummer for drinking hot toddy from the 1770s. May also be a larger goblet holding one and a half pints or more for preparing this drink, with an ovoid bowl, then followed later by bucket and barrel shapes, often engraved, on a short thick stem and a thick foot which may be square.

trailed ornament Heated ribbons of glass applied quite often in loops and blobs over the surface of ornaments and around the rims of sweetmeat glasses. Thicker than threading.

translucent Allowing the passage of light, as in frosted windows but no clear detail.

tumbler Drinking vessel, originally self-righting with a heavy round base, but later a simple handleless cylinder with straight sides and a heavy base.

twist See air or opaque or colour twist.

vaseline glass Glass with a greenish yellow tone resembling the ointment which was introduced in 1873.

Venetian glass A fragile soda glass made into intricate designs of useful and decorative wares and much sought after by those who could afford it. The craft was concentrated on the island of Murano from 1291 and its decline in the late seventeenth century has been linked to the development of lead crystal in England.

Verzelini, G (1522-1606) An Italian working in London from the 1570s-92 who introduced the manufacture of thin soda glass tablewares, now known as Anglo-Venetian glass.

Waterford glass Seemingly making flint table glass that was even more brilliant than Cork or Dublin but indis-tinguishable from English flint which also used fine Derbyshire lead oxide which gave the famous blue tint to the wares.

Whitefriars Important London makers of flint glass tablewares from the early eighteenth century. Became James Powell & Sons in 1834. Closed 1980.

Williamite glass Portrait glasses and decanters and inscriptions such as 'To the glorious memory' of William III (William of Orange) commemorating the battle of the Boyne. Mainly after 1780.

wine glass cooler Individual bowl for each diner from the 1750s to the 1850s with one or two pinched shapings in the rim to hold the stems of inverted glasses in iced water.

witch ball Evolved from spherical flasks for holy water to become popular cottage ornaments by the early nineteenth century

writhen A term applied to the surface twisting of a drinking glass stem or bowl, practical in helping to obscure the sediment in early eighteenth century concoctions.

yard of ale glass A drinking vessel holding about a quart that had to be drained in a single draught. It has a flared mouth and a narrow tubular body and, by the nineteenth century a hollow bowl at the lower end, which tricked the drinker into splashing the liquid all over the face.

zaffre blue A powder prepared from cobalt to colour glass.

Index

The Index is compiled from the descriptions attached to the images from 2,365 sales from dozens of auctions nationwide. These descriptions are not edited as they represent the actual market. Occasionally certain key words do not appear in a description and in these cases the cross reference may be absent from the Index. It is also possible in a very small number of cases that certain manufacturers may have been wrongly identified or the names of patterns or figures mistaken. Again this reflects the actual market and the difficulties of identifying and cataloguing sales. Factories are emboldened and colour coded. Names of patterns are colour coded in italics.

Registered Design Information
1842 - 1980

1842 - 1867
In the first cycle the year is represented by the letter at the top of the diamond, the month by the letter on the left and the day of the month by the figure on the right. The parcel number is at the bottom of the diamond. The ring at the top enclosing Roman numerals indicates the class of goods e.g. III for glass. This cycle ends after 26 years; i.e. the number of letters in the alphabet.

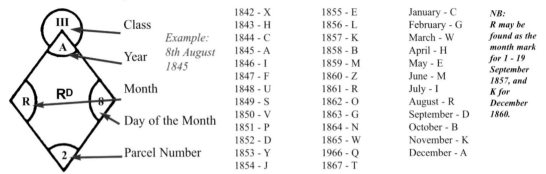

1842 - X	1855 - E	January - C
1843 - H	1856 - L	February - G
1844 - C	1857 - K	March - W
1845 - A	1858 - B	April - H
1846 - I	1859 - M	May - E
1847 - F	1860 - Z	June - M
1848 - U	1861 - R	July - I
1849 - S	1862 - O	August - R
1850 - V	1863 - G	September - D
1851 - P	1864 - N	October - B
1852 - D	1865 - W	November - K
1853 - Y	1966 - Q	December - A
1854 - J	1867 - T	

NB:
R may be found as the month mark for 1 - 19 September 1857, and K for December 1860.

1868 - 1883
In the second cycle the year of registration moves to the right of the diamond, the month to the bottom and the day of the month to the top. The parcel number appears on the left. In 1883 the Patents, Designs and Trade Marks Act merged the categories into serialised registration numbers beginning on the 1st January 1884.

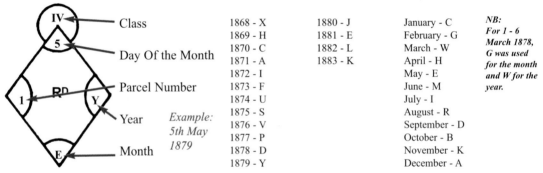

1868 - X	1880 - J	January - C
1869 - H	1881 - E	February - G
1870 - C	1882 - L	March - W
1871 - A	1883 - K	April - H
1872 - I		May - E
1873 - F		June - M
1874 - U		July - I
1875 - S		August - R
1876 - V		September - D
1877 - P		October - B
1878 - D		November - K
1879 - Y		December - A

NB:
For 1 - 6 March 1878, G was used for the month and W for the year.

1884 - 1980
In 1884 the various classes of goods were amalgamated, and a single numerical series of numbers was issued to designs for goods of every category. The list below shows the approximate number at the 1st January each year. The number is prefixed with the abbreviation 'Rd. No.' starting with no 1 on the 1st January 1884.

1 = 1884	368154 = 1901	662872 = 1918	799097 = 1935	866635 = 1952	939875 = 1969
19754 = 1885	385088 = 1902	666128 = 1919	808794 = 1936	869300 = 1953	944932 = 1970
40480 = 1886	402913 = 1903	673750 = 1920	817293 = 1937	872531 = 1954	950046 = 1971
64520 = 1887	424017 = 1904	680147 = 1921	825231 = 1938	876067 = 1955	955432 = 1972
90483 = 1888	447548 = 1905	687144 = 1922	832610 = 1939	879282 = 1956	960708 = 1973
116648 = 1889	471486 = 1906	694907 = 1923	837520 = 1940	882949 = 1957	965185 = 1974
141273 = 1890	493487 = 1907	702671 = 1924	838590 = 1941	887079 = 1958	969249 = 1975
163767 = 1891	518415 = 1908	710165 = 1925	839230 = 1942	891665 = 1959	973838 = 1976
185713 = 1892	534963 = 1909	718057 = 1926	839980 = 1943	895000 = 1960	978426 = 1977
205240 = 1893	552000 = 1910	726330 = 1927	841040 = 1944	899914 = 1961	982815 = 1978
224720 = 1894	574817 = 1911	734370 = 1928	842670 = 1945	904638 = 1962	987910 = 1979
246975 = 1895	594195 = 1912	742725 = 1929	845550 = 1946	909364 = 1963	993012 = 1980
268392 = 1896	612431 = 1913	751160 = 1930	849730 = 1947	914536 = 1964	
291241 = 1897	630190 = 1914	760583 = 1931	853260 = 1948	919607 = 1965	
311658 = 1898	644935 = 1915	769670 = 1932	856999 = 1949	924510 = 1966	
331707 = 1899	653521 = 1916	779292 = 1933	860854 = 1950	929335 = 1967	
351202 = 1900	658988 = 1917	789019 = 1934	863970 = 1951	934515 = 1968	

Monarchs of England, Great Britain (after 1707) and United Kingdom (after 1801)

1066-87	William I		1727-60	George II
1087-1100	William II		1760-1820	George III
1100-35	Henry I		1820-1830	George IV
1135-41	Stephen		1830-37	William IV
1141	Matilda		1837-1901	Victoria
1141-54	Stephen (restored)		1901-10	Edward VII
1154-89	Henry II		1910-36	George V
1189-99	Richard I		1936	Edward VIII
1199-1216	John		1936-52	George VI
1216-72	Henry III		1952-	Elizabeth II
1272-1307	Edward I			
1307-27	Edward II			
1327-77	Edward III			
1377-99	Richard II			

Monarchs of Scotland (from 1306)

1399-1413	Henry IV
1413-22	Henry V
1422-61	Henry VI
1461-70	Edward IV
1470-71	Henry VI (restored)
1471-83	Edward IV (restored)
1483	Edward V
1483-85	Richard III
1485-1509	Henry VII
1509-47	Henry VIII
1547-53	Edward VI
1553	Jane
1553-58	Mary I
1558-1603	Elizabeth I
1603-25	James I (VI of Scotland)
1625-49	Charles I
1649-1660	Commonwealth
1660-85	Charles II
1685-88	James II (VII of Scotland)
1688-89	Interregnum
1689-1702	William III co-ruled with
1689-94	Mary II
1702-14	Anne
1714-27	George I

Monarchs of Scotland (from 1306):

1306-29	Robert I
1329-32	David II
1332-38	Edward
1338-71	David II (restored)
1371-90	Robert II
1390-1406	Robert III
1406-37	James I
1437-60	James II
1460-88	James III
1488-1513	James IV
1513-42	James V
1542-67	Mary
1567-1625	James VI